SCRIBNER READING SERIES

CLIMB THE HILLS

Jack Cassidy

Doris Roettger   *Karen K. Wixson*

SCRIBNER EDUCATIONAL PUBLISHERS
New York

ACKNOWLEDGMENTS

"Alive with Music" by William B. McMorris. Photographs by William B. McMorris. Reprinted from *Boys' Life* with permission.

"Artifact Games" is abridged and adapted from pp. 3, 40–41 in DIGGING THE PAST by Bruce Porell. Copyright © 1979 by Bruce Porell. Reprinted by permission of Harper & Row, Publishers, Inc.

"The Big Race" from MISTY OF CHINCOTEAGUE by Marguerite Henry. © 1947 by Rand McNally & Co., renewed 1975 by Marguerite Henry. Published in the U.S. by Rand McNally & Co.

"Blue Beach" from CARLOTA by Scott O'Dell. Copyright © 1977 by Scott O'Dell. Reprinted by permission of Houghton Mifflin Company and McIntosh & Otis, Inc.

"Birdfoot's Grampa" from ENTERING ONONDAGA by Joseph Bruchac, Cold Mountain Press, Austin, Texas. Copyright © 1975 by Joseph Bruchac. Reprinted by permission of the author.

"Bad Day" from THE WAY THINGS ARE AND OTHER POEMS by Myra Cohn Livingston. Copyright © 1974 by Myra Cohn Livingston. Reprinted with the permission of Atheneum Publishers, Inc. and Marian Reiner for the author.

"The Big River" is an abridgment and adaptation of Chapter 7 from GONE TO TEXAS by Richard Wormser. Copyright © 1970 by Richard Wormser. By permission of William Morrow & Company.

"The Casserole Threat" is abridged and adapted from ARTHUR, FOR THE VERY FIRST TIME by Patricia MacLachlan. Copyright © 1980 by Patricia MacLachlan. Reprinted with the permission of Harper & Row, Publishers and Curtis Brown, Ltd.

"Charlie" is adapted from THE SUMMER OF THE SWANS by Betsy Byars. Copyright © 1970 by Betsy Byars. Reprinted by permission of Viking Penguin, Inc.

"Collecting Autographs" is from COLLECTING AUTOGRAPHS by Herman M. Darvick. Copyright © 1981 by Herman M. Darvick. Reprinted by permission of Julian Messner, a division of Simon & Schuster, Inc.

"The Comeback Dog" is adapted from pp. 35–6 from THE COMEBACK DOG by Jane Resh Thomas. Copyright © 1981 by Jane Resh Thomas. Reprinted by permission of Ticknor & Fields/Clarion Books, a Houghton Mifflin Company.

"Cousin Carrée's Cubic Cuisine" from THE PHANTOM ICE CREAM MAN by X. J. Kennedy. Copyright © 1975, 1977, 1978, 1979 by X. J. Kennedy. Reprinted by permission of Curtis Brown, Ltd.

"A Day to Remember" is from SCRUB DOG OF ALASKA by Walt Morey. Copyright © 1971 by Walt Morey. Reprinted by permission of the publisher, E. P. Dutton, a division of New American Library and Burda & Richards for the author.

"The Daring Doctor of Brazoria" by Janelle D. Scott is from WE CAN FLY: STORIES OF KATHERINE STINSON AND OTHER GUTSY TEXAS WOMEN by Mary Beth Rogers, Sherry A. Smith and Janelle D. Scott. Copyright © 1983. By permission of the Texas Foundation for Womens Resources and Ellen C. Temple—Publisher.

"Digging into the Past" is from GOING ON A DIG by Velma Ford Morrison. Copyright © 1981 by Velma Ford Morrison. Reprinted by permission of Dodd, Mead & Company, Inc.

(Acknowledgments continued on page 623)

SCRIBNER EDUCATIONAL PUBLISHERS
866 Third Avenue
New York, NY 10022
Collier Macmillan Publishers, London
Collier Macmillan Canada, Inc.

Printed in the United States of America

ISBN 0-02-256120-X
9 8 7 6 5 4 3

CLIMB
THE HILLS

Contents

STRATEGIES
TO USE WHEN YOU MEET A NEW WORD

PRONOUNCE THE WORD

Is it a word you know?
Is it a word you have heard other people use?

EXAMINE THE WORD

Is it a compound word? Do you know the meanings of the smaller words?
Are any parts of the word like another word you know? Does it have a familiar base word? Does it have a familiar prefix or suffix?

EXAMINE THE SENTENCE IN WHICH THE WORD APPEARS

Are there any clues that help you understand the meaning of the new word?

If you are still not sure what the word means, look it up in the glossary or a dictionary to find out its meaning.

STRATEGIES
TO USE WHEN YOU WRITE

PREWRITING—Before you write,

- choose a topic.
- consider your purpose and audience.
- take notes and make an outline.

WRITING—When you write your first draft,

- use your notes.
- compose a topic sentence.
- compose detail sentences that support your topic.
- vary sentence length and structure for interest.

REVISING—When you revise,

- edit your first draft. Be sure you have kept to your topic, arranged your sentences in the best order, used vivid words, and achieved your purpose for writing.
- proofread. Be sure the punctuation, spelling, and grammar you have used are correct.

Use these marks when you edit and proofread.	¶	Start new paragraph
	∧	Add This
	℘	Delete this
	lowercase	Make this lowercase
	capital	Make this uppercase

- copy your revised draft neatly on a clean sheet of paper.

1

IT HAPPENED ONE DAY

Most of the time, life goes along without too much change. One day is not very much different from the day before or the day after. But every once in a while, a special time comes along—a time when thoughts and feelings and actions seem to have greater importance. Sometimes this special time lasts a single moment. Sometimes it lasts a week. For some people, these times are special because of what they learn. For others, these times are special because of what they do.

As you read the selections in this unit, think about how each of them describes a special time. Think about how and why the people in each selection might remember that day or time.

From the Diary of
Leigh Botts

by BEVERLY CLEARY

Leigh Botts has two problems. He has no friends at his new school, and someone keeps stealing things from his lunchbag. The thief doesn't take his sandwich. He or she only takes the special treats that Leigh's mother, who works for Catering by Katy, adds to his lunch.

What three attempts does Leigh make to "foil" the thief before he comes up with a successful solution? Does Leigh ever find out who the thief is?

Friday, December 22

If I eat my lunch on the way to school, I get hungry in the afternoon. Today I didn't, so the two stuffed mushrooms Mom packed in my lunch were gone at lunch period. My sandwich was still there, so I didn't starve to death, but I sure missed those mushrooms. I can't complain to the teacher because it isn't a good idea for a new boy in school to be a snitch.

All morning I try to keep track of who leaves his seat to go behind the partition where we keep our lunches, and I watch to see who leaves the room last at recess. I haven't caught anybody chewing, but Miss Martinez is always telling me to face the front of the room. Anyway, the classroom door is usually open. Anybody could sneak in if we were all facing front and Miss Martinez was writing on the blackboard.

Hey, I just had an idea! Some authors write under made-up names. After Christmas vacation I'll write a fictitious name on my lunchbag. That will foil the thief, as they say in books.

Tuesday, January 9

My little cheesecake was missing at lunchtime, which made me mad. I guess somebody noticed Joe Kelly's lunch was really mine. When I went to throw my lunchbag in the garbage, Mr. Fridley, the custodian, said, "Cheer up, Leigh, or you'll trip over your lower lip."

I said, "How would you feel if somebody was always stealing the good stuff from your lunch?"

He said, "What you need is a burglar alarm." A burglar alarm on a lunchbag. I had to laugh at that, but I still wanted my cheesecake.

Tomorrow I am going to wrap my lunchbag in a lot of tape so nobody can sneak anything out of it.

Tuesday, February 6

Today I felt so tired I didn't have to try to walk slow on the way to school. I just naturally did. When I got there, I just threw my lunch down on the floor and didn't care if anybody stole any of it. By lunchtime I was hungry again, and when I found my cheesecake missing, I was mad all over again.

I'm going to get whoever steals from my lunch. Then he'll be sorry. I'll really fix him. Or maybe it's a her. Either way, I'll get even.

Today during spelling I got so mad thinking about the lunchbag thief that I asked to be excused to go to the bathroom. As I went out into the hall, I scooped up the lunchbag closest to the door. I was about to dropkick it down the hall when I felt a hand on my shoulder, and there was Mr. Fridley.

"What do you think you're doing?" he asked, and this time he wasn't being funny at all.

"Go ahead and tell the principal," I said. "See if I care."

"Maybe you don't," he said, "but I do."

That surprised me.

Then Mr. Fridley said, "I don't want to see a boy like you get into trouble, and that's where you're headed."

"I don't have any friends in this rotten school." I don't know why I said that. I guess I felt I had to say something.

"Who wants to be friends with someone who scowls all the time?" asked Mr. Fridley. "So you've got problems. Well, so has everyone else, if you take the trouble to notice."

I thought of Dad up in the mountains chaining up eight heavy wheels in the snow, and I though of Mom squirting deviled crab into hundreds of little cream puff shells and making billions of tiny sandwiches for golfers to gulp and wondering if Catering by Katy would be able to pay her enough to make the rent.

"Turning into a mean-eyed lunch-kicker won't help anything," said Mr. Fridley. "You have to think positively."

"How?" I asked.

"That's for you to figure out," he said and gave me a little shove toward my classroom.

Nobody noticed me put the lunchbag back on the floor.

Thursday, February 8

Today when I came home from school, I leaned over the fence and yelled at a man who works in the gas station next door, "Hey, Chuck, what's in that box that says Alarm System on the side of the station?" I know his name is Chuck because it says so on his uniform.

"Batteries," Chuck told me. "Batteries and a bell."

Batteries are something to think about.

If I took my lunch in a black lunchbox, the kind workers carry, and got some batteries, maybe I really could rig up a burglar alarm.

Thursday, March 1

I bought a beat-up black lunchbox in the thrift shop down the street and started carrying my lunch in it. The kids were surprised, but nobody made fun of me, because a black lunchbox isn't the same as one of those square boxes covered with cartoon characters that first and second graders carry. A couple of boys asked if it was my Dad's. I just grinned and said, "Where do you think I got it?" The next day my little slices of salami rolled around cream cheese were gone, but I expected that. But I'll get that thief yet. I'll make him really sorry he ate all the best things out of my lunch.

Next I went to the library for books on batteries. I took out a couple of easy books on electricity, really easy, because I have never given much thought to batteries. About all I know is that when you want to use a flashlight, the battery is usually dead.

Saturday, March 3

Today I took my lunchbox and the twenty dollars Dad gave me to the hardware store and looked around. I found an ordinary light switch, a little battery, and a cheap doorbell. While I was looking around for the right kind of insulated wire, a man who had been watching me (boys my age always get watched when they go into stores) asked if he could help me. He was a nice old gentleman who said, "What are you planning to make, son?" I didn't want to tell the man, but when he looked at the things I was holding, he grinned and said, "Having trouble with your lunch, aren't you?" I nodded and said, "I'm trying to make a burglar alarm."

He said, "That's what I guessed. I've had workers in here with the same problem."

It turned out that I needed a 6-volt lantern battery instead of the battery I had picked out. He gave me a couple of tips and, after I paid for the things, a little slap on the back and said, "Good luck, son."

I tore home with all the things I bought. First I made a sign for my door that said

**KEEP OUT MOM
THAT MEANS YOU**

Then I went to work fastening one wire from the battery to the switch and from the other side of the switch to the doorbell. Then I fastened a second wire from the battery to the doorbell. It took me a while to get it right. Then I taped the battery in one corner of the lunchbox and the doorbell in another. I stood the switch up at the back of the box and taped that in place, too.

Here I ran into a problem. I thought I could take the wire clamp meant to hold a thermos bottle inside the lunchbox lid and hook it under the switch if I reached in carefully as I closed the box. The clamp wasn't quite long enough. After some thinking and experimenting, I twisted a wire loop onto it. Then I closed the box just enough so I could get my hand inside and push the wire loop over the button on the switch before I took my hand out and closed the box.

Then I opened the box. My burglar alarm worked! That bell inside the box went off with a terrible racket that brought Mom to my door. "Leigh, what on earth is going on in there?" she shouted above the alarm.

21

I let her in and gave her a demonstration of my burglar alarm. She laughed and said it was a great invention. One thing was bothering me. Would my sandwich muffle the bell? Mom must have been wondering the same thing, because she suggested taping a piece of cardboard into the lid that would make a shelf for my sandwich. I did, and that worked, too.

I can't wait until Monday.

Monday, March 5

Today Mom packed my lunch carefully, and we tried the alarm to see if it still worked. It did, good and loud. When I got to school, Mr. Fridley said, "Nice to see you smiling, Leigh. You should try it more often."

I parked my lunchbox behind the partition and waited. I waited all morning for the alarm to go off. Miss Martinez asked if I had my mind on my work. I pretended I did, but all the time I was really waiting for my alarm to go off so I could dash back behind the partition and tackle the thief. When nothing happened, I began to worry. Maybe the loop had somehow slipped off the switch on the way to school.

Lunchtime came. The alarm still hadn't gone off. We all picked up our lunches and went off to the cafeteria. When I set my box on the table in front of me, I realized I had a problem, a big problem. If the loop hadn't slipped off the switch, my alarm was still triggered. I just sat there, staring at my lunchbox, not knowing what to do.

"How come you're not eating?" Barry asked with his mouth full. Barry's sandwiches are never cut in half, and he always takes a big bite out of one side to start.

Everybody at the table was looking at me. I thought about saying I wasn't hungry, but I was. I thought about taking my lunchbox out into the hall to open, but if the alarm was still triggered, there was no way I could open it quietly. Finally I thought, Here goes. I unsnapped the two fasteners on the box and held my breath as I opened the lid.

Wow! My alarm went off! The noise was so loud it startled everyone at the table including me and made everyone in the cafeteria look around. I looked up and saw Mr. Fridley grinning at me over by the garbage can. Then I turned off the alarm.

Suddenly everybody seemed to be noticing me. The principal, who always prowls around keeping an eye on things at lunchtime, came over to examine my lunchbox. He said, "That's quite an invention you have there."

"Thanks," I said, pleased that the principal seemed to like my alarm.

Some of the teachers came out of their lunchroom to see what the noise was all about. I had to give a demonstration. It seems I wasn't the only one who had things stolen from my lunch, and all the kids said they wanted lunchboxes with alarms, too, even those whose lunches were never good enough to have anything stolen. Barry said he would like an alarm like that on the door of his room at home. I began to feel like some sort of hero.

One thing bothers me, though. I still don't know who's been robbing my lunch.

Tuesday, March 6

Today Barry asked me to come home with him to see if I could help him rig up a burglar alarm for his room because he has a bunch of little sisters and stepsisters who get into his stuff. I thought I could, because I had seen an alarm like that in one of the electricity books from the library.

Barry lives in a big old house that is sort of cheerful and messy, with little girls all over the place. As it turned out, Barry didn't have the right kind of battery so we just fooled around looking at his models. Barry never uses directions when he puts models together, because the directions are too hard and spoil the fun. He throws them away and figures out how the pieces fit by himself.

Thursday, March 15

This week several kids turned up with lunchboxes with burglar alarms. You know that song about the hills ringing with the sound of music? Well, you might say our cafeteria rang with the sound of burglar alarms. The fad didn't last very long, and after a while I didn't even bother to set my alarm. Nobody has robbed my lunchbox since I set it off that day.

I never did find out who the thief was, and now that I stop to think about it, I am glad. If he had set off the alarm when my lunchbox was in the classroom, he would have been in trouble, big trouble. Maybe he was just somebody whose mother packed bad lunches—jelly sandwiches on that white bread that tastes like tissues. Or maybe he had to pack his own lunches, and there was never anything good in the house to put in them. I have seen people look into their lunches, take out the cookies and throw the rest in the garbage. Mr. Fridley always looks worried when they do this.

I'm not saying robbing lunchboxes is right. I am saying I'm glad I don't know who the thief was, because I have to go to school with him.

CHECK FOR UNDERSTANDING

1. Why didn't Leigh tell his teacher that things were disappearing from his lunchbag?
2. What three attempts did Leigh make to "foil" the thief before he came up with a successful solution?
3. When Leigh put a fictitious name on his lunchbag and his cheesecake disappeared anyway, what conclusion did he draw? Was it a correct conclusion? Explain why or why not.
4. What happened when Leigh set off the burglar alarm in the cafeteria?
5. How did the burglar alarm help Leigh to solve both his problems?
6. Did Leigh ever find out who the thief was?

WRITE ABOUT *"From the Diary of Leigh Botts"*

Pretend that you are Leigh Botts. So many people have asked you to explain how you built your burglar alarm that you decide to hand out written directions. Reread the entry in Leigh's diary for Saturday, March 3. Note what he bought at the hardware store and what he did to assemble the alarm. Then prepare the written directions. First list the materials needed. Then write step-by-step directions.

BAD DAY

by MYRA COHN LIVINGSTON

Yesterday it was great,
A yellow day. It made my feet run
And my arms flap
And my voice sing

     (Oh sing aloud
     If sing you can!)

And I was alive.
Really alive.

Other things have happened today
And

     (Oh sing aloud
     If sing you can!)

I cannot sing.

What comes into my head
Is nothing but knowing
That it is gray
Today
And I am sad.

27

Context Clues

When you read a story or article, you sometimes come across words whose meaning you don't know. When this happens, you can look the word up in a dictionary. But if you don't have a dictionary handy, or if you don't want to stop reading to look up the word, you may be able to figure out the meaning of the word yourself.

The way you can do this is by using **context clues.** *Context* means the words and sentences surrounding an unfamiliar word. Sometimes clues to a word's meaning can be found in the same sentence in which the unfamiliar word appears. Sometimes you need to think about what was said one or two sentences earlier. At other times you need to read on for a few sentences to find the clues that help you figure out what an unfamiliar word means.

Context gives you different kinds of clues. One kind of clue is a **synonym,** or a word that has almost the same meaning as the unfamiliar word. Look at these sentences from "From the Diary of Leigh Botts." Which word has almost the same meaning as *fictitious?*

> Hey, I just had an idea! Some authors write under made-up names. After Christmas vacation I'll write a fictitious name on my lunchbag.

In these sentences the context tells you that *fictitious* means "made-up." *Fictitious* and *made-up* are synonyms.

Now read these sentences. Which word is a synonym that can help you figure out the meaning of *cuisine?*

> Before Mom went to Chef Pierre's School, she was pleased if we complimented her on her cooking. Now she expects us to tell her the cuisine was excellent.

What do you think the word *cuisine* means? What other word in the sentences helped you figure this out?

Antonyms are words that have opposite meanings. Antonyms can also help you understand the meaning of an unfamiliar word. Read this sentence and find a word that means the opposite of *hostile.*

> After the argument, Suzannah tried to be friendly and patch things up, but Kit continued to behave in a hostile way toward her.

The word *hostile* is an antonym for *friendly.* In this sentence the word *but* gives a clue that Suzannah and Kit have different feelings. Often such words as *but, however, on the other hand* appear in sentences that contain antonyms.

Now read these sentences. Which word can help you figure out the meaning of *adamant*?

> Mr. Perkins was willing to change their plans and postpone the trip. Mrs. Perkins, on the other hand, was adamant. They needed a vacation and they would *have* a vacation.

What does *adamant* mean? Which words in the sentences gave you a clue that to be adamant was the opposite of being willing to change?

Often the context does not include a specific synonym or antonym for an unfamiliar word. This does not necessarily mean there are no context clues to help you deal with an unfamiliar word. Look at the way the word functions in the sentence. Think about what the sentence is saying. Try to think of another word that would make sense in place of the unfamiliar word.

Read this passage from "From the Diary of Leigh Botts." Imagine that you did not know the meaning of *snitch.* What clue would help you figure out its meaning?

> I can't complain to the teacher because it isn't a good idea for a new boy in school to be a *snitch.*

THE RESCUE

by BARBARA CORCORAN

Laurie is making a long journey with an important purpose. She doesn't want to waste time or go out of her way. Yet an emergency puts Laurie's goal in conflict with her sense of what is right.

What emergency interrupts Laurie's journey? At the end of the story, what choice must Laurie make?

Laurie has lived most of her life with her grandfather in an abandoned mining town. They keep to themselves and have little contact with the rest of the world. Now, because of her grandfather's failing health, Laurie must ride her horse, Hook, across the state of Montana to get help from her uncle in Butte.

In the middle of the day, Laurie came to a campground. There were picnic tables and fieldstone fireplaces and piped-in water and rest rooms. People sure went to a lot of trouble to make things fancy. If they wanted to camp out, why didn't they just camp out? Still, it was nice. She took a long drink of the good cold water and filled her canteen. She built a fire in one of the fireplaces and made some soup. Then she took a little time to explore.

Off in the woods at the end of a grass-covered road there was a small trailer. No one seemed to be around.

She rested for a while, lying on the warm pine needles. It was a nice place. Before she left she put her face under the cold water and let the water run for a minute.

"There," she said to Hook, as she came up dripping, "I guess I'm ready to go." She hated to leave the quiet sheltering place, but she got into the saddle and rode down the grassy lane until she heard a car coming. She veered off into the trees and waited while the car went by, a yellow pickup with the Montana Forest Service emblem on the door.

She left the road, and after a few minutes came to a game trail that ran more or less parallel to the road. She could hear a river off to her right, and she rode over to take a look at it. It was a wide foaming river down in a deep canyon. The cliff on which she stood dropped away sharply to the bottom. On the other side of the river a mountain reared abruptly upward so that the river was in shadow.

She went back to the game trail and continued on. A magpie swooped in front of her, flashing his shining black and white plumage. Hook shied. "Steady, boy," she said, "it's only an old magpie."

31

The limbs of the trees hung low, and she had to ride slowly, parting them so she could get through. All at once she thought she heard something. She stopped and listened. It sounded like a child crying. Then someone called "Mama!" It came from the direction of the river. She looped Hook's reins around a tree and went on foot to see what it was, moving carefully, not knowing what she might meet. But she saw no one. She went to the edge of the cliff and looked down. A few feet below her on a narrow ledge huddled a small child. Her face was tear-stained, and when she saw Laurie, she began to howl.

"How did you get down there?" Laurie said.

The little girl stopped crying. "I fell down."

"Where are your parents?" She was testing the edge of the cliff cautiously with her foot.

"They're lost," the little girl said. She wailed again.

"Stop crying," Laurie said sharply. She was afraid the child would fall off the ledge. There was a long drop to the foaming river. Laurie lay down on her stomach and reached her hand down. She could just barely touch the child. She didn't dare move out any further on the ledge or she would fall over herself. But there had to be a way. She thought of the rope she always carried.

"Don't move and don't cry," she said sternly to the little girl. "I'm going to get you out of there. Just stay still a minute."

"Are you going to get my mama?" the little girl asked.

"We'll find her as soon as I get you out of there."

Laurie ran back to Hook and unsnapped the strap that held the lariat.

"Why does everything happen to me," she said.

She ran back and tied one end of the rope around a sturdy pine, talking to the little girl all the time that she was doing it. She measured the distance, and then tied the other end of the rope around her own waist. Now if she slipped over the edge, she could make it back up with the rope. But she had better not slip; if she did, the child might fall.

Very slowly and cautiously, talking steadily to reassure herself as much as the little girl, she inched out over the edge. "Hold your arms up straight," she said. The little girl held up her arms. "Now when I get hold of you, I want you to grab my arms. Don't grab me around the neck. Take hold of my arms tight and hold on. Understand? And don't grab this arm too high up." She moved her injured arm.

"Understand," the little girl said. She was watching Laurie with bright, intelligent eyes.

Laurie lay out over the ledge as far as she dared. She tried not to look at the dizzy drop below her as she reached down first one arm and then the other. "Try not to grab me where the bandage is," she said, warning the child again.

"Did you fall down and hurt yourself?" the child said.

"Yes." She touched the child's

hands. First the little girl took hold of her wrists. She felt the tight grip of the small hands. "That's right. Now move your hands up my arms, up above the elbows. That's the way. You're doing fine." When the child had a good hold, Laurie began to pull up. It was a terrible strain on her shoulders and back, and her wounded arm hurt. She was not sure she could do it. Then she got her good arm around the child's waist and that gave her more leverage. She began inching backward on the edge of the cliff.

The little girl said "Ouch!" as her knees scraped the rocks of the cliff.

"Hang on," Laurie said. "We'll have you up in a minute." She used her free hand to hold onto the rope, pulling herself up with it. The child was small, but she was dead weight. When Laurie had moved back far enough so that she was not in danger of falling, she put her other hand under the child's arm and put all her strength into a great heave upward. The child cleared the top of the cliff. Laurie fell over backward, the little girl on top of her. Laurie lay still a minute, trying to get her breath.

The little girl sat up. "Well," she said calmly, "we did it."

Laurie laughed with relief. "We sure did." Her voice trembled from the exertion, and her arm was throbbing. "Now what am I going to do with you?" She sat up and untied the rope.

"Take me home. I want Mama."

"Where do you live?"

"I live in Montana," the child said, proud of her knowledge.

"For Pete's sake!" Laurie said. "Montana is a big place." She took the child's hand and led her toward Hook. "How old are you?"

The little girl held up three fingers. "I'm this many."

"What's your name?"

"Sandy."

"Sandy what?"

She thought a minute. "Patterson. I have a Mama and a Daddy and a dog named Harry. Harry is my best friend in all the world."

Laurie was trying to think what to do with her. The road that led from the campground probably went to a town. She guessed she

would just have to take her into town and see if she could find her parents.

"Is that your horse?" Sandy asked.

"Yes."

"Do I get to ride it? Sometimes my daddy lets me ride on his horse with him." She looked up at Laurie, excited. She had short red-blonde hair and green eyes. She was a very pretty little girl. Her parents should

take better care of her, Laurie thought.

"How did you get way out here anyway?" Laurie swung Sandy up onto the front of the saddle.

"We went on a picnic. I went to look for flowers. I found some pretty flowers, but I dropped them down that big hole when I fell down. Can we go get my flowers?"

"Not now," Laurie said. "We have to find your mama." She swung into the saddle. She had not wanted to go into town. It meant another delay. And who knew what all this with the little girl would lead to. But she had no choice. She wished the Forest Service truck would come back; then she could turn the child over to them.

Sandy looked around at her.

"You are my very best friend," she said.

Laurie couldn't help smiling. "I thought Harry was your very best friend."

"And you, too," Sandy said. She leaned back comfortably against Laurie. "What is your horsie's name?"

"Hook."

"Fishhook?"

"Just plain Hook."

Hook flicked his ears at hearing his name. Laurie got away from the game trail and went back to the road.

"I'm hungry," Sandy said.

"So am I, as a matter of fact," Laurie said.

"I'm thirsty, too," Sandy said.

Laurie unscrewed the top of the canteen and gave her a drink. The water ran down her chin and made rivulets in the dirt on her face.

"That was good," she gasped. "Do you have any purple juice?"

"No, I don't."

"Purple juice is my favorite," Sandy said.

They came at last to the main road where there were some road signs. The nearest town was four miles north. That meant she would have to backtrack. Eight extra miles

altogether. She groaned wearily. But then she noticed another sign that said, "Butte—20 miles." Maybe she would get there after all. Twenty miles was not so bad. If only she could strike right out for Butte and not do all this backtracking. A car whizzed past them. For a moment she thought of hailing a car and asking them to take Sandy home. But she dismissed the idea. Who knew what kind of people they might be. They might hurt the child or kidnap her or something.

The child lay limp against her, and Laurie saw that she had fallen asleep. Poor little kid, she thought; she must have been awfully scared. She was a game little girl. Laurie liked her. She turned Hook north.

CHECK FOR UNDERSTANDING

1. What emergency interrupted Laurie's journey?
2. Laurie might have gone to look for help to rescue Sandy, but she never even considered it. What does this tell you about Laurie's character?
3. At the end of the story, what choice must Laurie make?
4. Why did Laurie decide not to flag down a passing car and ask the driver to take Sandy home?
5. When Laurie turned Hook north, what decision had she made?
6. When Laurie locates Sandy's parents, what do you think will happen?

WRITE ABOUT *"The Rescue"*

Think about what might happen when Laurie gets to town. Will she ask people in town if they know the Pattersons? Will she take Sandy to the sheriff's office?

Write a continuation of the story. Tell how Laurie finds Sandy's parents and what they do when they get their little girl back.

News is reported in the newspaper and on radio and TV. If you have ever wondered how reporters decide which events and stories they will cover, this selection will help you understand.

What three different kinds of news do we get from newspapers, radio and TV? Would the story of Laurie rescuing Sandy make a good news story?

What's News?

by RUTH and MIKE WOLVERTON

It began to rain suddenly at one o'clock Friday afternoon. It was one of those heavy rains that happen quite frequently in the summertime. It was nothing new.

The city editor of the local newspaper got to his desk at three o'clock. He started getting together the news for the next morning's early edition. By that time the weather bureau was reporting that more than three inches of rain had fallen. But unless there was a lot more rain, most people would have forgotten about the downpour by the time the early edition hit the streets at five o'clock, Saturday morning. The city editor stifled a yawn.

Across the city, the assignment editor at the television station checked the stories scheduled for the six o'clock news.

They included reports of flash flooding at the usual low-water crossings. So far, there was nothing very exciting about that.

At 3:05 P.M. a news reporter at a city radio station finished her five minutes of hourly news. She ended with a weather report. The report predicted that the rain was likely to continue. It also mentioned that the water level in the reservoir, or lake, behind the city dam was rising rapidly. Something about that weather report made her feel uneasy. She went to the morgue, a filing cabinet in which all the old newscasts for the past two years were filed. She was looking for a story on the dam the station had reported many months ago. It was more of a hunch than anything else. She remembered that the U.S. Army Corps of Engineers had worked on the dam and found it somehow unsatisfactory. . . .

"Probably grasping at straws," she told herself. "But on a dull news day, any straw in the wind is welcome."

What Is News?

News doesn't always mean something completely new and different. News does not have to be something that has never happened before. We wouldn't have much news if that were the case. Some events such as the first moon landing or a brand new invention or discovery are new. But the old saying that there is nothing new under the sun is usually true.

What we see on TV, read in the paper, and hear on the radio, and call "the news" can be different things. News can be true stories about people's unusual experiences. News can be warnings of danger to ourselves, our homes and businesses, our animals and plants. Or it can be important new information that helps us live our lives.

An unusual happening can be almost anything that is rare in a particular place at a given time. For instance, a lion walking down the street in New York City is definitely news. A lion walking along a road in Peru, Indiana, would be unusual, too, but not as newsworthy. Circuses often winter in Peru each year and lions sometimes do get out of their cages. In an African village, next to a wildlife preserve with a large lion population, the story of a lion walking down the street would be news only if the lion happened to hurt or kill someone.

If there is a two-inch snowfall in San Antonio, Texas, the news is proclaimed in big newspaper headlines. It is told in news bulletins on the radio and on TV. Why? Because in San Antonio it snows only once every ten years or so. A snowfall of two inches in Denver, Colorado, however, is not newsworthy because Denver has a lot of snow every winter. However, if there were a two-inch snowfall in Denver on the Fourth of July, it *would* be news. Snow is rare in the summer, even in Colorado.

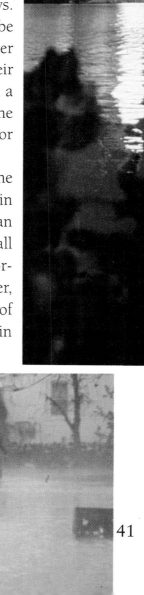

Some events are news everywhere. A long search for a lost child is always news. A natural disaster, such as an earthquake or flood is always news. So is a visit by a famous person. In fact, news doesn't have to be sad or frightening at all. It's news if someone wins a million dollars. It's news if someone is saved from a disaster or wins a medal at the Olympics. It's news if someone has invented a new gadget. It's news if scientists discover new facts about the human body, the age of the Earth, or the composition of the planet Jupiter.

Another kind of news is information that helps people lead better lives. The latest reports on energy conservation help people decide which new heating system would be best for them. Stock market reports let people know which stocks would make a good investment. Consumer news informs people about goods and services.

News warnings do not only inform the public about danger. They also advise them on what to do. They give

alternate routes if roads are blocked. In case of disasters, they give evacuation routes and advice on how to protect homes and businesses.

How News Becomes History

When the news is "hot," that is, when a news story first breaks, we usually get it in the form of news flashes. A news flash is a brief statement that tells us what has just happened. As the story unfolds and more facts become known, reporters bring us the story during regular newscasts. Often they report directly from the scene.

Newspapers will carry the story on the front page of one of their regular editions or in a special edition. Newspapers often have several regular editions in a single day, changing the front page in order to keep pace with fast-breaking news. Newspapers go into much greater detail than radio or television newscasts do. They give "background" material to provide a better understanding of the story.

For the next day or two, or for as long as the story is "alive," further details and developments will be reported on the newscasts and written up in the daily papers. Weekly news magazines will also cover the story in detail. They give background information that helps us put together the pieces and see a whole picture.

Finally, the event ends its life as "news" and enters its new life as "history."

There is one important difference between news and history, however. History is not just a collection of old news. While historians—the people who write history—do rely on news reports, they do not give the same emphasis to events that news reporters and editors do.

It is often difficult to predict how important a news event will be several years after it happens. Events that seem very important at the time they happen may turn out to be of little importance when compared to the news of the next week or next month. More often, though, it is the other way around. Events that seem to be hardly newsworthy at all at the time may turn out to be turning points in history. That is why nearly all events get at least some attention from the people who bring us the news.

That is why even a Friday afternoon rainstorm got some attention.

The reporter at the city radio station found what she had been looking for in the morgue. It was an old news story. It told how the U.S. Army Corps of Engineers had made some temporary repairs on the city dam. But they had warned that

the dam might not be safe. Very rapidly rising water might be dangerous if it built up quickly behind the dam. And that was exactly what was happening now!

The reporter quickly put in a phone call to the nearest office of the U.S. Army Corps of Engineers. She would try to get some more information about how much extra water the dam could hold. Then she began to write a story for her four o'clock newscast. She would inform her listeners that experts had said the city dam was not very safe.

CHECK FOR UNDERSTANDING

1. What made one reporter think the day's rainfall might be news while other reporters didn't?
2. What three different kinds of news do we get from newspapers, radio, and TV?
3. If there were a two-inch snowfall in your community in December, would it be considered news?
4. Would the story of Laurie rescuing Sandy make a good news story? Why or why not?
5. Imagine that you were putting out a class newspaper. Give some examples of news you would include in the newspaper that would not be included in your local newspaper. Explain why.

READING MAGAZINES AND NEWSPAPERS

Sophie and Yolanda were looking at the magazines in the airport newsstand. They were waiting to board the plane for their trip to Texas to visit Yolanda's grandmother.

"Will we get a movie on the flight?" Sophie asked.

"No, there's not enough time for a movie. There's only enough time to get bored if you don't have a book or some good magazines to read," Yolanda said.

Sophie watched her friend look through the magazines on the rack, read a bit of one or two, then choose three magazines to buy. "Why did you buy those magazines?" Sophie wanted to know.

"They each have an article I want to read," Yolanda answered.

"How could you tell?"

"I looked at the table of contents of a few science magazines until I found one with an article that interested me."

This is what the contents page of *Young Science* looked like.

What's Happening in Space	**12**
A report from a space probe	
Seeing Eye Robots Help the Blind	**16**
Dogs are more fun, but robots never eat	
Tornado Tracker	**19**
Secrets from a top Texas tornado-watcher	
Desert Sand—a New Kind of Soap	**23**
Your next shampoo may be a dry one	

"When I saw the word *tornado*, I thought I might be on the right track."

"That was all you had to do—just read the contents?"

"No," admitted Yolanda. "The contents page told me that the magazine had something that *might* interest me, but I wanted to make sure before I spent my money."

"How did you do that without reading the whole thing?"

"You can get a pretty good idea of what the article is going to be like by looking at the first page."

Yolanda pointed out the parts of the first page that she used to get information about the article. First, she looked at the *headline* under the title. This told her what kind of article it was going to be, in this case, an article about a scientist who studies tornadoes. Then, she looked at the *illustration*—in this case there was a photo with a *caption*, words that explain the picture. She also checked the *author's name* to see if she recognized it and read the *background note* at the foot of the page that told about the author. The background note explained that the article had been written by someone who knows about weather—particularly about tornadoes that have struck the Texas Panhandle. Finally, she read the *opening paragraph* to find out the following:

1. Does the author open with a good story or something else to grab the reader? *What is the grabber in the sample selection?*

2. Does the author let the reader know what the article will cover? *What will the article in the sample selection cover?*

3. Is the author's style of writing clear and easy to understand? *How would you describe the author's style in the sample selection?*

TORNADO TRACKER

A scientist with an unusual hobby roams the roads of northern Texas studying one of the most dangerous forces of nature.

Shirlee K. Applebee

Whenever people in the small towns of the Texas Panhandle learn that "Tornado Ed" McCausland is in the neighborhood, they move fast. Windows are boarded up, entire families hide in their cellars. Some people even jump in their cars and leave town.

No. "Tornado Ed" isn't a famous Western gunman. He's a professor of weather science at Panhandle University. But he has an odd hobby. He tracks down and studies tornadoes—those deadly funnel-shaped clouds of whirling winds that frequently form over the western plains. The force of a tornado can shatter an entire block of houses in a few seconds. It isn't Ed McCausland that people fear. It's the tornadoes he tracks.

What does it take to be a tornado tracker? "Well, first you have to enjoy being a few hundred feet away from something that's a mile high, spinning at more than 200 miles an hour, and can jump in any direction at any minute," says Professor McCausland.

SPINNING LIKE A TOP, and towering thousands of feet into the atmosphere, the funnel of a tornado creates a path of destruction wherever it touches the ground.

"Second, you have to enjoy chasing across the country after something that may not happen. Tornadoes don't always show up where you expect them to."

Shirlee K. Applebee is the weather reporter for Station KTEX-TV in the Panhandle. She has been the chief eyewitness reporter during six tornadoes.

When they boarded the plane, the flight attendant handed Sophie a national newspaper. "Can I use the same techniques for finding an article in a newspaper?" Sophie asked.

"Almost, but sometimes it helps if you know ahead of time what you want to read about."

"Since you're reading about tornadoes, I want to check the weather in Texas. Where will I find that?"

"Start with the contents. It's usually on the front page."

WORLD NEWS TODAY 3 SECTIONS

News

Editorial, Opinions	7-8A
Nation/State	5-6A
World	1-2A
Weather	3-4A

Sports/Finance

Pro Sports	1-2C
School Sports	3-4C
Stock Exchange	5-6C

Entertainment

Food	1-2B
Fashion	3-4B
Movies, Books	5-6B
TV Listings	7-8B

When Sophie turned to pages 3 and 4 of Section A, she saw a huge map of the United States that covered the top half of the page. Alongside the map was a boxed section listing all the symbols used and what they meant. At the bottom of the page was a series of boxes describing the weather in twenty cities around the country. The box for Lubbock looked like this.

LUBBOCK

Tornado warning
Stay tuned to local stations
for further advice.

49

Using What You Have Learned

Read the first page of this article and answer the following questions:

1. Does the author seem to be someone who knows the subject?

2. What words in the headline are used to describe mud in order to make you feel strongly about the topic?

3. How does the first paragraph expand on this description and engage the reader's interest?

4. Does the author's style of writing suggest that the article will be easy to understand and interesting to read?

5. How do the caption and illustration add to this description?

Expanding Your Skills

Bring in a number of magazines of all kinds to build a class collection. Review the table of contents in each magazine to find at least five articles that interest you. Then read the first page of each article and decide which of the five articles you would *most* like to read. Write down the information that helped you make your decision. Then read the article you selected. When you have finished reading, discuss your choice with the class. Explain why you decided to read the article and tell whether or not you feel you made a good choice.

MUD

An unlikely destroyer has buried thousands of square miles and killed hundreds of thousands of people throughout history. Milt Johnson

If you were asked to name the most destructive forces in nature, your list might include fire, flood, windstorms, or earthquakes. It is not likely that you would mention mud. To most of us, the worst damage mud can do is to soil the rug or the floor if we are careless enough to track it into the house.

Throughout history, mud has been as great a destroyer as hurricanes or tornadoes. Giant floods of mud, some more than a hundred feet high, have buried the landscape in many places around the world. In 1985, a huge mudflow in South America overwhelmed the Colombian town of Armero, killing thousands.

Great mudflows like these start on the side of volcanoes. During an eruption, dirt and volcanic ash may mix with steam from the inside of the volcano and with water melted from snowfields on its sides. The result is a sudden, monstrous river of sticky mud that flows at a rate of more than sixty miles an hour and topples everything in its path. Even when the flow stops, the mud may harden like concrete, trapping forever everything that lies beneath.

Milt Johnson is a ranger on Mt. Rainier and writes science articles for many magazines.

SOURCE OF A PREHISTORIC MUDFLOW is Mt. Rainier in the state of Washington. About 5,800 years ago, a volcanic explosion caused the collapse of the top two thousand feet of the mountain. The eruption caused a 100-foot-high mudflow that traveled more than 80 miles to the waters of Puget Sound.

Good Evening, This Is Elma Barrera...

by CHRISTOPHER McMILLAN

Have you ever wondered what the people you see on the evening news do during the rest of the day? In this article, you will follow Elma Barrera, a TV reporter in Houston, Texas, through a long and busy day.

What three different kinds of news stories does Elma cover during her day? What personal qualities make Elma Barrera a good reporter?

52

On September 19, Elma Barrera, a news reporter for Channel 13 in Houston, wakes up at seven in the morning. She wants to be at the station by eight o'clock.

Today is Thursday. Thursday is always an extra heavy day. Not only will she do her regular story or two for the six o'clock news, she will also return to the station after dinner to tape the weekly show she hosts called "Viva Houston." It is too soon for her to know that a tragedy in a city south of Houston will make her day even more demanding.

As soon as Elma arrives at the station, she is on the phone. She wants to set up an interview with a police officer named Alan Johnson about a law that has just been adopted by the state of Texas. But Officer Johnson is a busy man. "Yes, yes," she says over the phone, "but when can I see him?"

Elma's eyes flash when she is told that she may not be able to interview the police officer that day. She is eager to get the interview. Elma is not the sort of person who gives up easily.

A tall man with glasses comes up to Elma's desk.

"Are you ready to go?" Elma asks him.

This is Steve Ladecke, one of the cameramen at the station. Steve and Elma will be working together today. Each reporter on an assignment is paired with a cameraman or camerawoman. This person films the videotapes that are included in the news reports on television.

"I've got to get the camera and the power pack," Steve says. "I'll meet you at the car."

When Elma gets to the parking lot, Steve is already loading the cumbersome camera into the car. The camera has a microphone attachment. There is also a heavy pack that powers the camera and the lights.

The car has a two-way radio so that the reporters and the people at the station can communicate with each other all the time. Right now, Elma and Steve are having trouble finding the office building where Elma is going to interview a social worker. The woman's job will be affected by the new law. Elma wants to get her reaction in a taped interview. Elma picks up the radio.

"How do we get to 4040 Milam?" she asks the station.

Someone at the station starts to give directions. Before the person is finished, Elma recognizes the office building. Once inside, Elma begins talking to the woman while Steve sets up the camera, lights, and tape recorder.

The interview itself lasts only a few minutes. Elma thinks the interview is good but not great. She is not sure it will be seen on television later that night.

"The station has less than an hour to cover all the day's news," she explains. "Usually we reporters bring back more tape than the station has time for. That means some of the tape has to be left out. I'll edit this interview myself and leave in only the best questions and answers. But even so, there may be other news stories that the station thinks are more important than this interview."

The next stop is the Houston Police Station, where Officer Johnson works. Elma and Steve have no problem finding this place. They have both been here often covering stories.

Elma and Steve head down the hall and enter a door marked Juvenile Division. Elma asks if she can see Officer Johnson. She is told he is just on his way out the door. Sure enough, a man with a blond mustache is putting on his jacket, getting ready to leave.

"Is that him?" Elma asks. Before the officer at the desk can answer, Elma is in the room and standing in front of Officer Johnson.

"Excuse me, I'm Elma Barrera, a reporter for Channel 13. I would like to ask you some questions about the new law."

"I'm afraid I have to leave right now for a case," the officer says.

"May we come with you?" Elma asks quickly.

Officer Johnson smiles and shakes his head. "Sorry," he says and begins to move toward the door.

"Well, can we follow you?" Elma asks

He shakes his head to that suggestion, too.

"I'd really like to get more information about the new law," Elma continues. "Could I interview you when you get back?"

"I'm not sure when I'll be back," Officer Johnson says.

"We'll wait," Elma says cheerfully. Then she adds, "As long as we know we can talk to you when you *do* get back."

"OK," he says with a shrug, "if that's what you want to do."

It's not what Elma wants to do, but she is willing to wait if it means getting the interview.

"I hate to wait," says Elma, shaking her head. "But sometimes, for a reporter, waiting is more important than rushing off somewhere."

The wait finally pays off. When Officer Johnson strides down the hall a few hours later, Elma stops him with a smile.

"I'm still here," she says. "Could I ask you a few questions now?"

The police officer sighs and smiles. "Sure," he says. "Where do you want to set it up?"

Elma chooses a quiet corner of the Juvenile Division office for the taping. In a short time she has asked all the questions she needs. She thanks the officer and goes outside the station. Here, using the front of the police station as background, Elma wraps up her two interviews with a "stand-up." This is a summary or a wrap-up of the stories. When she tapes the stand-up, Elma looks straight into the lens of the camera. That way, she will seem to be talking directly to the people watching her on their TV sets.

Elma and Steve get back to the station about an hour before the five o'clock newscast. They are surprised to find the newsroom in even more of an uproar than it usually is at this time of day. Elma has been so busy with

her own story that she hasn't had a chance to listen to any news during the day. It is only now that she learns of a terrible catastrophe. This morning, while she was doing her first interview, a tremendous earthquake struck Mexico City, 1,200 miles south of Houston. The station has already sent one of its reporters to Mexico City. This reporter will give eyewitness reports of the efforts to rescue people buried under the rubble of buildings crumbled by the earthquake.

Many of the Mexican-Americans who live in Houston have relatives in Mexico. The earthquake has damaged telephone lines. It is impossible for people in Houston to find out if their relatives are safe. Many of the people whose families might be affected by the earthquake speak only Spanish. Reports about the earthquake given in English will not help them.

As soon as Elma walks in, her boss, Jim Topping, rushes over to her.

"Drop everything, Elma," he says. "You've got to do a report on the earthquake in Spanish for us at the beginning of the five o'clock news and the six o'clock news." He thrusts the latest reports about the earthquake into her hands.

Elma looks at the clock on the newsroom wall. She doesn't have much time to summarize all the reports, translate them into Spanish, and type up the Spanish script. She sets to work furiously, putting aside the story she has spent all day working on.

Somehow Elma manages to finish the script just before she hears the call "Stand by to roll." This is the signal that she is about to go on the air. Elma is worried because she has not had time to rehearse the Spanish script. She hates to fumble or make a mistake, particularly in Spanish.

But she does the report without fumbling. Elma knows she looks tense on camera. The earthquake has made everyone tense. Now she will have to wait another hour to make the same report, along with any fresh news of the disaster, on the six o'clock news. That's all right. She still has work to do to prepare for the taping of her show, "Viva Houston." She will have to forget about dinner, because after the taping she will have to update the earthquake report for a third time.

The report for the six o'clock news goes more smoothly. Elma is glad to see that her story about the new law and her interview with Officer Johnson have made it on the air. A lot of her interview with the woman was cut, but the basic story got told, and that's what counts.

Elma barely has time to take a deep breath and start to relax before a call comes from the reception desk. One of her guests for "Viva Houston" has arrived.

Part of the show tonight is on life-saving techniques for people who have stopped breathing because of drowning, shock, or heart attack. Elma flips through her notes

and finds that the woman in the reception area is someone whose life was saved by these techniques. The guest's case is unusual. She had stopped breathing after being struck by lightning. Only the quick work of a bystander familiar with these life-saving techniques had kept the woman from dying.

Other guests for the show arrive. Elma escorts them to the studio that will be used for the taping. The high ceilings of the studio are hung with banks of bright lights. Some of them are focused on the center of the studio floor. There on a platform is a couch, two easy chairs, and tables, to make the set look like a living room.

Taping the show takes almost two hours. When the show is finished, Elma thanks her guests and quickly says good night. She knows that they would like to linger and talk more, but Elma's work is not finished. There is the one final report on the earthquake to tape in Spanish for the ten o'clock news. Again Elma puts together the latest

bulletins on the earthquake and translates the report into Spanish. It is now nearly ten o'clock. It has been fourteen hours since Elma first arrived at the station.

"When you are tense or tired, you are more worried about making a mistake. So you make more," Elma explains later. "It's funny, but when you broadcast live and you don't have the second chance you have with tape, you almost never make mistakes. When you know you can retape if you make a mistake, you make more of them."

It is a struggle for Elma to get through the taping of the final earthquake report without making a mistake. The TelePrompTer that shows the script for the report is hard to read. By this time, Elma is exhausted.

"Please," she says to the cameraman in a strained voice. "Move the camera closer so I can read the script." The cameraman realizes how tired she is and quickly obliges.

On the third try, the report is taped without a mistake. Elma can't help letting out a whoop of relief. She thanks the cameraman for his patience and practically runs to her desk to get her purse.

"Going to dinner?" the cameraman asks.

"Dinner?" Elma says. "I'm going to get some sleep. I have to be back here again in a few hours."

As Elma closes the newsroom door behind her, the screens of all the television sets in the room are suddenly filled with the same image. On every screen an attractive dark-haired woman looks steadily at the viewer and says with energy and confidence: "Good evening, this is Elma Barrera for Channel 13 News."

CHECK FOR UNDERSTANDING

1. Who goes with Elma on an assignment? Why?
2. How does Elma succeed in interviewing Officer Johnson?
3. What special responsibilities does Elma have on this day that she doesn't ordinarily have?
4. What three different kinds of news stories does Elma cover during her day?
5. What personal qualities make Elma Barrera a good reporter?

WRITE ABOUT *"Good Evening, This Is Elma Barrera . . ."*

What would Elma Barrera's day have been like if she had been a reporter in Mexico City on the day of the earthquake? Write a short description of her day. What kinds of facts and information would she have gathered? What kinds of interviews would she have had?

When the Earth Explodes

by FRED GEBHART

Earthquakes, like the one in Mexico City, and other natural disasters cause death and destruction. Scientists work hard to find ways to predict when these events will happen in order to save lives. This article tells how the scientists at the Hawaii Volcano Observatory study volcanoes.

What are the first signs that a volcano is about to erupt? What special instruments do scientists use to study volcanoes?

On a warm spring day, early morning visitors were already exploring Hawaii Volcanoes National Park. They were walking over crunchy lava rock and looking at ancient craters. Even though the people were close to a volcano, they felt safe. But soon they would see more of that volcano than they had ever expected.

"I felt the first earthquakes about 8:45 A.M.," remembers a park ranger. "At 8:55, the call came to close the road around the crater." Two and a half hours later, the ground broke open. Kilauea (kē' lou' ā' ə) volcano began spewing fiery streams of red-hot lava.

Park visitors were surprised by the eruption. But thanks to a team of nearby scientists, no one got hurt. The scientists work at the Hawaii Volcano Observatory (HVO). Perched on the rim of Kilauea, it is the world's oldest volcano research lab. Its scientists predict when the volcano will blow its top.

Because these researchers are experts at their work, no one has been hurt by an eruption for many years. Kilauea can start forest fires or burn houses. But the HVO team's forecasting ability helps limit the damage that the volcano can do.

Watching and Waiting

"Most volcanoes erupt, then lie quiet for many years, but not Kilauea," explains Reggie Okamura, an HVO scientist. "It's the most active volcano in the world."

"A volcano never erupts without warning," says Okamura. He has been studying Kilauea for

twenty-five years. "It's up to us to understand the warnings." Reggie Okamura and other HVO team members are **volcanologists** (vol' kə nol'ə jists). By studying Kilauea, they are learning to predict when volcanoes will erupt in other parts of the world. This has helped to save many lives.

Before Kilauea's eruption on that spring morning, the HVO team had been watching the volcano night and day. But there wasn't much for them to see on the earth's surface.

The first signs of the coming eruption actually happened miles underground. The volcano watchers used special instruments to track the movements of liquid rock deep inside the earth. Liquid rock is called **magma**.

Tilt!

The HVO team noted another early sign of the coming eruption. Rock was bulging from Kilauea's crater to make way for the rising magma. The crater was inflating like a slightly blown-up balloon. This bulging is called **tilt**. The greater the tilt, or bulge, of a volcano, the bigger its coming eruption will be.

To measure tilt, Reggie and the HVO team used an instrument called a **tiltmeter**. It is very sensitive. If you were to put a dime under a board 3000 feet long, a tiltmeter could measure the slight difference in the board's angle.

The volcano watchers used another instrument, a **seismograph** (sīz'mə graf'), to help predict *where* the eruption would take place. Seismographs detect and record earthquakes. Forty-six of these instruments cover the island of Hawaii. They pinpoint every earthquake that takes place, even ones you can hardly feel.

Before the eruption, the quakes moved closer to the surface along with the rising magma. "We traced magma through the moving quakes," explains Fred Klein, another member of the volcano watchers' team. He knew that an eruption was coming very soon. Kilauea was going to blow.

Eruption

"The quakes tell us exactly which part of Kilauea's crater will erupt," Reggie Okamura says. "Then we call the park officials to suggest safety measures." In this case, a road had to be closed. At other times, people must be moved back for safety.

HVO suggestions are serious business. Park official David Ames remembers a 1971 eruption. HVO suggested that he close a visitors' viewing platform. He did. An hour later, the empty platform fell into a lake of boiling lava.

Predicting when Kilauea will erupt is only part of the job the HVO team handles. "We study everything that happens during an eruption," Okamura explains. "We collect samples of hot lava and take lots of photos." Later, these lava samples are studied to help figure out where gold and other precious minerals can be found.

Of course, the team members who collect lava have a very hot job. To get near the glowing lava, they have to put on special suits.

The suits are covered with a shiny metal that reflects heat. Lava erupts at more than 2100 degrees Fahrenheit (1149°C). That's hot enough to melt ordinary steel as if it were candle wax.

HVO team members grab chunks of lava with tongs made out of special steel. Then they get out as quickly as possible! Fortunately, lava from Kilauea moves slowly, like thick mud. "It's hot as a furnace," says a sweaty scientist. "But you can walk faster than it flows."

After a couple of hours, HVO team members put on extra-heavy boots. It's time to replace the seismographs and tiltmeters that got caught in the lava flows. The machines have melted completely.

"Sometimes we put out new instruments every day," says Okamura, laughing.

All the watching, waiting, and measuring is worth the effort to the HVO team. The spring eruption of Kilauea came just as they had predicted. There was no panic among park visitors and no injuries. In fact, thousands of people rushed to the park when the road reopened about noon. Red rivers of melted rock were only a few hundred feet away. But thanks to the HVO team, people could safely watch one of nature's most incredible displays of fireworks.

CHECK FOR UNDERSTANDING

1. Why did no one get hurt when Kilauea erupted in the middle of a busy national park?
2. What is *magma*?
3. What are the first signs that a volcano is about to erupt?
4. What special instruments do scientists use to study volcanoes? Explain what information each of these instruments gives the scientists.
5. What do the scientists do during an actual eruption?
6. What do the scientists have to do after a volcano has erupted? Why?

Cause and Effect

The scientists who predict when volcanoes will erupt can do so because they understand cause and effect. They know that the movement of liquid rock, or magma, causes a volcano to erupt. They also know that this movement has a series of effects. The first effect is tilt. The rising magma causes the rock of the crater to bulge. The next effect is a series of small earthquakes. The final effect is the volcanic eruption.

Leigh Botts was able to build his lunchbox burglar alarm because he understood cause and effect, too. Opening the lunchbox caused the switch to be triggered. Triggering the switch caused electricity to flow from the battery. The flow of electricity caused the bell to sound. Of course, in the case of Leigh's burglar alarm, the series of causes and effects happened in a split second.

For readers, too, it is important to understand cause and effect. To understand a story it is important to identify the events and circumstances that bring about other events and circumstances.

Many Causes for One Effect

Part of the fun of reading is figuring out all the causes that lead to a single effect. Think of Leigh Botts's burglar alarm as the effect. What would you say caused Leigh to build the alarm? Did he build it because someone was taking things from his lunch? Did he build it because Mr. Fridley jokingly suggested that he needed a burglar alarm? Did he build it because he found out what was in the box marked "Alarm System" at the gas station?

Actually all three situations and events led to the single effect: Leigh built a burglar alarm. If someone had not been stealing from Leigh's lunchbag, Mr. Fridley would not have suggested that Leigh needed a burglar alarm. If Mr. Fridley had not made the suggestion, Leigh would not have asked about the box marked "Alarm System." If Leigh had not asked about the alarm system, he probably would never have built his own alarm. The major cause for building the alarm was that someone was taking things from Leigh's lunch. But without the other causes, the particular effect probably would never have occurred.

Many Effects from One Cause

An effect can turn around and become a cause itself. For example, you have seen how Leigh's burglar alarm was an effect caused by several things—the thefts, Mr. Fridley's suggestion, the alarm system at the gas station. At the end of the story, Leigh's burglar alarm becomes a cause. As a cause, it had several effects. Can you remember any of them?

First, the alarm caused a new problem for Leigh. He could not open his lunchbox in the cafeteria without setting off the alarm. Another effect was that when Leigh did open it, everybody began to notice him. Still another effect was that the principal admired Leigh's invention. Another important effect was that Leigh discovered that someone had been taking things from other kids' lunches, too. A final effect of the alarm was Leigh's new friendship with Barry, who wanted Leigh to help him make an alarm for his room. All in all, the lunchbox alarm was the cause of all the positive effects that happen at the end of the story.

When you read "The Big Race," try to identify the causes that lead to Grandma's suggestion and the effects that occur as a result of her suggestion.

THE BIG RACE

by MARGUERITE HENRY

Some communities have special days that everyone in the community prepares for and takes part in. The special day on Chincoteague Island, where this story takes place, is Pony Penning Day. For Maureen and her brother Paul, this Pony Penning Day is going to be more special than ever. But before the day comes, one of them must deal with bitter disappointment.

Why is this Pony Penning Day a very special day for Maureen and Paul? What disappointment must one of them face?

Chincoteague is an island off the coast of Virginia. Across a channel from Chincoteague is another island called Assateague, which is inhabited by wild ponies. Every year on Pony Penning Day, the people of Chincoteague round up wild ponies on Assateague and swim them across the channel to Chincoteague. When the ponies arrive, there is a festival with a picnic, a race, and other events.

Last year Paul Beebe took part in the roundup for the first time. He brought back a wild pony called Phantom. Paul and his sister Maureen have trained Phantom all year for the big race this Pony Penning Day.

It was the early morning when the world was all red and gold with the rising sun that Paul and Maureen chose for Phantom's training period. They would take turns riding her—across the tundra-like beach, hard packed after a rain; up and down Main Street, where her hooves sounded like seashells pinging against the pavement; over trails carpeted with pine needles, where she made no sound at all.

They rode her out to the pony penning grounds, getting her used to the feel of the track and the sight of the white fence.

Before long the Phantom came to be a familiar and glorious sight. Her fame grew and spread. Now, on pleasant Sundays, visitors from the mainland began coming to see her.

Finally, on the Monday morning before Pony Penning, Grandma asked the question right out. She and Maureen were hanging up clothes at the time, while Paul, perched on top of a chicken coop, was silently whittling a pole into a clothes prop.

"Which of you," Grandma said, as she removed a clothespin from her mouth, "which of you will ride Phantom in the big race?"

A long silence was the only answer.

"Well! Well!" said Grandma brightly. "If you won't state your rathers, I got a fine idea."

Still no answer. Maureen

71

shook the creases out of a table-cloth as if her life depended on it. Paul kept on whittling furiously.

Just then Grandpa Beebe came by. He glanced around sharply. "Why's everyone so hushed?"

"Why, I just asked who's to ride Phantom come Pony Penning Day," replied Grandma, hanging her clothespin bag on the line and looking from one to the other.

"Oh," and Grandpa strung the little word out until it seemed to have springs in it. He dropped the posthole digger he was carrying and toed it with his boots.

Seconds went by.

Grandma straightened up from the clothesbasket.

"Clarence!" she said, speaking loud enough so her voice would reach Paul. "Seems like something told me to save the pully bone from that marsh hen. It's hanging above the almanac in the kitchen."

Grandpa slapped his thigh. "Nothing could be fairer than a pully bone!" he exclaimed. "The one that breaks off the biggest part gets to ride."

"I'll fetch it," Maureen called

over her shoulder as she disappeared into the kitchen. She came out holding one end of the wishbone very gingerly, as though it might break off in her hand.

"Now then!" Grandpa cleared his throat nervously.

Grandma picked up the empty clothesbasket, then set it down again in the very same spot.

"Now then," Grandpa repeated, "stop that whittling and step up, Paul."

Paul's legs seemed as wobbly as a colt's. He came forward very slowly, and his hand shook as he grasped the other end of the wishbone with his thumb and forefinger.

"Squinch your eyes tight," Grandma directed. "Make yer wish. And when I count three, pull!"

Paul and Maureen each took a long, deep breath as they clutched the tiny wishbone that was to decide their fate.

"One," Grandma counted slowly. "Two it is—and three!"

With a slight cracking noise, the wishbone broke. The larger half was in Paul's hand.

He gave a whistle of joy. Then his face sobered as he caught sight of Maureen, who was burying her half of the wishbone in the sandy soil. She looked up, trying to cover her feelings with a little smile.

"You won, Paul," she said, blinking. "You'll ride her better anyhow."

The last Wednesday in July dawned hot and still. Another Pony Penning Day had come!

By sunup the causeway between the mainland and Chincoteague was choked with traffic—trucks, station wagons, jeeps, cars of every description, bringing visitors to the island. They watched excitedly as the wild ponies swam ashore after the roundup. They lined the streets to see the procession to the pens; they cheered the broncobusters. But even after these events were over, the crowds kept on coming. For this year the big event was the race. Phantom was running! A wild sea horse against the sleek, well-trained Black Comet, winner for three years.

Toward evening a light wind came up, whisking sheep clouds before it. The sun was a huge red balloon hovering over the bay as Paul and Maureen, riding double on Phantom, turned into the pony penning grounds.

73

Maureen slid to her feet, and before she could whisper a word of encouragement into the Phantom's ear she was caught like a fly in a web. Her schoolmates, her uncles and aunts—everyone wanted to be with her during the race. They felt sorry for her because she was not riding. They seemed to wrap themselves about her until she could hardly breathe. Oh, how she longed to be by herself! Then she could race *with* Paul and Phantom! Only by being alone could she *be* Paul and Phantom both.

It was the voice over the loudspeaker that came to her rescue.

"Tonight, ladies and gentlemen!" the voice blared. "Tonight Black Comet from Pocomoke races against Firefly and the Phantom."

Everyone began running toward the track. Maureen slipped away from her friends and lost herself in the crowds. She wedged her way into a small opening between strangers and soon she was standing at the rails, her stomach against a fence post. She heard strange voices all about her. But now there was no need to listen to them. They were as unimportant as the little insect voices of the night.

She drew a deep breath as the

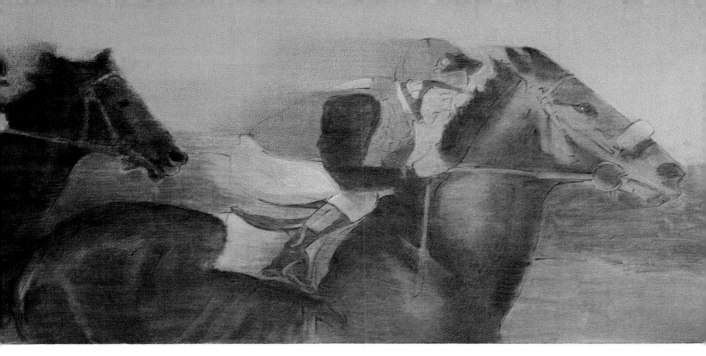

names of the three entries were announced again.

"There comes Black Comet!" the cry went up on all sides. "There he is!"

She saw Black Comet amble out on the track, aloof and black as night. He seemed bored with the entire business. Maureen would not have been surprised to see him yawn.

Now Firefly, a tall, rangy mare, pranced nervously to the starting post. Maureen's eyes passed over her lightly, then lingered on the Phantom who was parading to the post with dignity in her manner. She seemed unaware of the crowds, as if for her they did not exist. Her head was uplifted, her nose testing the winds, her body trembling. She could not understand the delay. She snuffed the wind hungrily. The wind was calling her, yet Paul was holding her back.

At last the signal was given. A roar went up from the crowd.

"They're off!"

"Black Comet at the rail," came the clipped voice over the loudspeaker, "Phantom on the outside. But it's Firefly who's taking the lead!"

From then on no one could hear the announcer for all the yell-

ing. The changeable crowds were calling, "Firefly! Firefly!"

Firefly held the lead the first quarter, then Black Comet shot forward and pulled out in front.

Maureen dug her fingernails into the fence rail. "Phantom!" she urged. "Oh, Phantom! Get going! It's a race."

But the Phantom was not running a race. She was enjoying herself. She was a piece of thistledown borne by the wind, moving through space in wild abandon. She was coming up, not to pass Firefly and Black Comet, but for the joy of flying. Her legs went like music. She was sweeping past Firefly now. She was less than a length behind Black Comet.

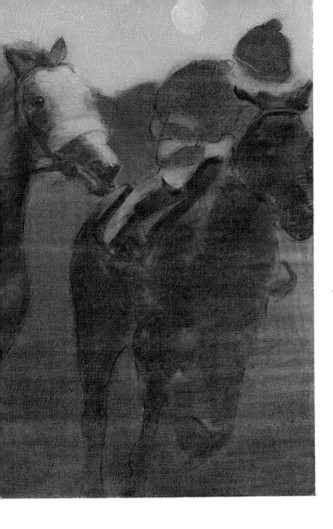

winging around the curve, her nostrils fire-red in the dying sun. She was Paul, leaning forward in a kind of wild glory.

Phantom was drawing close to Black Comet. Now she was even. She was sailing ahead. She was over the finish line. She was winner by a length!

The crowds grew hysterical. "It's Phantom! Phantom! She won!" But there was no stopping the Phantom! She was flying on around the track.

The voice over the loudspeaker was laughing. "Only once around," it was saying. "Only once around." Paul pulled back on the wickie and spoke softly in Phantom's ear. Gradually he brought her to a stop.

Maureen was laughing and crying too. The crowds pushed past her, dived between the rails, flocked around the Phantom. They yelled and thumped one another on the back as the judge handed Paul a purse.

Paul felt of its bulging contents. Then his eyes swept the crowds.

The people climbed up on the fence rails in a frenzy of excitement.

"Come on, Black Comet!" screamed the crowds from Pocomoke. "Come on!"

"Gee-up, Phantom!" cried the island folk.

Maureen was no longer an onlooker. She was the Phantom

"Here—here I am!" cried Maureen.

Every eye turned to see whom Paul wanted. When they discovered Maureen, standing on the top rail of the fence like a bird on a twig, friends and strangers, too, clapped and cheered. In an instant Paul was riding through the little opening they had made. With the fence as a mounting block, Maureen swung up behind Paul.

The island folk went mad with happiness.

"Hoo-ray for Paul and Maureen!"

"Hoo-ray for the Phantom!" they rejoiced.

But Paul and Maureen found only one face in all that sea of faces and heard only one voice in all that blur of noise. It was Grandpa Beebe's. "Get home," he bellowed. "Tell Grandma."

All the way home Paul talked to the Phantom. "Do you know," he murmured, "do you know you won twelve whole dollars? And

we're going to spend it all on you?"

"We could buy her red plumes, and ribbons to braid in her mane," suggested Maureen.

Paul leaned far forward to get as close as he could to Phantom's ear. "We could buy you shiny brass and leather trappings," he said. "You could be handsomer than any horse in the king's guard."

The Phantom let out a long whinny into the deepening twilight.

Paul laughed and laughed. "Want to know what she said?"

"What'd she say, Paul?"

"She said, 'Buy a toaster for Grandma and Grandpa. As for me,' she said, 'all I want is wings on my feet!' "

CHECK FOR UNDERSTANDING

1. Why was this Pony Penning Day a very special day for Maureen and Paul?
2. What disappointment did one of them have to face?
3. What method did Grandma suggest for settling the question of who would ride Phantom?
4. Why did Maureen want to be alone during the race?
5. In what way was the way Phantom ran the race different from the way the other horses ran?
6. What kind of relationship did Maureen and Paul have? What events in the story reveal this?

WRITE ABOUT *"The Big Race"*

What might have happened if Maureen had gotten the larger half of the wishbone? How do you think Paul might have reacted to the disappointment? What things would he have said and done? Rewrite the wishbone scene. In your version have Maureen be the one who gets the larger half.

DREAMS

by LANGSTON HUGHES

Hold fast to dreams
For if dreams die
Life is a broken-winged bird
That cannot fly.

Hold fast to dreams
For when dreams go
Life is a barren field
Frozen with snow.

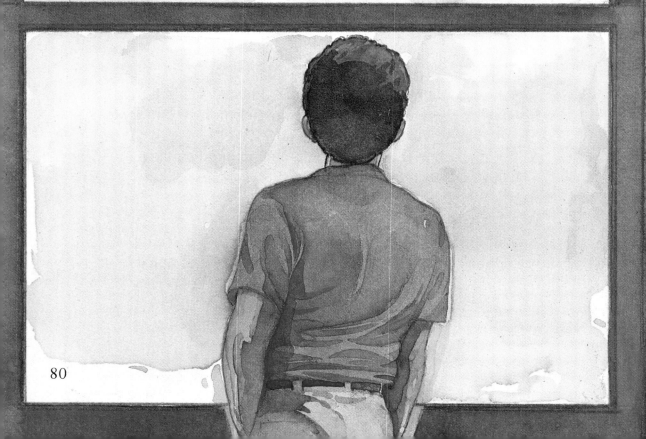

A Special Dream

by HARRIETTE GILLEM ROBINET

Things that are easy for most people may be difficult for others. For Jerome, almost everything is more difficult than it is for other people.

What two things does Jerome teach himself to do? Why is it so important to Jerome that no one know what he is doing?

Once he had liked the word *special*, special classes, special bus. Then he decided it meant "not like other boys."

The trouble was that people were always helping him. His speech was slow and slurred, and someone was always finishing what he wanted to say. When he played baseball, he would kneel to bat the ball and someone would run the bases for him. When he tried to roll his wheelchair at school, one of the kids would insist on pushing it. Everything happened to him, but he never got a chance to make things happen himself. Like a chick breaking out of an egg, he wanted to break free.

Jerome had a dream, a special dream. He knew what he must do. He would learn to ride a tricycle. And he would do it alone.

Jerome's father agreed to buy him a tricycle and fixed it up with a special seat belt and straps to hold Jerome's feet on the pedals. Each day Jerome sat on the cycle outside his house, but no one ever saw him even trying to ride it. Training himself to ride was something he did in secret. Alone in an alley, with no one watching except his sister Tilly, Jerome struggled each morning to ride his red cycle.

Three weeks passed and school was out. Every morning Tilly and Jerome went on their secret trip for a couple of hours. When Mama asked them where they went all morning, Jerome said, "Uh beennn near." Mama accepted the fact that he stayed close.

Soon Jerome could shake the cycle enough on the slope so that his right leg got down fast enough for the left leg to reach the top of its pedal. Then he could grunt the stiff left leg down. He pedaled, but not always. He

82

never could be sure. The dream of success was becoming a nightmare. He felt foolish and silly, not being able to depend on his rotten old legs.

"Tilly donnn' tellll," he begged. Every day they went to the alley. Tilly pulled the cycle out of the way when the trucks came up to the factory. Then she put her brother back on the slope and sat yawning, chin in hands, watching him struggle with the red cycle. What was simple for a three-year-old was hard for her eleven-year-old brother!

Sometimes she wished he were somebody else's brother; sometimes she almost hated him, he was so stubborn and mean. Her head got all confused when Jerome was mean, and she often felt she didn't love him at all, but she stuck by him all the time.

By July he could ride down the slant, but he fought and struggled to ride up. Soon his legs moved one after the other, and he was riding. Some days Jerome nearly burst with triumph, and Tilly wanted to tell Mama and Papa right away. But other days there was only failure. On those days his legs wouldn't push as he wished; in fact, they wouldn't move at all. He had nightmares about his legs not working when he tried to show Mama. In his dreams, Mama and Papa were watching and his legs wouldn't budge. His legs must learn to move one after the other all the time. He knew it wouldn't be easy, and he was fighting hard. Gradually he became more sure of being able to pedal; his legs worked more often than they didn't.

In August smothering heat arrived, but Jerome forced his legs to move in spite of the sweat pouring off him. Besides Tilly, no one else knew how hard he was trying.

At home Mama was afraid to hope; it broke her heart to watch him sit still out front on that red cycle. Papa was afraid not to hope.

By then the kids on the block had decided that Jerome would never ride. He had been fun the way he was; if only he would be satisfied with himself. What was so important about riding that cycle?

The summer before, he had played baseball with the other kids, and Tommy usually ran bases for him. But this summer he tripped Tommy and made his nose bleed. Then David ran his bases one day, and Jerome threw a stone at him and David needed an ice pack. Now all Jerome did was sit alone on the big red cycle. The kids thought he was mean, and they stopped playing with him. Why did he want that big cycle anyway?

But Jerome had his dream, and he had chosen it carefully. It was something he could do, it was possible, and he would do it. It was one thing he would get to do all by himself. Tilly, it was true, brought him to the slanted drive, but *he* was the one fighting his legs to ride. He'd show Tommy and David and all the kids—he'd even show Tilly, because there was something secret he was practicing late at night all by himself.

By the end of August he could hardly wait to show off. As he became sure of himself, the perfect occasion

came up. The neighbors planned a block party for Labor Day weekend.

That Saturday morning police closed the street at both ends, and teenagers decorated trees with yellow crepe-paper banners. Neighbors held brightly colored balloons, and marching music filled the air. Everyone was dressed in cool, colorful clothes for the hot summer day.

In the morning there was a pet parade, then games with water-filled balloons. Artists of all ages drew pictures on the sidewalk with colored chalk. In the afternoon there was a program of local talent.

David played drums, Liza sang a funny song, and another girl arranged a mushroom dance with five little girls. Jerome knew that Tilly had put his name next on the program.

For the mushroom dance, the little girls held umbrellas covered with brown paper. Everyone liked the silly twirling dance. When they finished, Mrs. Mullarkey called out, "And next on our program is Jerome Johnson who will, who will . . . Jerome Johnson, folks!"

Everyone clapped politely. Then there was an eerie quiet. Adults and kids looked at one another to see if

anyone knew what was going to happen. What was he going to do?

Tilly pulled her brother out into the street at the end of the block and left him sitting on the shiny orange red cycle. Her heart was pounding, and she lowered her head and stuck her hands in her jean pockets as she strolled away from him. He was on his own.

Mama folded her arms to calm herself; Papa sat down on the curb because his knees grew weak. Liza hugged Gordon, and they watched their brother and waited.

Jerome, frowning and gritting his teeth, struggled for what seemed like hours to get his legs moving. After two long minutes, slowly but firmly, he began pedaling—gripping the handles and leaning forward as though he were speeding along. There was no wind whipping in his face, but that didn't matter. He was riding his cycle himself; he was riding. That was all he would think.

The neighbors murmured and nodded to each other. Mrs. Mullarkey forgot she was holding the loudspeaker and blew her nose. The noise made everyone giggle nervously.

His progress down the street was slow, deliberate, and strangely rhythmic. People could hardly wait to applaud. As he neared the end, clapping burst forth and the kids cheered, but he remained calm and cool.

"OK," he muttered to himself, "wid Tilly's help Uh learnnnn tuh ride. But nnnnnn-now Uh really show um."

He stopped in the middle of the street, opened the seat belt, and bowed with a flourish to the people on his right. When he bowed, he made sure he slipped his right foot out of the pedal strap. He bowed and waved to the people clapping on his left and slipped his left foot out of the pedal strap just as he had planned. His hands trembled.

Tilly wondered why he had stopped in the middle. She started toward him, but he stopped her with an icy scowl. Papa stood up, but Jerome frowned at him, too.

Mama muttered, "It's not enough he can ride, that boy has to crawl off in the middle of the street."

The neighbors got quiet again.

Carefully Jerome slid his right leg around and off the cycle. He stood crouched on both feet, his knees and hips bent under this weight. He was grateful for the braces that kept his feet flat on the ground. At night when he had practiced this with his braces off, he stood on his toes.

He heard himself saying, "Uh wannn-na tank evv-body help muh, 'pecially muh sister Tilly and muh Papa and muh Mama." There was a mild sprinkling of applause.

Then, while eighty people held their breath, he let go of the cycle. His arms wavered at his sides, balancing him.

His head was high, his chin jutted forward. In spite of his eyeglasses, everybody was blurred.

He slid his stiff left leg forward, feet and knees twisted in. Then he stepped jerkily off on his right foot. He dragged his left leg, stepped with his right. Deliberate, slow, arms waving in the air, one leg after the other, Jerome Johnson walked. It was stiff and clumsy walking, with twisted legs, but these were his first steps, practiced late at night.

Before he reached his wheelchair, he fell to the street. No one moved toward him. Clapping and cheering could be heard for five blocks. It was almost like thunder in the sky. His dream had come true.

He didn't try to get to his feet again; he crawled to his wheelchair. He'd work on walking with his physical therapist now that it wasn't a secret anymore. Now that he'd shown them how much he could do all by himself.

Mama was thanking the Lord; Papa cried and didn't care who saw him. Liza and Gordon were staring with mouths hanging open.

Tilly rolled on the grass, laughing and crying and hugging herself for joy. Her tough, stubborn little brother had learned to ride a cycle and had taught himself to walk.

Jerome saw Tommy and David among the neighbors. Maybe he'd play some baseball with them. After all, he could walk now. Maybe next summer he would be running—even running his own bases.

Maybe he'd even . . .

Jerome was dreaming again.

CHECK FOR UNDERSTANDING

1. What two things did Jerome teach himself to do?
2. Why was riding the red cycle a good goal for Jerome to set for himself?
3. Why was it so important to Jerome that no one know what he was doing?
4. Why do you think Jerome seemed stubborn and mean so much of the time?
5. How did everyone at the block party react when Mrs. Mullarkey announced that Jerome Johnson was next in the program?
6. In what ways was Jerome's performance at the block party different from the things the other neighborhood children did?

WRITE ABOUT *"A Special Dream"*

Imagine that you are Tilly and that you have kept a record of Jerome's progress in a diary or journal. Write what you think Tilly would write in her journal the night of the Labor Day block party.

Point of View

> I was nearly twenty years old and about to take my first trip in an airplane. I had questions that I wanted to ask the flight attendants, but if I asked them they would know I'd never flown before. That would have been too embarrassing. It wasn't as if I'd never traveled anywhere before. I'd been lots of places. But Mom and Dad always liked seeing the countryside. So wherever we went, we went by car.

> At twenty, Hilary was about to take her first trip in an airplane. She had questions about the flight, but she didn't want to ask the flight attendants. She didn't want them to know that she had never flown before. It was not the case that Hilary had never traveled before. Actually she had traveled a great deal. But her parents enjoyed seeing the countryside. For Hilary, family vacations had always involved traveling by car.

What is different about these two paragraphs? They both describe the same situation. They both seem to be about the same person. The difference is the point of view. The first paragraph is written as if the character were telling you the story herself. It uses the first-person pronouns *I, my,* and *we.* This paragraph is written from first-person point of view. The second paragraph is written as if someone who knows a great deal about the character, Hilary, were telling the story. This paragraph uses the pronouns *her* and *she.* This paragraph is written from third-person point of view.

A story told from the first-person point of view has the excitement of making the reader an eyewitness to the events in the

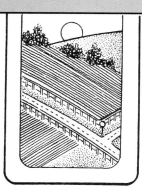

story. The reader has the feeling of discovering things just the way the teller of the story discovers them. The reader also learns first-hand what the character thinks and feels. At the same time, a story told from this point of view is limited. It shows only the events seen by the person telling the story.

By using the third-person point of view, the writer is not limited to only the events seen by one person. A writer can show the reader two events happening at the same time in different places.

The first story you read in this unit, "From the Diary of Leigh Botts," is told in the first person. So is the selection you are about to read, "The Mountains of the Sangre de Cristo."

It is possible to blend the excitement of a first-person point of view and the flexibility of the third-person point of view. An example of this is the "The Rescue." The story is told in the third person. The main character is called *Laurie* or referred to as *she* throughout the story. But the story has a flavor of the first-person point of view because everything in the story is witnessed by this main chracter. The reader gets the feeling of standing beside Laurie throughout the story as things happen to her.

Keep in mind the point of view as you read "The Mountains of the Sangre de Cristo." Ask yourself how the story would be different if it had been told from a third-person point of view. Try to figure out why the author chose to tell the story from the first-person point of view.

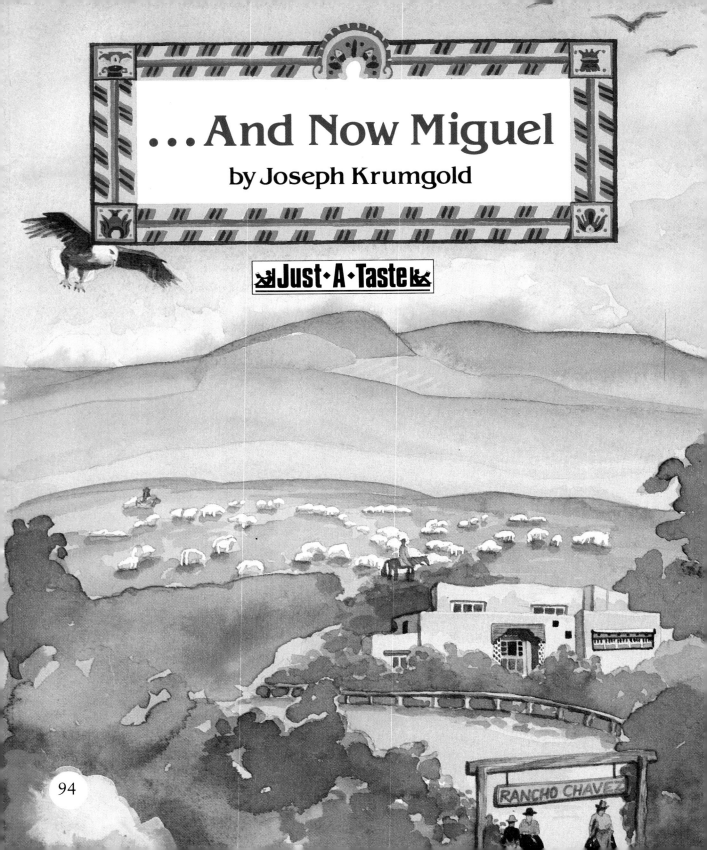

...And Now Miguel

by Joseph Krumgold

Just·A·Taste

The Mountains of the Sangre de Cristo

Miguel's family raises sheep in New Mexico. Every spring, his father, uncles, and older brothers drive the sheep to pasture in the Mountains of the Sangre de Cristo. Twelve-year-old Miguel longs to go with them. But to be asked to go, Miguel must find a way to prove that he is ready.

Why is it so important to Miguel to go with the flock to the mountains? Why are the Mountains of the Sangre de Cristo important to the Chavez family?

To be me, Miguel, and to have a great wish—that is hard.

I had such a wish. It was a secret and yet not a secret. For how secret can you keep high mountains that one can see for hundreds of miles around, mountains that face me when I first open my eyes every morning and are the last thing I see in the night.

This was my wish, to go up there—into those mountains that are called the Mountains of the Sangre de Cristo. If you are ready and the time comes, then you will go.

To get ready, it is first necessary to be of my family, a Chavez, and that I have come to be without even trying. Then, one must be a shepherd and know all about how to take care of the sheep. It is likewise a help to know how to bake bread and be a good cook as well as to ride a horse and shoot a gun and catch fish. When you can do these things, then you are ready.

And all that must be done then is to wait until the time comes.

And it always does. Every year. It comes as sure as the time for the lambs to be born, and the time for the Fiesta de San Ysidro, and then the shearers arrive and the wool is clipped. Just so sure as all these things happen, comes the time for the flock to go up into the Mountains of the Sangre de Cristo.

Then you will go along. If, that is, everyone knows you are ready.

But if they don't, then you must wait again for another whole year. And even another year and another.

Each year, after the last heavy snows are over, the time comes to show that I am ready and that it is different this year for me, Miguel, than it was last year. It is in this early part of the year that the new lambs are born. Then the sheep are brought in from the pueblo land of the Indians, from the big mesa where they have spent the winter. The sheep wagon is brought in, too. Now the flock must stay close to the house so that everyone can help with the birth of the lambs.

At this time there is no question of who is Pedro and who is Gabriel and who am I. Everyone helps without it making any difference who he is.

Even in the middle of the night someone can come into the bedroom where Faustina sleeps in one bed and me and Pedro in another. This one can say, "Come on, they need water."

There is no question who asks for the water or who goes to fetch it. We are quick to find our clothes and run to the spring, which is down the hill behind the tool shed. We carry the water to where it is needed, to the lambing pens where the fires are kept going all night and the men must help the newest lambs who are having a hard time to get born. Or to the kitchen where my mother is always cooking during this time, because someone is always eating.

The lambs come at all different hours, and all our uncles and cousins stay at our house to be ready to help, and there is no breakfast time or dinner time or bed time. Everyone sleeps and eats when he can, no matter who he is, as long as he is ready when something is needed.

I would like it to matter who he is, especially if it's me, Miguel. But that has never happened.

"Behind the tractor," my father will talk to me without even turning around, "in the tool shed there on the shelf is the liniment. The brown bottle. Hurry!"

My father will be busy bending over a ewe who tries hard to give birth to a lamb, working together with Uncle Eli. He will not even look up when I bring the medicine and put it into his hand.

Once I tried to make my father see who I am. When he asked for some burlap bags to wrap one small lamb who was cold, I brought him the bags. When he took them from me, I said, "Here are the bags."

My father said nothing. He rubbed the lamb and wrapped it up.

"All right?" I said. "OK?"

My father felt the neck of the lamb. "He'll be all right. It'll live."

"No," I shook my head. "I ask about the bags."

"What about the bags?"

"Are they all right?"

"What can be wrong with bags?"

"Wrong? Nothing. Except sometimes—" This is not what I wanted to talk about at all. "There can be holes in them."

"For our purpose, to wrap up new lambs, holes make no difference. That's why we use old bags."

I knew all this. But I couldn't stop him from saying it.

"If we wanted to put something into them, like grain or wool, then we use new bags without holes." My father stood up now, looking down at me. "You didn't bring me any of the new wool bags, those that are in the corner of the shearing shed?"

"Me?" I said quickly. "Not me!" This is why it is hard for me to be Miguel sometimes, getting people to understand.

"Then what is all this talk about bags?" My father put his hands in the back pockets of his pants and waited.

"I'm sorry." I looked around trying to find some way to leave. But it was too late.

"Miguel, what's the trouble?"

"Nothing." When my father looks at you, then there is no place to go. "It's only that I wanted you to know that it was me—I brought you the bags when you asked for them."

"Of course. They were needed. That's why I asked."

"I know, but—" It was no use. It could not get any better. "That's all."

"Ai Blas." Uncle Bonifacio yelled to my father from across the corral. "This ewe here, with twins. Looks bad."

"Be right with you," my father called to him, but he looked back. "Let me understand this, Miguel. This is nothing but a question of bags, yes?"

"That's all."

"Nothing else?"

"No."

"Very well," said my father, and he hurried through the sheep to the other side of the corral.

It is different in school. There, when the teacher asks you to write in your book the capital of the State of New Mexico, and you write "Santa Fe," the matter does not come to an end. If you do what she asks, then you get a star in your book. And after you get enough stars, you get a G on your report card instead of an F.

But here with the family and with the sheep, to bring an old bag is nothing but the question of a bag. And if you talk about it, all you do is to get into trouble. And liniment is nothing else but liniment. And when you bring water, that is the end of it. There are no stars.

Soon the days pass and all the lambs are born, and then the shearers arrive and not many days are left.

And even though everyone gets busy again at the shearing, it's not like when the lambs come. To shear and to bag the wool, to tie the fleeces, you have to be an ex-

pert to do these things. Even a little mistake is bad. All I can do is to sit on a fence, with Pedro, and watch the others hard at work under the shearing sheds.

"And after so many years," like I once told Pedro, "it's not enough, just to watch anymore."

"Why?" said Pedro. "This is fine. Nothing to do. No school. What could be better than this?"

"It would be better to help, like our brother Blas over there, pushing the sheep into the pen for the shearers."

"Such hard work. What for?"

I had not told Pedro, or anyone else, about my wish to go to the Sangre de Cristo. Nor did I tell him now. Instead I said, "When we work with the others, as at the lambing, we are less by ourselves. It is not so lonesome."

"We're together," said Pedro. "That's not lonesome."

"I mean alone by ourselves. When the others are working."

"You know as well as I do," said Pedro, "when we run and fetch and help at lambing time, no one even knows we're there."

This is true, as I have said. "But even so, it would be better to help," I said once again. "Much better."

"It is better to be sitting here on the fence," said Pedro, "just watching and doing nothing else."

That's the way it is with Pedro. Everything he has is enough. But for me, I have the wish to be part of everything that happens, even if it is not happening to me. Like when the shearers leave and the day comes for the men to leave with the flock, to start for the Mountains. Even though I have never gone with the others, that day for me is the biggest day of the year.

Hardly anyone goes to sleep because the start is very early in the morning, before it gets light, and because there is so much to prepare. We all work to get everything together the men will need—the horses and a tent, the blankets and the food and the guns and a stove. Each man who is going must take everything for the whole time he is away.

And I, too, in secret, have for many years now prepared a bundle for myself, which I keep underneath the bed without anyone knowing. In it I put all my clothes of the winter, though it is by then summer, because it is cold, they have told me, on the high ridges and on the top peaks. In it, too, I pack my best fish hooks, the luckiest ones. I put this bundle beneath my bed because you never know. It could happen at the very last that my father, or my brother Blas, or Uncle Eli will say, "One moment,

100

Miguel. It has been decided among us that you are ready and that this year you will come with the flock, with the rest of us, to the Sangre de Cristo. You are needed."

"If I am needed," I will say, "then of course I will be glad to go."

Then they will say, "The only trouble is we forgot to tell you until it is late. Can you get ready in time?"

And because my bundle is already under the bed, I will say, "Yes. Sure. No trouble."

It could happen this way. Though it never has. But until the very last minute, until the very start, the chance remains that it might. And until then, it is good to be in our house. For everyone talks of nothing but the Mountains of the Sangre de Cristo. And because the men are going away for so long, not less than three months, they like to talk to the rest of us who are staying. Even when Faustina cries because they are leaving, my father will stop his work and take her on his lap.

"Tinga mia," he will tell her. "It is not forever. At the end of the summer, we will be back."

"Why?" Faustina squeaks very high like a lamb when she cries. "Why don't you stay here, in the house?"

"We must feed the sheep. There is good grass, the best in the world, on the Sangre de Cristo."

"Here is grass. On the farm is grass. What's grass?"

My father always has to wipe her nose. It runs like a spring when she cries. "There's not enough, Tinga," he tells her, "for so many sheep. On this farm we can feed no more than fifty sheep. We have many hundreds and each one with a lamb. That's why in the winter we must rent from the Indians to pasture the flock. You remember how it is in the winter?"

"Yes," says Faustina. If my father holds her long enough on his lap, pretty soon she quiets down.

"But in the summer, the pueblo lands on the mesa get very dry. There is very little grass for the sheep to eat. We are lucky we have the mountains so close. Up there it

101

is never dry. The grass is always green and rich. It makes the sheep and the lambs fat and healthy. Isn't that good, Tinga?"

"OK," says Faustina, as if she understood what it was all about.

The truth is we are lucky indeed to be able to take the sheep to the Sangre de Cristo. Not everyone can go there for pasture. All this was explained to me by Uncle Bonifacio.

"No one owns the mountains." We were packing flour and bacon and all kinds of food in bags when he told me this. "No one except the government. And the government name for the Sangre de Cristo is the Carson National Forest."

"Carson—he is part of the government."

"No, he's just a man by the name Kit Carson who fought with the Indians and killed buffaloes and was a soldier, and now he is dead. So instead of putting up a statue for him where the birds can sit when they get tired of sitting in trees, they set aside the mountains so that no one can own them and

gave his name, Carson, to the whole place." Uncle Bonifacio smiled as we kept putting food into the bags. Often he smiles, my Uncle Bonifacio, but I have never seen him laugh.

"Now people come from far away to go up in the mountains because it is beautiful there."

"Like I say," I said. "Wonderful."

"That's also true." Uncle Bonifacio nodded. "Wonderful. Almost anything you like, you can find in the mountains. Great sights to see. Good fishing, bass in the lakes and trout everywhere. Animals to hunt, in the proper season, even bears and wolf and deer."

"And lions and tigers?"

"There are mountain lions. But tigers? This is the Sangre de Cristo after all, Miguel, not a traveling circus. And there are trees everywhere, good for making lumber if one gets permission from the government and promises not to cut down all the trees. In which case, the birds would have to go back to the statues after all. And fine pasture for cattle and sheep. But in order to graze our stock on the mountains, you must also get permission, and this is difficult."

"With the mountains so big? Stretching as far as you can see?"

"Even so, there are men in the government who say even less sheep should graze in the Sangre de Cristo than now. For there is a danger if all the grass is eaten. Then when it rains on the bare earth, the dirt will wash away, and the water will run off the hills as from a roof, making one day a flood and the next day dry, bare rocks under the sun. That is why only a few are given the permit to pasture their sheep in the mountains. And that is why we of the Chavez family are lucky to have such a permit."

"Thank goodness we are lucky!"

"Thank goodness if you wish," Uncle Bonifacio closed the bag now and tied it up, "but also thank

103

your grandfather for being such a wise man. It was he, many years ago, who got the permit for our flock. If not for him you would have to be a police officer when you grow up, or an airplane pilot," he smiled.

I don't think to be a police officer or an airplane pilot is anything so terrible. But still I am glad that I am growing up to be a shepherd,

if only it doesn't take too long. And so, as Uncle Bonifacio said, I thanked my grandfather.

It was during the last hour of the night. I helped my grandfather tie the canvas bag filled with blankets onto the mule, Herman. My grandfather is almost eighty years, which is as old as most people get. He no longer goes to the mountains, but nothing is done without his help. Tying the pack, he worked very slow and every knot was tight. He stopped and shook his head when I thanked him.

"The permit, it is only a piece of paper of the government. The paper will go and the government will go, but still the mountains will remain."

"Yes, Padre de Chavez," I said.

He turned from the mule, and slowly he pointed with his hand from the north to the south. It was not yet dawn, but already the sky looked to be in two parts. The part that was really the sky was not so dark, and the part that was the mountains still black. "When you wish to see what is ahead, in the time to come, you look to the

mountains. If it is white on their peaks with snow, like blessed white clouds that have come to rest, it will be a good year. There will be much water all through the months from the snows that melt, and we and the sheep will have it good, here and far from here. All down the Rio Grande valley, they will rejoice. Even in Texas and Arizona and in Old Mexico they will give thanks for the Mountains of the Sangre de Cristo. Give thanks, too, Miguel, for the year that is ahead.''

And I did. Though last year, when we spoke, it was not the year for which I wanted to thank anybody. Last year it happened like all the years before.

When the time came, my father kissed my mother and then each one of us. Then we all went outside, and everybody hugged everybody else and said good-by. No one said anything special to me, not even at the last moment.

One could see the mountains with the tops all white as they started out, for it was getting day. Gabriel was on his horse Blackie, leading the three pack horses. And

105

Uncle Eli, too, was on a horse. My father, my brother Blas, and Uncle Bonifacio went on foot, driving the flock with the dog Cyclone.

We stood watching them. My mother stood with my grandfather, and my big sisters were with the little ones, Faustina and Pedro. And me, not big or little, I stood there alongside the others.

The flock sent up a big cloud of dust as it started out. And after a while there was nothing to watch but this brown, dirty cloud coming up and moving slowly toward the high mountains. By then the others had gone back into the house. Soon, even the dust of the cloud disappeared, and nothing was left to look at except the tops of all the Mountains of the Sangre de Cristo, standing clean and shining and high in the sun. At the end it was no good to stand there anymore looking up at them. It made you to feel more little than you are.

So I went back into the house. I took the bundle out from underneath the bed. I put everything back in its place.

It happened this way last year. And this is the last time, I have promised myself, it will happen in such a way. For now it is a new year, with the winter coming to an end, and I have become twelve.

Now that he is twelve, Miguel believes things will be different. To find out what happens this year when Miguel's family prepares to take the sheep to the mountains read the rest of the novel... **And Now Miguel,** *by Joseph Krumgold.*

106

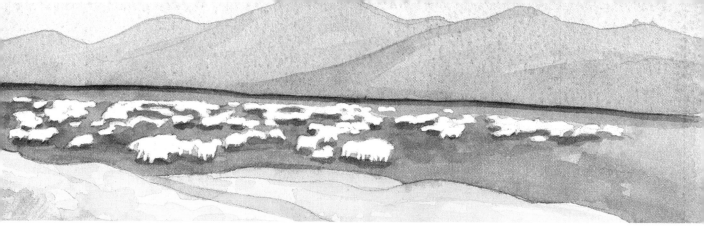

CHECK FOR UNDERSTANDING

1. When Miguel brought his father the burlap bags, what did Miguel try to make his father do? Why?
2. In what way are Miguel and his little brother Pedro different?
3. What did Miguel do the year before to prepare for the trip to the mountains?
4. Why is it so important to Miguel to go with the flock to the mountains? What does the journey mean to Miguel?
5. Why are the Mountains of the Sangre de Cristo important to the Chavez family?

WRITE ABOUT

"The Mountains of the Sangre de Cristo"

Imagine that Miguel's father had discovered the bundle under Miguel's bed and asked Miguel about it. What would Miguel have told him? Would Miguel's father have agreed to let him go to the mountains when he realized how much Miguel wanted to go? If not, how would he have explained that Miguel was not ready?

Pretend you are Miguel telling about the talk you had with your father. Write what you think they might have said to each other.

THINK ABOUT IT

Think about the events that took place in each story.

- For Leigh, opening his lunch box and setting off the alarm was a turning point in his feelings about his new school, his classmates, and himself.
- For Laurie, choosing to help the little girl meant risking a goal that was important to her.
- For Elma Barrera, a routine day of news reporting is dramatically changed by a tragedy in Mexico City.
- For Maureen, the chance to participate in a special event is lost, so she must find another way to share the moment.
- For Jerome, all his effort and courage are required to make Labor Day the moment when people will see that he is "special" for a new reason.
- For Miguel, the day the men take the sheep to the mountains will always be special, whether he goes or stays.

Some events—even those that people look forward to and plan for—just happen and are forgotten. Other events—some that happen quite unexpectedly—are never forgotten. They are remembered; they become part of a person's "history." What makes the difference? What makes an event memorable?

WRITE ABOUT IT

Special moments create changes. Some of the changes may be small; others may be long-lasting. Choose one of the stories that you liked. Write two paragraphs explaining how the character's life or way of looking at life might be different in the future.

Explain how the change—whether it is a minor change or a dramatic one—may be a result of a special moment the character experienced in the story you read.

READ ABOUT IT

Portrait of Ivan by Paula Fox. Bradbury Press, 1969. When a lonely boy has his portrait painted, he finds that it is easy to talk to the young painter and to the woman who reads to him during the sittings.

Philip Hall Likes Me, I Reckon, Maybe by Bette Greene. Dial Books for Young Readers, 1974. In this novel set in rural Arkansas, Beth is the leader when she and Philip catch turkey thieves, run a fruit stand, and share other adventures.

When Hitler Stole Pink Rabbit by Judith Kerr. The Putnam Publishing Group, 1972. This is the story of a Jewish family who left Germany for France in 1933, to avoid Hitler's persecution.

The Dancing Cats of Applesap by Janet Taylor Lisle. Bradbury Press, 1984. Jiggs' Drug Store has cats everywhere—even on top of the counters. Passersby think this is odd, but Melba Morris knows that the cats are special.

In the Year of the Boar and Jackie Robinson by Bette Bao Lord. Harper & Row, Publishers, 1984. Shirley Temple Wong, otherwise known as Bandit, sails to New York in 1947 to live in Brooklyn. There she discovers something remarkable—baseball.

2

NOT WHAT YOU THINK

You've probably heard jokes like this.

Why did the chicken cross the road? To get to the other side.

What time is it when an elephant steps on your clock? Time to get a new clock.

The answers are obvious, but they are not what you would expect. That is what makes them funny.

In this unit, you should expect things to be a little different from what the characters think they are. The selections are full of surprises. Sometimes the surprising things that happen will make you laugh. Other times, you may find yourself scratching your head in puzzlement. As you read the selections, think about why *the characters—and perhaps you, too—think things are different from what they really are.*

The Lost Umbrella

by ELEANOR ESTES

Have you ever suspected something was true but didn't know for sure? Often your suspicion grows, and everything you see makes you more and more certain that you are right. In this story, Kim Chu and Mae Lee are sure they know who took Kim's father's umbrella.

Why is Kim afraid to speak to the millionaire man? What happens to give Kim the courage to accuse the man?

Kim Chu's father had a very special umbrella. It had been given to him by the leaders of Chinatown in New York City for his contribution to the neighborhood's New Year's celebration. The umbrella was the only one of its kind. The bamboo handle twisted off, and inside there was a secret scroll.

*Kim's whole family valued the umbrella, but one day Kim lost it at the library. She **had** to get it back.*

Kim and her friend Mae Lee trail a well-dressed man—"a millionaire man"—onto the Staten Island Ferry. They are convinced that he has Kim's father's umbrella. Together Kim and Mae keep watch on the man and his companion—the "laughing lady."

Kim caught up with Mae as she was rounding the bend at the front of the boat. "Wait, Mae!" she said. "Come back! News!"

At the meeting place she said, "Mae. They're sitting together now! He's in my seat!"

"In your seat?" repeated Mae Lee incredulously. "Shows they are in cahoots! The lady laughs all the time

to throw you off the track . . . make you think what a nice jolly lady she is. But all along she's been a partner of the man and . . . she must know the secret of the handle."

"Yes!" said Kim indignantly. "Asking me was I lost! Right this minute we should say to the two of them sitting in my seat, 'We know you have my father's umbrella! Give it back!' " Kim was so angry she could not help but speak loudly.

"Sh-sh-sh!" Mae Lee cautioned her and looked from left to right and behind them. But no one was around. "All right then," she said. "I'll go back my usual way and you go back yours. Then we, the two of us, will meet in front of them . . . the two of them. Two in cahoots against two in cahoots. That's fair!"

"We must hurry!" said Kim. "They must be thinking something . . . plotting something . . . they know we suspect them and they want to outwit us. But . . . Mae. When we get there, what will we say?"

"Say? Well . . . that will come to us, the right thing to say. And we will say it politely, nicely . . . Just say, 'We want that umbrella back! Come across!' "

Mae hurried off, not sauntering this time, on her regular beat around the boat.

Kim did not have as far to go as Mae. So she sauntered back to where the two were sitting. In her mind she rehearsed what she might say . . . just say . . . nicely . . . "There must be a mistake. But the nice man has my umbrella, my father's umbrella, and please give it back quietly . . . nicely . . ." She wouldn't say they'd call the police or anything to scare the man . . . or the jolly lady either, if she was in cahoots . . . Oh! But what a hard thing to do! she thought. As she rounded the bend she reminded herself of Mae's words: "Courage, my friend!"

But—around the bend now, all steeled to say what she had been thinking to say . . . and how to say it, like lines in a play, to the two of them together—she saw that the jolly lady was sitting alone again and that the millionaire man had gone back to his seat. Again he had the umbrella tightly clutched between his knees and had *The Wall Street Journal* spread out in front of him. Kim sat down in her seat next to the jolly lady who was having

quite a fit of chuckling . . . her shoulders were shaking. She was staring at page forty-nine and her forefinger still marked the same place in line five.

Maybe Kim had imagined it all . . . that the man had been sitting in her seat just a few minutes before!

Then Mae Lee came. Pretending no surprise at finding the man back in his seat, she took up her usual position at the railing nearby, leaned on her elbows, and rocked on her feet, as usual. But a dark frown was on her face and her eyes flashed anger. Very soon she signaled Kim to join her at the meeting place. Once there, she said ominously, "They're trying to throw us off the track. They're stalling. They know we don't have many minutes left before the ferry docks. Anyway, one good thing . . . it's much easier to speak to one crook at a time. You speak! This minute. It's *your* father's umbrella, not my father's . . ."

"Supposing it isn't my father's umbrella anyway after all?" asked Kim. "Would I be arrested?"

"I'll come to see you in jail . . . bring you your homework and something to eat," Mae comforted her. "But I don't think you will be arrested . . . he's the one to be arrested," said Mae. "Racing up to the Chatham Square

El Station, and all. You know . . . he probably saw me going into the library as he was coming out. And he probably thought *I* had seen *him* with your father's umbrella. Then . . . when he saw me on the elevated train, then he may have missed it on purpose . . . to give me the slip! But he didn't . . ." said Mae proudly. "We have him cornered!"

"Yes . . ." said Kim dolefully. "But I wish I'd already said, 'Give it back!' Come what, come may . . ."

"Courage, friend," said Mae. "We have to work fast now. You see that buoy bobbing in the ocean there? The minute we pass that buoy, the captain gives a toot. So people in Saint George can hurry down the hill and catch the boat going back to the city."

"O-o-oh!" gasped Kim and she hurried away. But as she rounded the bend, she stopped short. For there were the two sitting together again! Kim tore after Mae and this time the girls hurried through the cabin of the boat to the wide open door beside which, on the outside, on the deck, the two suspects were sitting, heads together as before behind *The Wall Street Journal,* plotting something . . . how to make their getaway with the stolen umbrella, probably, before the buoy bonged its somber tune.

The girls listened. The two of them were talking out of the side of their mouths to each other, but not in any code . . . in plain English. And they talked more loudly than Mae and Kim had talked at their meeting place. The girls could hear every single word the two were saying.

"George!" said the laughing lady.

"Yes, Daisy . . . yes?" said the millionaire man.

(Kim and Mae exchanged glances. This showed that the two were in cahoots for they knew each other by first names. So, why hadn't they tried to sit together? To throw Kim and Mae off . . . that's why . . .)

The lady said, "I knew you could carry it off, George. I just knew it. You're a winner, a born winner . . . you get everything you go after, George. 'Go-getter George!' You deserve the nickname. And this is so important! The most important thing you've set your sights on so far. You've carried it this far. Do you think you can carry it off?"

("O-o-oooh!" gasped Kim. "He'll probably leap over the rope . . . like when he got on . . ."

"Sh-sh-sh . . ." said Mae.)

"With you behind me, Daisy," said the man, "I can carry anything off!" Then he said, "Say, Daisy, by the way, have you noticed those two little girls . . . the one who stands behind me at the railing, and the other who sits beside you? One or the other of them has had her eyes on me the whole way over."

("Oh, we haven't," said Kim indignantly. "Sometimes we were at the meeting place."

"Anyway, we know how to watch so no one knows we are watching . . ." said Mae.)

The jolly lady chuckled. She could hardly talk she thought this was so funny. "Yes, George. I have noticed that . . ."

("I told you she was pretending to read," said Kim, "staying on page forty-nine!"

"Yes! And *The Wall Street Journal* . . . It's fine print, but you don't stay on page two forever!" said Mae.)

"George!" said Daisy. "What is there about you that is so special in the minds of these little girls?"

"I'm sure I don't know," said George with a shrug of his shoulders.

("Throwing us off," said Kim.)

"H-m-m," mused Daisy. She turned toward Go-getter George and peered at him through the top no-glass part of her glasses and then the glass part (the girls could see this through the window), and she said, "Nothing so very unusual about you . . . dressed nicely as always, carrying your umbrella neatly clasped together . . ."

("Throwing us off," said Mae.)

"There are probably a dozen or more men on this ferry boat, all nicely dressed, as you so charmingly put it, carrying umbrellas exactly like this one, neatly fastened together . . ." said Go-getter Terwilliger.

The lady mused. She said, "Well, George. I don't know . . . but there *is* something odd about the way you are holding your umbrella, clutching it so tightly between your knees. And it's so wet!"

"Listen to me, Daisy!" said the man. "I have to clutch this umbrella. I have to hang onto it by hook or by crook. Because this umbrella . . ."

Kim and Mae were listening intently. But the word that came next was lost because, at that very moment,

"TOO-OOT! TOO-OOT!" sounded the long, deep whistle of the ferryboat.

As though pressed by a button, passengers appeared from all sides, coming up from below and down from above. And true enough, exactly as the millionaire man had said, many men appeared and some of them had umbrellas that looked exactly like the one that the millionaire man was clutching.

The last thing Kim and Mae heard the man say was, "Well, nice talking to you, Daisy. I'm counting on you. But I have to hurry . . . Think I can carry this off?"

"Of course, George! Good luck!"

Kim gasped. "Hurry, Mae. We have to beat them to the front!"

"It's now or never!" said Mae.

They tore through the cabin and to the front of the boat as it began to bump and thrash its way into the slip. The man who was in charge of the heavy rope was already standing at the hook end. He was all set to unclasp the heavy hook the minute the boat docked. And that was to be right now!

Kim and Mae ran to the rope, ducking between people to get there. They stretched their arms straight out, fingers barely touching in the middle to give each other courage. And they needed it! For at this very moment the millionaire man, in a desperate hurry, rushed to the rope also.

"He wants to jump over again!" said Kim.

"Wait!" cried Mae Lee.

"Stop!" yelled Kim Chu. "There is a thief aboard!" She felt brave now that come what, come may was here. "An umbrella thief!" she and Mae cried out together. They could have made a wish had the time been suitable.

The rope man held his hand uncertainly on the heavy hook. But he did not unhook it. For the captain had sounded a special piercing whistle that meant, "HOLD EVERYTHING!"

And now the captain of the boat in his shiny blue suit and gold braid left his place at the helm and descended the little winding stairway. When he reached the deck he boomed, "What's all this about? What thief is on board this Staten Island ferry? Explain!" he said. "Explain!"

Is the millionaire man really an umbrella thief? Will Kim and Mae get into trouble for accusing him? To find out what happens, read The Lost Umbrella of Kim Chu, *by Eleanor Estes.*

CHECK FOR UNDERSTANDING

1. Why did Kim and Mae think the jolly lady was in cahoots with the millionaire man?
2. Why was Kim afraid to speak to the millionaire man?
3. What did Kim think the woman was talking about when she said to the man "I knew you could carry it off"?
4. What do you think the millionaire man was about to say when the ferryboat whistle sounded?
5. What happened to give Kim the courage to accuse the man?

WRITE ABOUT *"The Lost Umbrella"*

When the ferryboat captain comes down from his place at the helm, he demands that Kim explain what she is talking about when she says that there is a thief on board the ferry. Write the next scene of the story. Write Kim's explanation of why she said there was a thief aboard and why she thinks the millionaire man is that thief.

123

Word Histories

Kim Chu's father's umbrella was special. It had a story behind it. It had a history. Words can have histories, too. Several of the words used in "The Lost Umbrella" have quite interesting histories. Knowing the history of a word—what language it came from and what it originally meant—is interesting and fun. It gives you a better understanding of the meaning of words by showing you how the meaning may have changed over time. Knowing word histories also gives you a sense of the richness of language.

Take the word *umbrella,* for example. It comes from a Latin word *umbra,* which means "shade." We think of an umbrella as something that protects us from the rain. If we wanted something that would shade us from the sun, we might carry a *parasol.* The word *parasol* is made up of an Old Italian verb that means "shield" and the Latin word for sun, *sol.* It is interesting that although we think of an umbrella primarily as rain gear and a parasol as an old-fashioned protection from the sun, the histories of these words show that both umbrellas and parasols were originally intended to shade people from the sun.

The laughing lady in the story is sometimes referred to as the jolly lady. The word *jolly* has an interesting history. It probably comes from the word *jol,* a very old name for a midwinter festival. When this festival occurred, the shortest day of the year was past. The days were beginning to get longer again, and that was a sure sign that spring and the growth of living things would return once again. At the ancient *jol* celebration, people were happy and hopeful. They were *jolly.*

In the story, Mae says to Kim, "Courage, my friend!" *Courage* also has an interesting history. It comes from the Latin word for heart, *cor.* In the Middle Ages, the English word was spelled *corage,* and it meant heart as the center of a person's character and seat of inner strength. In modern English, *heart* is often a synonym for *courage. Heart* is a synonym for *courage* in the expression *take heart,* which means "be brave, don't give up." *Heart* is also a synonym for *courage* in the expression *lose heart,* which means "become discouraged."

In the story, the millionaire man is reading *The Wall Street Journal. The Wall Street Journal* is a daily business newspaper. It is named *Wall Street* after the major street in the financial district in New York City. The word *journal* has an interesting history. The base word for *journal* is the French word for day, *jour.* In French, the word *journal* means literally "daily." In English, a *journal* is a book in which people keep daily entries or records or it is a newspaper that is published daily.

There are other words in the story with interesting histories. See if you can figure out which words they are. One of the words comes from the Latin word for book, *liber.* Which word do you think it is?

Another expression used in the story may be related to a French word for hut or cabin, *cahute.* What is the expression? How do you think that meaning of the expression might be related to the French word *cahute?*

Another word in the story comes from the Old English word *daegeseage,* which meant "day's eye" and named a flower that opened in the morning and closed again in the evening. Which word do you think this is? Here is a hint. In the story, the word is a person's name.

Another word comes from the word *mus,* which is an Old French word for "snout." The verb form of this word, *muser,* meant "sniff around for a scent." Which word in the story comes from these Old French words? How is the meaning of the English word related to the meanings of the Old French words?

The Last of the
DRAGONS

by E. NESBIT

In the days when knights roamed the countryside doing
brave deeds, every prince was expected to rescue a princess
from a fierce dragon. This story has a prince, a princess, and a
dragon. But what happens in the story is not what you'd expect.
   What makes the princess wrong for the role of the person
who must be rescued? How does the dragon feel about its role
in the story?

Of course you know that dragons were once as common as motorbuses are now, and almost as dangerous. But as every well-brought-up prince was expected to kill a dragon and rescue a princess, the dragons grew fewer and fewer, till it was often quite hard for a princess to find a dragon to be rescued from. And at last there were no more dragons in France and no more dragons in Germany, or Spain, or Italy, or Russia. There were some left in China, and are still, but they are cold and bronzy. There never were any, of course, in America. But the last real live dragon left was in England. Of course that was a very long time ago, before what you call English History began. This dragon lived in Cornwall in the big caves amidst the rocks. It was a very fine dragon, quite seventy feet long from the tip of its fearful snout to the end of its terrible tail. It breathed fire and smoke. And it rattled when it walked, because its scales were made of iron. Its wings were like half-umbrellas—or like bat's wings, only several thousand times bigger. Everyone was very frightened of it, and well they might be.

Now the King of Cornwall had one daughter. When she was sixteen, of course, she would have to go and face the dragon. Such tales are always told in royal nurseries at twilight, so the Princess knew what she had to expect. The dragon would not hurt her, of course—because the Prince would come and rescue her. But the Princess could not help thinking it would be much pleasanter to have nothing to do with the dragon at all—not even to be rescued from it.

"All the princes I know are very silly little boys," she told her father. "Why must I be rescued by a prince?"

"It's always done, my dear," said the King, taking his crown off and putting it on the grass. They were alone in the garden, and even kings must unbend sometimes.

"Father, darling," said the Princess presently, when she had made a daisy chain and put it on the King's head, where the crown ought to have been. "Father, darling, couldn't we tie up one of the silly little princes for the dragon to look at? Then I could go and kill the dragon and rescue the prince. I fence much better than any of the princes we know."

"What an unusual idea!" said the King. He put his crown on again, for he saw the Prime Minister coming with a basketful of new laws for him to sign. "Dismiss the thought, my child. I rescued your mother from a dragon. You don't want to set yourself up above her, I should hope?"

"But this is the *last* dragon. It is different from all other dragons."

"How?" asked the King.

"Because it *is* the last," said the Princess. Then she went off to her fencing lesson, with which she took great pains. She took great pains with all her lessons—for she could not give up the idea of fighting the dragon. She took such pains that she became the strongest and boldest and most skillful and most sensible princess in Europe. She had always been the prettiest and nicest.

The days and years went on. At last the day came which was the day before the Princess was to be rescued from the dragon. The prince who was to do this deed of valor was a pale prince, with large eyes and a head full of mathematics and philosophy. Unfortunately, he had neglected his fencing lessons. He was to stay the night at the palace, and there was a banquet.

After supper the Princess sent her pet parrot to the Prince with a note. It said:

"Please, Prince, come onto the terrace. I want to talk to you without anybody else hearing.—The Princess."

So, of course, he went. He saw her gown of silver a long way off shining among the shadows of the trees like water in starlight. When he came quite close to her he said:

"Princess, at your service," and bent his cloth-of-gold-covered knee and put his hand on his cloth-of-gold-covered heart.

"Do you think," said the Princess earnestly, "that you will be able to kill the dragon?"

"I will kill the dragon," said the Prince firmly, "or perish in the attempt."

"It's no use your perishing," said the Princess.

"It's the least I can do," said the Prince.

"What I'm afraid of is that it'll be the most you can do," said the Princess.

"It's the only thing I can do," said he, "unless I kill the dragon."

"Why you should do anything for me is what I can't see," said she.

"But I want to," he said. "You must know that I love you better than anything in the world."

When he said that he looked so kind that the Princess began to like him a little.

"Look here," she said, "no one else will go out to-morrow. You know they tie me to a rock and leave me. Then everybody scurries home and puts up the shutters and keeps them shut till you ride through the town in triumph shouting that you've killed the dragon. And I ride on the horse behind you weeping, for joy."

"I've heard that that is how it is done," said he.

"Well, do you love me enough to come very quickly and set me free? We'll fight the dragon together."

"It wouldn't be safe for you."

"Much safer for both of us for me to be free, with a sword in my hand, than tied up and helpless. *Do* agree."

He could refuse her nothing. So he agreed. And next day everything happened as she had said.

When he had cut the cords that tied her to the rocks, they stood on the lonely mountainside looking at each other.

"It seems to me," said the Prince, "that this ceremony could have been arranged without the dragon."

"Yes," said the Princess, "but since it has been arranged with the dragon—"

"It seems such a pity to kill the dragon—the last in the world," said the Prince.

"Well, then, let's not," said the Princess. "Let's tame it to not eat princesses but to eat out of their hands. They say everything can be tamed by kindness."

"Tamed by kindness means giving them things to eat," said the Prince. "Have you got anything to eat?"

She hadn't, but the Prince said that he had a few biscuits. "Breakfast was so very early," said he. "I thought you might have felt faint after the fight."

"How clever," said the Princess, and they took a biscuit in each hand. They looked here and they looked there, but never a dragon could they see.

"But here's its trail," said the Prince. He pointed to where the rock was scarred and scratched so as to make a track leading to the mouth of a dark cave. It was like ruts in a road, mixed with the marks of sea gulls' feet on the sea sand. "Look, that's where it's dragged its brass tail and planted its steel claws."

"Let's not think how hard its tail and claws are," said the Princess, "or I shall begin to be frightened. I know you can't tame anything, even by kindness, if you're frightened of it. Come on. Now or never."

She caught the Prince's hand in hers, and they ran along the path towards the dark mouth of the cave. But they did not run into it. It really was so very *dark*.

So they stood outside, and the Prince shouted: "What

ho! Dragon there! What ho within!" And from the cave they heard an answering voice and great clattering and creaking. It sounded as though a rather large cotton mill were stretching itself and waking up out of its sleep.

The Prince and the Princess trembled, but they stood firm.

"Dragon—I say, Dragon!" said the Princess. "Do come out and talk to us. We've brought you a present."

"Oh, yes—I know your presents," growled the dragon in a huge rumbling voice. "One of those precious princesses, I suppose? And I've got to come out and fight for her. Well, I tell you straight, I'm not going to do it. A fair fight I wouldn't say no to—a fair fight and no favor. But one of these put-up fights where you've got to lose? No. So I tell you. If I wanted a princess I'd come and take her, in my own time. But I don't. What do you suppose I'd do with her, if I'd got her?"

"Devour her, wouldn't you?" said the Princess in a voice that trembled a little.

"Devour a fiddlestick end," said the dragon very rudely. "I wouldn't touch the horrid thing."

The Princess's voice grew firmer.

"Do you like biscuits?" she asked.

"No," growled the dragon.

"Not the nice little expensive ones with sugar on the top?"

"*No*" growled the dragon.

"Then what *do* you like?" asked the Prince.

"You go away and don't bother me," growled the dragon. They could hear it turn over. The clang and clatter of its turning echoed in the cave like the sound of jack hammers.

The Prince and Princess looked at each other. What *were* they to do? Of course it was no use going home and telling the King that the dragon didn't want princesses. His majesty was very old-fashioned. He would never have believed that a new-fashioned dragon could ever be at all different from an old-fashioned dragon. They could not go into the cave and kill the dragon. Indeed, unless it attacked the Princess it did not seem fair to kill it at all.

"It must like something," whispered the Princess, and she called out in a voice as sweet as honey and sugar cane:

"Dragon! Dragon, dear!"

"WHAT?" shouted the dragon coming towards them through the darkness of the cave. The Princess shivered and said in a very small voice:

"Dragon—Dragon, dear!"

And then the dragon came out. The Prince drew his sword and the Princess drew hers—the beautiful silver-handled one that the Prince had brought for her. But they did not attack. They moved slowly back as the dragon came out, all the vast scaly length of it, and lay along the rock. Its great wings were half spread, and its golden sheen gleamed and sparkled in the sun. At last they could retreat no further. With their backs to the rock they stood, swords in hand, and waited.

The dragon drew nearer and nearer. Now they could see that it was not breathing fire and smoke as they had

expected. It came crawling slowly towards them wriggling a little as a puppy does when it wants to play and isn't quite sure whether you're cross with it.

And then they saw that great tears were rolling down its cheeks.

"Whatever's the matter?" said the Prince.

"Nobody," sobbed the dragon, "ever called me 'dear' before!"

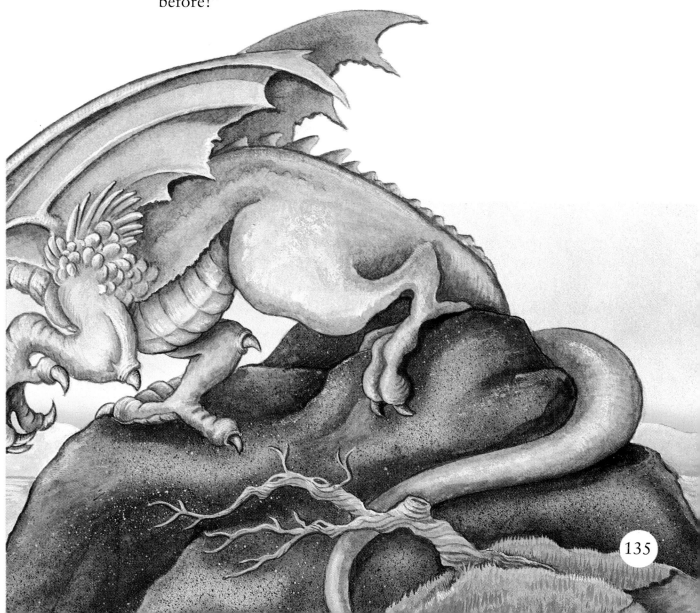

"Don't cry, dragon dear," said the Princess. "We'll call you 'dear' as often as you like. We want to tame you."

"I *am* tame," said the dragon. "That's just it. That's what nobody but you has ever found out. I'm so tame that I'd eat out of your hands. If I might make so bold," continued the dragon, "perhaps you'd be so kind as to call me 'dear' again. And if you'd shake claws with a poor old dragon that's never been anybody's enemy but its own, the last of the dragons'll be the proudest dragon there's ever been since the first of them."

It held out an enormous paw. The great steel hooks that were its claws closed over the Princess's hand as softly as the claws of the Himalayan bear will close over the bit of bun you hand it through the bars at the zoo.

And so the Prince and Princess went back to the palace to be married in triumph, the dragon following them like a pet dog. And all through the wedding

festivities no one wished the bride and bridegroom happiness more earnestly than the Princess's pet dragon, whom she had at once named Fido.

And when the happy pair were settled in their own kingdom, Fido came to them and begged to be allowed to make itself useful.

"There must be some little thing I can do," it said, rattling its wings and stretching its claws. "My wings and claws and so on ought to be turned to some account—to say nothing of my grateful heart."

So the Prince had a special saddle made for the dragon. It was very long, like the tops of many tramcars fitted together. One hundred and fifty seats were fitted to this, and the dragon, whose greatest pleasure was now to give pleasure to others, delighted in taking parties of children to the seaside. It flew through the air quite easily with its hundred and fifty little passengers. Then it would lie on the sand patiently waiting till they were ready to return. The children were very fond of it and used to call it Dear, a word which never failed to bring tears of affection and gratitude to its eyes. So it lived, useful and respected, till not too long ago—when someone happened to say, in its hearing, that dragons were out of date, now so much new machinery had come. This so distressed it that it asked the King to change it into something less old-fashioned. And the kindly monarch at once changed it into a mechanical contrivance. The dragon, indeed, became the first airplane.

CHECK FOR UNDERSTANDING

1. What made the Princess wrong for the role of the person who must be rescued?
2. What plan did the Princess get the Prince to agree to?
3. Why did the Prince and the Princess decide to tame the dragon with kindness?
4. How did the dragon feel about its role in the story?
5. When the dragon came out of its cave, what did the Prince and Princess expect it to be doing? How did it really approach them?
6. Why is *Fido* a good name for the dragon?

WRITE ABOUT *"The Last of the Dragons"*

Suppose that when the dragon wanted to make itself useful, the Prince and Princess couldn't think of anything for it to do. Imagine that the dragon decided to take out an ad in the newspaper, offering itself for work. Write the ad the dragon might have written. Include suggestions for different kinds of useful work the dragon might do.

Lost and Found

by LILIAN MOORE

LOST:
A Wizard's loving pet.
Rather longish.
Somewhat scaly.
May be hungry or
upset.
Please feed daily.

P.S. *Reward*

FOUND:
A dragon
breathing fire.
Flails his scaly
tail
in ire.
Would eat twenty LARGE meals
daily
if we let him.
Please
Come and get him.

P.S. *No reward necessary.*

COMPREHENSION

Drawing Conclusions

In "The Lost Umbrella," Kim and Mae suspect that the millionaire man has taken Kim's father's umbrella. They watch the man on the ferry. They eavesdrop on his conversation with the laughing lady. They draw the conclusion that they were right about him all along when they hear the laughing lady say this:

> "I knew you could carry it off, George. I just knew it. You're a winner, a born winner...you get everything you go after, George. 'Go-getter George!' You deserve the nickname. And this is so important! The most important thing you've set your sights on so far. You've carried it this far. Do you think you can carry it off?"

The laughing lady's comments convince Kim and Mae that the millionaire man has indeed made off with the rare and treasured umbrella. The conclusion they draw is false, but it can help us understand the process involved in drawing conclusions.

When you draw a conclusion, you work like a detective to figure out things that are not completely explained. To do this, you use whatever clues there happen to be. In addition to the clues, you use your own knowledge. Your own knowledge helps you to understand the meaning and importance of the clues.

Think about the things the laughing lady says. What clues are found in what she says?

The first clue is that the millionaire man has done something difficult. He has managed to get something he has gone after. He has managed to carry something off. The second clue is that whatever he has managed to carry off is important. It is the most important thing he has set his sights on so far. The third clue is that the task—whatever it is—is not quite finished.

Kim and Mae combine these clues with their own knowledge and draw a conclusion. For Kim, in particular, the most important thing anyone could imagine is her father's treasured umbrella. The umbrella was "carried off" from the library. They suspect that the millionaire man carried the umbrella from the library to the ferry. They fear that he intends to carry the umbrella off the ferry when they get to Staten Island. Kim and Mae understand the clues that the laughing lady gives in light of their own knowledge. Their conclusion—that the millionaire man took the umbrella on purpose—is based on a combination of those clues and what they already know.

Think about the clues the laughing lady gives. Then think about other details in the story. The millionaire man and the laughing lady are sitting with their heads together behind *The Wall Street Journal*. Suppose you knew that a certain stock had gone up in value tremendously. Suppose also that you knew this had been reported in *The Wall Street Journal.* If you combined the laughing lady's clues with this knowledge, what conclusion might you draw? Now suppose you knew that the millionaire man was running for mayor? How would that knowledge affect the conclusions you would draw based on what the laughing lady says?

In "The Last of the Dragons," the Prince and Princess draw their swords and prepare to do battle when the dragon starts to come out of its cave. What clues in the story cause them to draw the conclusion that they may be in danger? What knowledge leads them to draw this conclusion?

In "The Casserole Threat," the main character, Arthur, draws a conclusion. As you read the story, try to identify the clues and information that will be the basis for Arthur's conclusion.

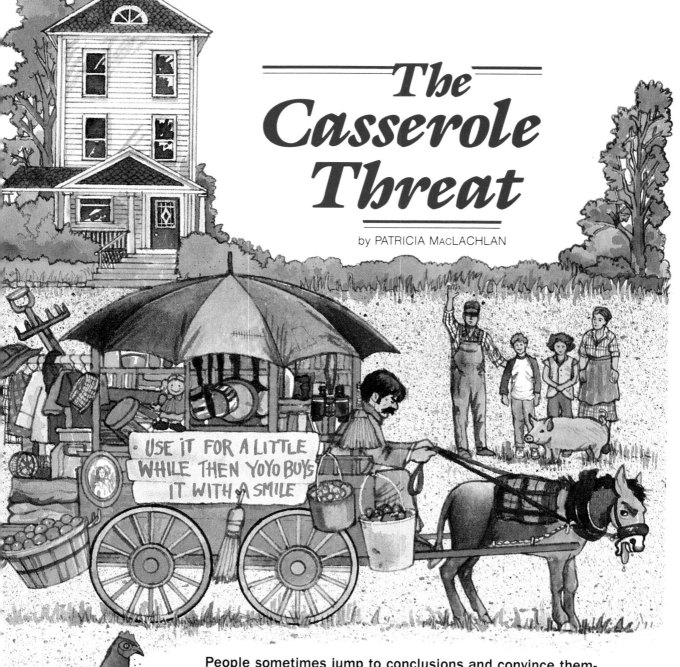

The Casserole Threat

by PATRICIA MacLACHLAN

USE IT FOR A LITTLE
WHILE THEN YOYO BUYS
IT WITH A SMILE

People sometimes jump to conclusions and convince themselves that something really awful has happened. In this story,
Arthur Rasby jumps to such a conclusion.

What awful thing does Arthur think has happened? What
does he do as a result of jumping to a conclusion?

Arthur Rasby is spending the summer in the country with his great-aunt and great-uncle. Aunt Elda and Uncle Wrisby are unusual people. They do things Arthur's parents—in fact, most grownups—would never do. They speak French to their pet chicken, Pauline, because French is sweet to a chicken's ear. Uncle Wrisby sings songs about fair and tender maidens to his pig, Bernadette, because she likes being sung to.

Many unusual things happen to Arthur during his visit with Aunt Elda and Uncle Wrisby, and he writes about all of them in his journal.

Five Dollars Even

On Wednesdays Yoyo Pratt came through the valley selling things from his donkey cart. The cart was painted red, had an old umbrella top and was pulled by a very nasty donkey called Jack. Jack would kick anyone who came close enough, and when approached from the front, he would pull his lips back to show his teeth.

Yoyo was the very picture of a villain. He had a black mustache that curled up at the ends and had one slightly yellow eye. It was said that he chewed adult aspirins. Yoyo wore a long gray coat, even in the warmest weather. That coat was the envy of every child in the county, for it had many pockets—twelve to be exact. They were full of nails, small wooden toys, sewing thread, nail clippers, perfume, jewelry, and dried soup. All for sale. The cart held secondhand clothes, canning jars, fresh fruit and vegetables (and nearly fresh fruit and vegetables), writing paper, metal pots, books, wooden spoons, yarn, cold remedies, and anything anyone wanted to be rid of or buy.

"Sooner or later, everything's bound to come back to me," Yoyo was fond of saying. "Just like the yo-yo comes back to the hand." On his cart was a sign that said:

USE IT FOR A LITTLE
WHILE THEN YOYO BUYS
IT WITH A SMILE

Aunt Elda didn't like Yoyo one bit.

"He's greedy, and he smells like cream of celery," she grumped. "And he could sell sewing needles to a porcupine."

"Elda knows," bellowed Uncle Wrisby.

"Oh, hush," said Aunt Elda.

She grabbed a broom and swept at Arthur's and Uncle Wrisby's feet, pushing them out the door.

Outside Jack turned to sneer at Arthur, and Pauline ran from the side yard, head stretched out, to peck at Yoyo's boots.

"Rotten chicken!" yelled Yoyo, kicking at her and running behind the cart. Jack shifted and rolled his eyes. Yoyo's coat flew out behind him as he ran, and Pauline grabbed it with her beak.

Uncle Wrisby and Arthur laughed.

"You'd better learn some French, Yoyo," called Uncle Wrisby. "*Allons! Arrêtes*, Pauline!"[1]

[1] *Allons* (a lôn') Come on; *Arrêtes* (ä ret') Stop it.

Pauline stopped, and Yoyo slunk out from behind his cart, eyeing her.

"I'll make French casserole out of that rascal someday," he threatened.

Uncle Wrisby's eyes narrowed to slits. "Don't you talk that way about Pauline. Ever," he said softly.

Arthur looked up, surprised. He'd never heard his uncle talk that way. So softly, yet so firm.

"Now, now, Wrisby. Just a joke," soothed Yoyo nervously.

Aunt Elda came out to buy pickle jars, a dollar a dozen, and Arthur looked through the cart. There were no prices written on anything, and he soon discovered that if he asked Yoyo the price more than once, it could go up or down depending on Yoyo's mood. It was like a game, knowing when to stop and when to ask again.

"This top, Mr. Pratt?"

"Seventy-five cents, Arthur. And call me Yoyo."

"How much is the animal book, Mr. Yoyo?"

"One dollar and fifty-nine."

"And the top?"

"Fifty cents even, boy."

So it went, a game of sorts amid a tangle of treasures.

"Well," said Yoyo finally. "Anything you want?"

There was something Arthur wanted. The minute he had seen the long canvas case he had known what was inside. His mother had a recorder, a wooden one, that she kept in such a case. Once she'd let him play it, showing him how to finger some of the notes. He remembered the mellow, sad notes that had made the hair on his neck rise when his mother had played. He also remembered the rasping squawks when he had played.

Arthur pointed to the case.

"What's that?"

Yoyo opened the case and took out the recorder. He held it upside down, blower end down. Arthur felt the first pricklings of excitement in his stomach. Yoyo didn't know what it was.

"Looks like a musical instrument," said Yoyo slowly. "Five dollars even," he announced briskly.

Arthur forced himself to look at a box of fish hooks. He forced himself to think about the money in his pocket. Three dollars and seventeen cents. "How much are the fish hooks?" he heard himself ask. His throat felt dry.

"Thirty-five cents."

Arthur hesitated. "How much is the canvas case? Without that thing . . . the instrument?" asked Arthur.

"The case alone?" asked Yoyo, surprised.

"It would be just right for my knives and pencils," said Arthur.

Uncle Wrisby smiled and folded his arms, leaning on the cart. He looked at Yoyo.

"Well," said Yoyo, turning the case over in his hands. "I guess this case looks like a dollar."

"OK," said Arthur. He felt in his pocket and counted out a dollar. "Do you want an old rag or something to wrap the wood thing in?"

"Sure enough," called Uncle Wrisby. "Those things are kind of delicate. You might not be able to sell it if the air got at it too much."

"Oh, drat," complained Yoyo. "More trouble than it's worth."

Arthur started toward the house to find a cloth. Then he stopped.

"If you want," he called, "I'll take it off your hands for, say, fifty cents."

"Seventy-five," said Yoyo promptly.

"Oh, all right," said Arthur. His hands shook as he counted out the money.

Yoyo grunted his thanks and climbed back up on the cart.

"I'm late, Jack," he called. "Git up!" The donkey backed up, snorted and flattened his ears. Then the cart rattled off down the road. Yoyo turned once to look at Arthur and Uncle Wrisby. Then he was lost around the bend.

Uncle Wrisby began to laugh.

He laughed all the way up the path to the front steps. He took off his glasses and wiped his eyes. He hooted and slapped his pant leg. Arthur began to laugh, too.

"Yoyo," said Uncle Wrisby, stopping to catch his breath, "will get all the way to the Hotwaters' house before he realizes that he sold you a 'five dollar even' recorder for one dollar and seventy-five cents."

Aunt Elda came out of the house to see what the noise was about. Then she shooed them off to feed Bernadette.

"You should have had Arthur buy the pickle jars for you, Elda," he called over his shoulder. "Yoyo might have thrown in the lids!"

This put Aunt Elda in a wicked mood, and there was cold beet soup for supper with a hot dish of cut-up greens that Arthur suspected were dandelions. But he didn't care. He had his recorder.

After supper he hurried to his friend Moira's house to show her his new recorder. Pauline came after him, clucking softly behind him.

"Pauline, *vite*!"[2] urged Arthur impatiently. He looked back once. "*Vite*!" he called crossly, and Pauline came after him, running in slow and fast spurts.

"Why, Arthur," exclaimed Moira when he showed her the recorder. "You are really doing things."

[2] *Vite* (vēt) quickly

Arthur frowned. "You don't think Yoyo Pratt will think I cheated him, do you?"

"Not Yoyo," said Moira positively. "That's the way he does his business. That's the way he is."

Arthur practiced the recorder all evening, sitting cross-legged on his bed. But there was a soft prickling of worry, like the beginnings of a sore throat. It wasn't until early dawn that Arthur sat upright in bed, suddenly awake and knowing what it was. Pauline had not come home with him.

He ran downstairs and looked behind the stove. Pauline wasn't in her cradle. Her blanket wasn't even warm. Arthur searched the yard and the barn, but Pauline was nowhere.

Finally he went to Aunt Elda and Uncle Wrisby's bedroom, feeling sick with dread. He knocked at the door, and when Aunt Elda opened it, Arthur burst into tears.

"My fault," he sobbed. "She's gone. I've looked everywhere."

Aunt Elda gathered Arthur up in her arms while he blurted out the story. He laid his wet face against Aunt Elda's big, white night braid. And Uncle Wrisby threw on his clothes and went out in the stark morning light to look for Pauline.

"It was my dumb recorder," said Arthur tearfully. He sat up suddenly. "All I could think about was that recorder and playing it." He stood up and ran upstairs.

"Arthur," called Aunt Elda. She pulled her cotton robe around her and went into the hall.

Arthur appeared with his recorder. He ran into the kitchen, opening the door of the iron stove.

"Arthur!" shouted Aunt Elda at the top of her voice.

Arthur stopped, his hand on the stove door. Aunt Elda never shouted.

"You'd better chop it into smaller pieces," she said softly.

"What?"

"Here. Here's the hatchet. Go chop the recorder into pieces so it will burn better. That will be more likely to bring Pauline back home."

Arthur closed the stove door. He felt foolish. "I have to do something," he said helplessly.

"I've got a good idea," said Aunt Elda. "If it makes you feel better, go upstairs and throw the recorder out the window. Then put on your clothes, go get Moira, and find Pauline."

Arthur went over to Aunt Elda and threw his arms around her middle.

"I'll find her, I promise," he said, his voice muffled in the softness of her robe.

Upstairs, Arthur opened the big window and threw his recorder out. He looked down to see it lying in the flower bed. He felt better.

Uncle Wrisby was in the kitchen when Arthur came downstairs. Uncle Wrisby looked pale and thin, his long fingers clasped around a cup of tea. Aunt Elda made Arthur eat some toast.

"Arthur," she said before he went out the door. "Pauline's been gone before."

Arthur knew that she was trying to make him feel better. But when he looked back through the window, he saw Uncle Wrisby put his arms around her.

They're afraid, he thought. *They're afraid just like me.*

Pauline, Where Are You?

The valley rang with French. Arthur and Moira rustled the bushes, calling.

"*Bonjour*, Pauline. *Où es-tu?*"[3]

"Pauline! *Viens!*"[4]

Moira knew no French, so Arthur gave her his French phrase book and she called "Where is the restroom?"; "How old is your favorite uncle?"; and "Do you wish fresh towels brought to your room?" all in French.

"Maybe it doesn't matter what you say," said Arthur sadly. "As long as it's French."

They circled back to the gravel road again and walked toward Uncle Wrisby's.

"We could try Yoyo Pratt's," said Moira. "Maybe she followed his cart."

It was then that Arthur suddenly remembered and told Moira about Yoyo's threat: the casserole threat.

"He'd never really eat Pauline!" said Moira, indignant.

"But how do you know?" asked Arthur, miserably. "You're the one who told me that you could never tell what people would do."

Moira said nothing. They both sat still, the noises of the day surrounding them, closing them in. Finally, Moira got up. She went over to touch Arthur's arm.

"I think," she began softly, "we'd better get over to Yoyo's."

Arthur got up, his heart pounding. The sun was high overhead, and Arthur saw that it

---

[3] *Bonjour* (bôn zhur) Good morning; *Où es-tu?* ($\overline{oo}$ e t$\overline{oo}$) Where are you?

[4] *Viens* (vē en') Come on.

would be clear. The brightness of the day bothered him. He wished it were raining or gray. Chipmunks ran along the stone walls, plunging down, then popping up between the stones to watch them on their way to Yoyo's house. They stopped once to look at a large spiderweb stretched across the side of a juniper. It was shaded from the sun, still shining with the wet of early dew. But they just looked at it, not speaking.

Yoyo's house was a small, gray saltbox with weathered shingles, almost dwarfed by the large lilac

bushes that grew around it. A larger barn stood behind, with Jack's cart waiting in front.

"See the cart," whispered Moira. "That means he's leaving."

The bush hid them well. Arthur sat with closed eyes and smelled the strong, sad scent of lilacs. He opened his eyes when he felt Moira stand up to look in the window.

"It's the kitchen," she whispered, pushing his head down. "There's a pot boiling. I can see the steam."

A pot. Arthur stretched up beside Moira just as Yoyo came in the kitchen door. They ducked down quickly, together, and crouched.

"Pot's simmering, Maggie," they heard Yoyo call to his wife. "Hurry up."

The palms of Arthur's hands felt wet. He rubbed them along his pants. "What's in the pot, Moira?" he asked.

"Can't see," she whispered. "They're leaving, though. Wait."

Moira moved closer to Arthur and looked over at him. She

151

reached out her hand and Arthur took it. He looked down at the big fist they made.

They heard the sounds of Yoyo yelling at Jack, then the grating of the wood plank across the barn door. The cart rattled, and from their hiding place, they watched it move slowly down the road. Yoyo drove, with Maggie sitting straight beside him.

Moira took a breath.

"OK," she said, her voice sounding suddenly loud. "I'm going in to look at the pot."

Arthur stood up. "I'm going, too."

The kitchen door wasn't locked, and they walked into the room. Dismayed, Arthur saw that the table was set for supper: two blue-flowered plates and silverware.

Moira lifted the lid and peered into the pot. She took a large fork, stretched up on her toes and poked the contents. Then she carefully closed the lid again.

"It's a chicken," she said.

"Oh, no," said Arthur. He felt tears at his eyes.

"What can I say to Aunt Elda and Uncle Wrisby?" he cried.

Moira didn't speak.

Arthur looked down at the table, staring at the plates. Then, angrily, he picked them up, along with the silverware, and put everything back in the cabinets.

"Yoyo's not going to eat Pauline, that's for sure," he said in a trembling voice.

Moira nodded.

"Let's bring the pot, too," said Arthur, his voice breaking. "We'll have a proper funeral."

Moira searched through the drawers and found two pot holders. She handed one to Arthur. And they walked out the door and down the road, each holding a handle of the pot.

Arthur began to cry, quietly. He was glad that Moira didn't say "Don't feel bad" or "Everything will be all right." He knew he would feel bad forever. But worse—much worse than feeling bad forever—he'd have to tell Aunt Elda and Uncle Wrisby about Pauline. Silently, they passed by the spiderweb in the juniper, now almost invisible in the sunlight. When Uncle Wrisby's barn came into view, Arthur felt a sharp jarring in his stomach.

"Wait," he cried out.

They put down the pot by the side of the road.

"I can't," moaned Arthur. "I can't tell them. I can't."

Moira touched his shoulder. "You can," she said softly. "You have to." She bent down and put her hand around one of the pot handles. "Lift."

Together they picked up the pot and walked slowly past the barn and turned into the yard.

"Arthur!" called Uncle Wrisby from the barn. "Where have you been?"

Aunt Elda opened the kitchen door and hurried out.

"We've been calling and calling you," she said. She stopped when she saw the tear smudges under Arthur's eyes and the look on Moira's face.

Arthur went over to Aunt Elda and put his arms around her.

"She's gone." He lifted his face to look up at Aunt Elda's face. "I'm sorry. So sorry." He began to cry against Aunt Elda, his chest hurting and his body shaking.

"Arthur," said Uncle Wrisby softly. He came over and untangled Arthur from around Aunt Elda. "What are you talking about?" He brushed Arthur's hair from his eyes. "She's not gone anymore." He turned Arthur around and pointed his long finger toward the paddock fence. "See?"

A flash of rust flew to Arthur's feet and began pecking his shoelaces. Brisk, hard pecks that hurt.

"Pauline!" cried Arthur.

"It is Pauline!" shouted Moira.

Aunt Elda put an arm around Arthur.

"We looked and called for you all morning," she said. "We found Pauline sleeping in the tree outside your window." She pushed Arthur's hair back and wiped at his cheeks with her apron.

Arthur began to laugh and cry at the same time as Pauline pecked happily at his shoelaces. He knelt down and picked her up, burying

his face in her feathers. He couldn't remember, ever, being so happy.

"Oh, Pauline," he said softly. "*Je t'aime.*"[5]

Later, Arthur brought Pauline a pan of water and watched her drink. She tilted her head back so the water could run down her long neck.

"Never," he promised her, "never again will I forget you."

Suddenly Uncle Wrisby raised his head and sniffed. "I smell goose."

Moira looked up from where she sat beneath the tree. "Goose?" she said. "I don't smell goose."

"Well, I know goose smell when I smell it!" insisted Uncle Wrisby firmly.

There was a silence. Moira and Arthur stared at each other.

"Oh, no" said Arthur, breathlessly.

"It's Yoyo's chicken," cried Moira. "I forgot all about it!"

"That's no chicken!" boomed Uncle Wrisby. He followed his nose around the tree until he stood over Yoyo's tipped-over kettle, Bernadette's nose pushing the lid into the grass.

"Goose," announced Uncle Wrisby positively. "Greasy goose, too." Uncle Wrisby slowly folded his arms and looked down at Arthur and Moira. "No made-up stories," he said sternly.

"We thought it was Pauline," blurted Moira.

"Pauline!"

Arthur nodded. "Yoyo said he'd eat Pauline if she didn't stop chasing him. Remember?" he implored.

"We went to his house," said Moira. "There was a pot boiling." She pointed. "That pot. Arthur wanted a proper funeral."

Uncle Wrisby, arms still folded, walked off a bit and stared up the road while Moira and Arthur waited uneasily. Then Uncle Wrisby swung around. He stooped beside them, his long arms gathering them in.

"Now," he whispered. "Here is what we'll do."

---

[5] *Je t'aime* (zhə tem) I love you.

155

Thursday, July 8: It has been a long day. Uncle Wrisby went to bed early. To sleep off his day of crime, he says. Aunt Elda kept saying OH MY GOODNESS when we told her what we'd done and what we had to do. She was mad because she'd been cooking a chicken all day long, and what we did meant hot dogs for supper (only Aunt Elda calls them franks). Uncle Wrisby must be the most brilliant person alive, and we told him so. It made him happy, but it made Aunt Elda say OH MY GOODNESS three times in a row. We couldn't put the goose back because Bernadette had nosed it into the dirt. So we took Aunt Elda's chicken, put it into Yoyo's pot and carried it back to Yoyo's house. It was as simple as that. Maybe not that simple. We put the pot on Yoyo's stove and turned on the burner. Then we left. Then I remembered that I had to go back and set the table again. Then we left. Then, all of a sudden, Uncle Wrisby felt his nose and said, I LEFT MY EYE-GLASSES AT YOYO'S. This time

it wasn't so easy. Just as we got there Yoyo's cart came up the road. We hid behind a stone wall wishing we knew what to do when Uncle Wrisby stood right up and pulled us after him. He ran up to Yoyo and said, I WAS JUST WALKING BY YOUR HOUSE WHEN I SAW BIG AS LIFE A FURRY THING PUSH OPEN YOUR SCREEN DOOR AND WALK INTO YOUR HOUSE. LOOKED LIKE A WEASEL. Mrs. Yoyo screeched lots of real long screeches, and Yoyo galloped old Jack up to the barn. I'LL GO IN FIRST, yelled Uncle Wrisby, and he ran into the kitchen while Yoyo ran to the barn for his rifle. Mrs. Yoyo stood up in the cart and kept yelling and lifting up her skirt and jumping from one foot to the other as if she expected the weasel to run out, reach up and steal her patent leather shoes right off her feet. Pretty soon Uncle Wrisby came out and shrugged his shoulders. CAN'T SEE THE CRIT-TER, he called to Mrs. Yoyo, BUT SUPPER SURE SMELLS GOOD! He grinned at us, pulled out his glasses and put them on his nose, and we walked home. We had a supper of hot dogs (franks), and then we had a funeral for Yoyo's goose. We buried it in the back field and put flowers from Aunt Elda's front garden on its grave. No one could think of much to say except for Uncle Wrisby. He said, I SURE AM GLAD YOU WEREN'T PAULINE. Aunt Elda said, AMEN.

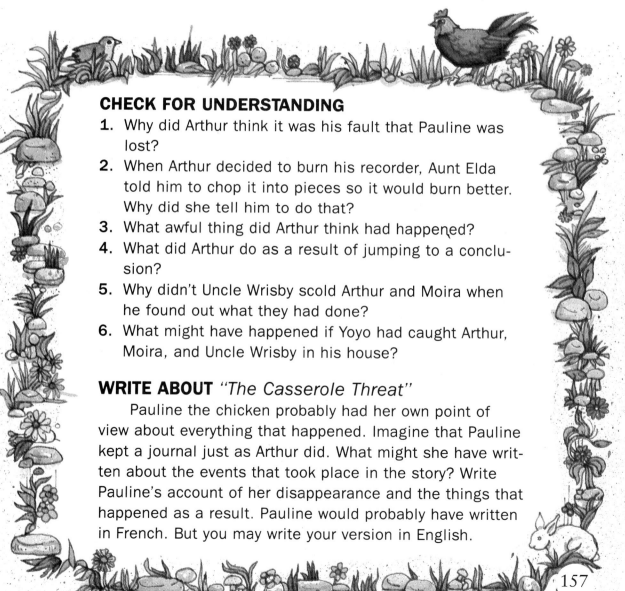

CHECK FOR UNDERSTANDING

1. Why did Arthur think it was his fault that Pauline was lost?
2. When Arthur decided to burn his recorder, Aunt Elda told him to chop it into pieces so it would burn better. Why did she tell him to do that?
3. What awful thing did Arthur think had happened?
4. What did Arthur do as a result of jumping to a conclusion?
5. Why didn't Uncle Wrisby scold Arthur and Moira when he found out what they had done?
6. What might have happened if Yoyo had caught Arthur, Moira, and Uncle Wrisby in his house?

WRITE ABOUT *"The Casserole Threat"*

Pauline the chicken probably had her own point of view about everything that happened. Imagine that Pauline kept a journal just as Arthur did. What might she have written about the events that took place in the story? Write Pauline's account of her disappearance and the things that happened as a result. Pauline would probably have written in French. But you may write your version in English.

157

DICTIONARY: PRONUNCIATIONS

Do you recognize any of these words?

estupefacción   Leichtsinnigkeit   citrouille

Do you know how to pronounce any of them? Suppose that you were a traveler in Spain, Germany, or France—the countries that these three words come from—and you did not know how to speak the language. Like many tourists, you might carry a little book of words and phrases to help you get around. It would tell you how to say "How much does that cost?" or "Where is the bus stop?" Most important of all, it would tell you how to pronounce these foreign words.

Pronunciation is not just a problem in a foreign language. English words can frequently be as difficult to pronounce as German, French, or Spanish ones. Do you know, for example, how to pronounce these words?

chasm   innocuous   sphagnum

They may look like foreign words, but they are all English. If you do not know how to pronounce them, there is help at hand...in your dictionary.

Open a dictionary and look at any page. Right after each entry word, you will find the *pronunciation respelling* enclosed in parentheses. It shows you how the word is pronounced.

In order to understand the pronunciation respelling, however, you need to know what sound each letter or symbol in it represents. The *pronunciation key* at the beginning of the dictionary is your guide to the pronunciation respelling. It shows what sounds the letters and symbols in the respelling stand for. For example, look at these lines from a dictionary pronunciation key:

oo   **oo** as in **wood, u** as in **put**

$\overline{oo}$ **oo** as in **fool, ue** as in **true**

k   **k** as in **kit, baking, seek, ck** as in **tack, c** as in **cat**

The first line tells you that the symbol oo stands for the sound that is spelled oo in the word wood and u in the word put. Look at the example again. What does the symbol $\overline{oo}$ stand for? What symbol represents the first sound in cat?

A shorter version of the pronunciation key is repeated throughout the dictionary. It includes the symbols for the sounds that cause most problems. For example, the line below is the beginning of a short pronunciation key.

at   **ā**pe   c**ä**r

The letters and symbols in dark type show that *a* stands for the first sound in *at,* *ā* stands for the first sound in *ape,* and *ä* stands for the middle sound in *car.*

You also need to understand the accent marks used in pronunciation respellings. In every word of two or more syllables, one syllable has a dark accent mark following it. This syllable is said with the most force, or emphasis.

carbon (kär′bən)

Some words have two syllables that are stressed. One is followed by a dark accent mark to show that it receives **primary stress,** or emphasis. The other is followed by a lighter accent mark to show it receives **secondary stress**—it is not emphasized as much as the syllable with primary stress.

carbohydrate (kär′bō hī′drāt)

159

Pronunciation Key

a	**a** as in **at, bad**
ā	**a** as in **ape, ai** as in **pain, ay** as in **day**
ä	**a** as in **father, car**
e	**e** as in **end, pet**
ē	**e** as in **me, ee** as in **feet, ea** as in **meat, ie** as in **piece, y** as in **finally**
i	**i** as in **it, pig**
ī	**i** as in **ice, fine, ie** as in **lie, y** as in **my**
o	**o** as in **odd, hot**
ō	**o** as in **old, oa** as in **oat, ow** as in **low, oe** as in **toe**
ô	**o** as in **coffee, fork, au** as in **author, aw** as in **law, a** as in **all**
oo	**oo** as in **wood, u** as in **put**
o͞o	**oo** as in **fool, ue** as in **true**
oi	**oi** as in **oil, oy** as in **boy**
ou	**ou** as in **out, ow** as in **cow**
u	**u** as in **up, mud, o** as in **oven, love**
ur	**ur** as in **turn, er** as in **term, ir** as in **bird, or** as in **word**
yo͞o	**u** as in **use, ue** as in **cue, ew** as in **few, eu** as in **feud**
ə	**a** as in **ago, e** as in **taken, i** as in **pencil, o** as in **lemon, u** as in **helpful**
b	**b** as in **bat, above, job**
ch	**ch** as in **chin, such, tch** as in **hatch**
d	**d** as in **dear, soda, bad**
f	**f** as in **five, defend, leaf, ff** as in **off**
g	**g** as in **game, ago, fog**
h	**h** as in **hit, ahead**
hw	**wh** as in **white, which**
j	**j** as in **joke, enjoy, g** as in **gem, dge** as in **edge**
k	**k** as in **kit, baking, seek, ck** as in **tack, c** as in **cat**
l	**l** as in **lid, sailor, feel, ll** as in **ball, allow**
m	**m** as in **man, family, dream**
n	**n** as in **not, final, on**
ng	**ng** as in **singer, long, n** as in **sink**
p	**p** as in **pail, repair, soap**
r	**r** as in **ride, parent, four**
s	**s** as in **sat, aside, cats, c** as in **cent, ss** as in **pass**
sh	**sh** as in **shoe, wishing, fish**
t	**t** as in **tag, pretend, hat**
th	**th** as in **thin, ether, both**
<u>th</u>	**th** as in **this, mother, smooth**
v	**v** as in **very, favor, salve**
w	**w** as in **wet, reward**
y	**y** as in **yes**
z	**z** as in **zoo, gazing, zz** as in **jazz, s** as in **rose, dogs**
zh	**s** as in **treasure, z** as in **seizure, ge** as in **garage**

From *Scribner Intermediate Dictionary*.
Copyright ©1986 by Scribner Educational Publishers,
A Division of Macmillan, Inc. Reprinted by permission of the publisher.

Using What You Have Learned

Use the pronunciation key to answer the following questions.

1. Does the symbol ē stand for the second sound in *tie* or the second sound in *tea?*

2. Which of the following sounds does the symbol ô stand for?
the sound written *a* in *talk*
the sound written *o* in *clock*

3. Which of the sounds below does the symbol o͞o stand for? Which does the symbol yo͞o stand for?
the sound written *ue* in *blue*
the sound written *u* in *refuse*

4. What symbol stands for the sound spelled by the letter in dark type in each word?
spok**e**n   **a**bove   ev**i**l   awf**u**l   ir**o**n

5. Match each pronunciation respelling on the left with a word on the right.
(hwis′əl)   circus
(kən klo͞o′zhən)   conclusion
(sur′kəs)   whistle

Expanding Your Skills

The passage below contains some words that you may not know how to pronounce. Each one is underlined. Use a dictionary to find out how these words are pronounced.

Dr. Bean was <u>implacable</u>. "We have a job to do," she <u>admonished</u> them. "I have in my hand a priceless <u>ewer.</u> On it is a message <u>inscribed</u> in code. If we can <u>decipher</u> that message, we will earn ourselves a place among the <u>laureates</u> of history. Let us <u>squander</u> our time no longer."

OPTICAL ILLUSIONS

by SEYMOUR SIMON

Optical illusions are tricks played on the eye. Things *appear* to be different from what they actually are. Optical illusions occur in nature, and they also occur in art.

What are some of the tools artists use to create three-dimensional effects? What kinds of things does M. C. Escher do to make his work puzzling?

Seeing Is Believing

Do you believe everything you see? Are you sure? Look at the two straight lines in Figure 1. Which is longer, line AB or line CD?

It certainly looks as though line CD is longer. But is it really? You'll need a ruler to tell for sure. Measure each line. Both lines are the same length, even though one *looks* longer.

Another example is Figure 2. Which line is longer, AB or BC? Again, the line that looks longer may not really be longer. Measure

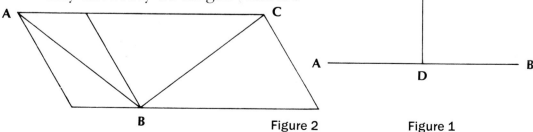

Figure 2   Figure 1

162

each line with your ruler. Surprised at the result? Both lines are exactly the same length.

You have been looking at two optical illusions. An optical illusion is something you see that is not exactly what is really there. You see one line to be longer than another, even though both really are the same size.

There are many different kinds of optical illusions. Some you see each day in nature, such as the way the sun or moon appears to move when clouds float by. Other illusions are done purposefully to fool you, such as the way artists make you see distance in a flat drawing.

Look at the three telegraph poles in Figure 3.

When you see them without any background, they are the same size. But look what happens when you place a few simple lines in the background as in Figure 4.

Now which telegraph pole looks bigger? To make them appear to be the same size, the artist would deliberately make each pole a different size. In so doing, the artist creates the illusion of distance in a picture that is really flat (Figure 5).

Figure 3

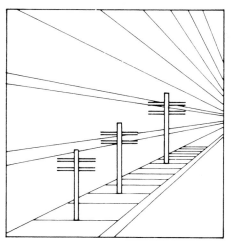

Figure 4

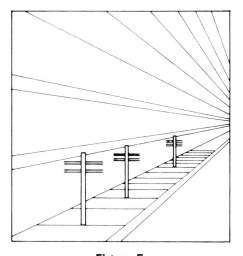

Figure 5

163

Figure 6

Optical Illusions in Art

Painters and other artists have used optical illusions since the early beginnings of art. As far back as prehistoric cave drawings, artists have tried to show the real, three-dimensional world on a flat two-dimensional surface. Perspective, light and shade, contrast, and color are some of the tools that artists use to achieve their effects.

It is interesting to look at drawings or paintings and to try to pick out the ways in which the artist uses materials to make you see with the artist's own vision. For example, look at the print of a landscape by the seventeenth-century artist Jacob van Ruisdael [yä′kōp vän rois′däl] (Figure 6).

Can you tell the materials that were used in the construction of the cottage? How does the artist set the mood of the day? Notice the use of shading and line to show the difference between water and land. Despite the many years that have passed since the print was made, the scene is a familiar one that we recognize quickly.

But look at the print made by the eighteenth-century artist Piranesi [pē′rä nā′zē] (Figure 7). The title of the print is *Prisons*, but no prisons such as these ever existed outside the artist's mind.

The artist makes you see huge and deep spaces with stone arches, timbers, and ropes. He uses perspective, light

Figure 7

Figure 8

and shade, and contrasting shades of gray. Bridges and
stairs seem to go no place and have no reason. You see a
solid structure made of huge blocks of stone. Yet it is
somehow unreal and shadowy.

Modern artists have gone even further with the use of optical illusions. One of the most interesting uses of different kinds of illusions is found in the works of the twentieth-century artist M.C. Escher [esh'ər]. Figure 8 is a work of his called *Day and Night*.

Look carefully at the picture and describe what you see. Do you see the white birds flying off to the right and the black birds flying to the left? Look how the birds merge into sections of the landscape. In the center of the print, each bird is outlined by the shapes of other birds. As you look, your perceptions change.

Figure 9, on page 168, is a print by Escher called *Another World*. The scene is startling. Not only does it show a weird figure against a strange background, but directions and distances are confused and meaningless. Which way is up or down? From what angle are you looking at the picture?

Escher used optical illusions to make you believe in impossible places. In a small area on a flat surface, Escher shows you the mind-spinning strangeness of distant universes.

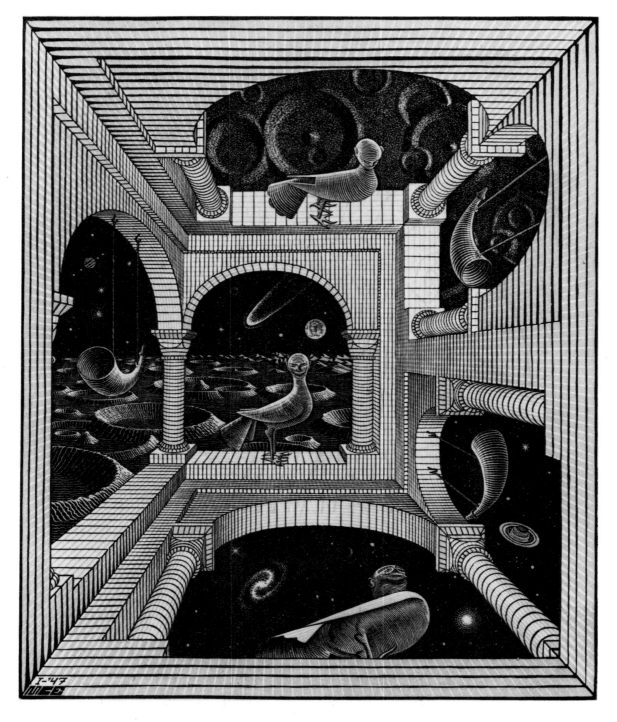

Figure 9

168

Figure 10

Figure 10 is another print by Escher that may remind you in certain ways of the Piranesi *Prisons*.

Stairs go up and down. But where do they lead? Who are the figures and what are they doing? It all depends on your point of view. After the great scientist Albert Einstein developed his theory of relativity, scientists were able to see and understand in new ways. Escher tries to make us see in new ways with his own "relativity."

Figure 11

Look at Figure 11. Follow the path of the waterfall all around the building. Do you believe what you see? How can water keep flowing around and around and yet downhill all the time? The illusion is so convincing that you'll have a hard time figuring out why you see it. One clue is to check the columns as they support each level.

Figure 12

There are many other artists who use optical illusions in important ways in their works. Figure 12 is a print of a painting called *Ondho* by the contemporary artist Victor Vasarely [vas'ə rel'ē]. Changes in the size and the shape of the squares and circles and the position of the lines make the figures appear to advance and retreat in our eyes.

Figure 13

Another contemporary artist who uses illusions is Josef Albers. Look at his *White Embossings on Gray VIII* (Figure 13). Are you sure you see them the way you think you do? Look again.

172

An Optical Illusion to Try

There are lots of optical illusions that you can try out by yourself or with your friends. Here's a sample.

You can make a cartoon character move very much the way they do in the movies. You will need a few sheets of typing paper, a pair of scissors, a stapler or a large paper clip, and a pen or pencil. Cut the paper into strips about 1½ inches wide by 3 inches long. You will need about thirty or forty strips. Stack them neatly and staple or clip them together along the bottom. Now draw a picture on each one of the strips that is just a little bit different than the one before it. For example, you might have a figure running or a rocket ship moving across the page as shown in Figure 14. Now hold the bottom of the stack firmly with your left hand. With your right hand, bend the strips backward and allow them to flip forward. You will get an illusion of motion. The rocket ship will appear to move or the figure will appear to run across the strips.

Flipping the strips uses the same principle as do regular movies. Your eyes keep an image for a short time. If you see

Figure 14

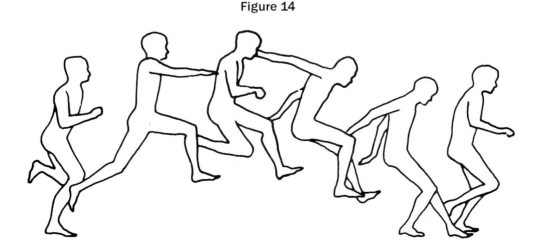

another image in quick succession, your eyes blend the images together and you see the illusion of motion. In the movies, still pictures are projected on the screen at the rate of twenty-four every second. Each still picture is slightly different from the one before just as in your book. You will see these still pictures with the illusion of movement.

Look at the spiral in Figure 15. Now revolve it around. When you revolve the spiral in one direction, the lines seem to move toward the center. When you revolve it in the other direction, the lines seem to move outward from the center. Perhaps you have seen a toy that works on the same principle. When you spin the toy, the spiral on it seems to become smaller or larger depending on the direction of the spin.

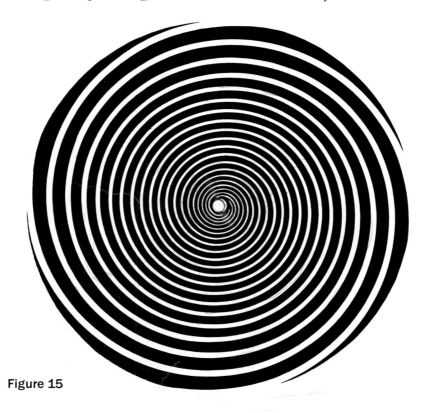

Figure 15

Draw a perfect square with exactly equal sides. Does it look perfect? Now draw a square a bit shorter than it is wide. Look at it side by side with the perfect square. You'll find that the unequal-sided square looks more equal than the perfect square.

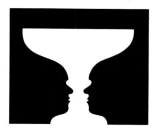

CHECK FOR UNDERSTANDING

1. What is an optical illusion?

2. What do you think makes two lines of equal length appear to be of different lengths?

3. What optical illusion in nature was mentioned in this selection? What other optical illusions occur in nature?

4. What are some of the tools artists use to create three-dimensional effects?

5. What kinds of things does M. C. Escher do to make his work puzzling?

6. In what way is the purpose of modern artists for using optical illusions different from the purpose of artists in earlier times?

WRITE ABOUT *"Optical Illusions"*

It is not just our sense of sight that can be fooled. The sense of hearing can also be fooled. Think of a way you could create the sound of thunder. Then write directions that explain step by step how you would go about creating the illusion of thunder.

The Snow in Chelm

ISAAC BASHEVIS
SINGER

Sometimes every attempt to solve a problem just creates new problems. This is exactly what happens to the wise leaders of the village of Chelm.

What is the problem that the Elders of Chelm try to solve in this story? What simple fact do the Elders keep overlooking in their attempts to solve their problem?

Chelm was a village of fools, fools young and old. One night someone spied the moon reflected in a barrel of water. The people of Chelm imagined it had fallen in. They sealed the barrel so that the moon would not escape. When the barrel was opened in the morning and the moon wasn't there, the villagers decided it had been stolen. They sent for the police, and when the thief couldn't be found, the fools of Chelm cried and moaned.

176

Of all the fools of Chelm, the most famous were its seven Elders. Because they were the village's oldest and greatest fools, they ruled in Chelm. They had white beards and high foreheads from too much thinking.

Once, on a winter night, the snow fell all evening. It covered all of Chelm like a silver tablecloth. The moon shone; the stars twinkled; the snow shimmered like pearls and diamonds.

That evening the seven Elders were sitting and pondering, wrinkling their foreheads. The village was in need of money, and they did not know where to get it. Suddenly the oldest of them all, Gronam the Great Fool, exclaimed, "The snow is silver!"

"I see pearls in the snow!" another shouted.

"And I see diamonds!" a third called out.

It became clear to the Elders of Chelm that a treasure had fallen from the sky.

But soon they began to worry. The people of Chelm liked to go walking, and they would most certainly trample the treasure. What was to be done? Silly Tudras had an idea.

"Let's send a messenger to knock on all the windows and let the people know that they must remain in their houses until all the

silver, all the pearls, and all the diamonds are safely gathered up."

For a while the Elders were satisfied. They rubbed their hands in approval of the clever idea. But then Dopey Lekisch called out in consternation, "The messenger himself will trample the treasure."

The Elders realized that Lekisch was right, and again they wrinkled their high foreheads in an effort to solve the problem.

"I've got it!" exclaimed Shmerel the Ox.

"Tell us, tell us," pleaded the Elders.

"The messenger must not go on foot. He must be carried on a table so that his feet will not tread on the precious snow."

Everybody was delighted with Shmerel the Ox's solution; and the Elders, clapping their hands, admired their own wisdom.

The Elders immediately sent to the kitchen for Gimpel the errand boy and stood him on a table. Now who was going to carry the table? It was lucky that in the kitchen there were Treitle the cook, Berel the potato peeler, Yukel the salad mixer, and Yontel, who was in charge of the community goat. All four were ordered to lift up the table on which Gimpel stood. Each one took hold of a leg. On top stood Gimpel, grasping a wooden hammer with which to tap on the villager's windows. Off they went.

At each window, Gimpel knocked with the hammer and called out, "No one leaves the house tonight. A treasure has fallen from the sky, and it is forbidden to step on it."

The people of Chelm obeyed the Elders and remained in their houses all night. Meanwhile the Elders themselves sat up trying to figure out how to make the best use of the treasure once it had been gathered up.

Silly Tudras proposed that they sell it and buy a goose which lays golden eggs. Thus the community would be provided with a steady income.

Dopey Lekisch had another idea. Why not buy eyeglasses that make things look bigger for all the

179

inhabitants of Chelm? Then the houses, the streets, the stores would all look bigger, and of course if Chelm *looked* bigger, then it *would be* bigger. It would no longer be a village, but a big city.

There were other, equally clever ideas. But while the elders were weighing their various plans, morning came and the sun rose. They looked out of the window, and alas, they saw the snow had been trampled. The heavy boots of the table carriers had destroyed the treasure.

The Elders of Chelm clutched at their white beards and admitted to one another that they had made a mistake. Perhaps, they reasoned, four others should have carried the four men who had carried the table that held Gimpel the errand boy?

After long deliberations the Elders decided that if next winter, a treasure would again fall down from the sky, that is exactly what they would do.

Although the villagers remained without a treasure, they were full of hope for the next year and praised their Elders, who they knew could always be counted on to find a way, no matter how difficult the problem.

CHECK FOR UNDERSTANDING

1. What happened when someone in Chelm saw the moon reflected in a barrel of water?
2. What was the problem that the Elders of Chelm tried to solve in this story?
3. Why did the Elders decide that the messenger should be carried on a table?
4. What ideas did the Elders have for using the treasure once they had gathered it up?
5. What simple fact did the Elders keep overlooking in their attempts to solve their problem?

WRITE ABOUT *"The Snow in Chelm"*

Imagine that you are a citizen of Chelm. You have heard what the Elders plan to do the next time it snows. Write a letter to the Elders. Explain why you think their plan won't work and suggest a better plan. But remember when you suggest your own plan that you are from Chelm, too.

181

What Hershel's Father Did

by ERIC A. KIMMEL

Hershel wants dinner, but he has no money. The people at the inn where Hershel stops for dinner suspect he has no money and refuse to serve him.

How does Hershel change the innkeeper's mind about giving him food? What does the innkeeper *think* Hershel's father did?

Hershel of Ostropol was a real person. He was born more than two hundred years ago in the Ukrainian village of Balta, but he didn't stay there, or anywhere else, for long. He spent most of his life wandering from village to village in search of a living.

Most often, he had no money and no place to go. But since he was leaving a village where he had no hope of finding work, Hershel knew that his chances in the next village could not be any worse. His sense of humor and his good sense kept him alive. The stories of his clever tricks and sayings have become so popular that, even though they all may not be true, they're still being told today.

One night, when Hershel was returning to Ostropol, he stopped at an inn along the side of the road.

"Please," he told the innkeeper, "give me something to eat. I've been walking all day, and I'm terribly hungry. I'm so hungry, I could eat an elephant."

Neither the innkeeper nor his wife thought much of Hershel. "Don't be fooled," the wife warned her husband. "I've seen his kind before. He'll eat an elephant, all right. If we let him, he'll eat everything we have. But when the time comes to pay for his meal, he'll tell us he has no money. If he wants, let him sleep in the stable. But don't give him anything to eat."

183

"What shall I tell him?"

"Tell him he came too late. Tell him dinner has been served and we have nothing left."

The innkeeper told Hershel just that. "I'm terribly sorry," he said. "We're all out of food."

"Not even a piece of bread?"

"No."

"A fishhead? A bone?"

"I'm sorry," the innkeeper said. "We have nothing."

Hershel's eyes flashed with anger. "If I don't get something to eat," he began very slowly, "if I don't get something to eat, I'll do what my father did."

The innkeeper was frightened. He backed away, and Hershel grabbed him by the collar.

"Do you hear me?" Hershel shouted. "IF I DON'T GET SOMETHING TO EAT, I'LL DO WHAT MY FATHER DID! I'LL DO WHAT MY FATHER DID!"

The innkeeper ran to his wife in the kitchen.

"What do you suppose his father did?" the wife asked.

"What kind of question is that?" the innkeeper shouted.

"Who knows what his father did? But whatever it was, his son will do it to us if we don't feed him. Hurry! Kill a goose and make him a supper. Give him the best food we have. Our lives depend on it!"

The innkeeper and his wife hurried. In no time a fine feast was spread on the table. Hershel's plate was piled high with food, and he ate it all. As soon as Hershel cleared his plate, the innkeeper and his wife served him more. Hershel ate until his buttons burst. He ate until he couldn't hold another bite. Ah, that Hershel could eat!

When Hershel was finished, when he couldn't eat another morsel, the innkeeper approached him timidly and asked, "Are you satisfied?"

"Am I satisfied?" Hershel replied. "I should say so!

It was a wonderful meal. It was the best meal I ever had."

"Are you sure you don't want anything else?"

"No. Not another thing."

"Then you're not angry with me?"

"Me, angry? Forget it!"

"In that case," the innkeeper began, "I was wondering . . . would you mind telling me what your father did when he didn't get anything to eat?"

Hershel laughed. "Since you've been so kind to me, I'll be glad to tell you. At night, when my father didn't get anything to eat . . . he went to bed hungry!"

CHECK FOR UNDERSTANDING

1. When Hershel asked for food, what did the innkeeper's wife tell her husband to say to Hershel?
2. How does Hershel change the innkeeper's mind about giving him food?
3. Who do you think would be more difficult to fool, the innkeeper or his wife? Why?
4. What did the innkeeper *think* Hershel's father did?
5. How would you continue the story? What do you think happened next?

LIMERICKS

by EDWARD LEAR

There was a Young Lady of Welling,
whose praise all the world was a-telling;
She played on the harp, and caught several Carp,
That accomplished Young Lady of Welling.

There was an Old Person of Rheims,
who was troubled with horrible dreams;
So to keep him awake they fed him with cake,
Which amused that Old Person of Rheims.

Humor

To understand the humor in some of the selections you have read in this unit, it is necessary to think seriously about the following question. Why did the grizzly bear buy running shoes? The answer is clear. The grizzly was getting calluses from running in bare feet.

Well? Did you laugh? Did you at least *smile?*

The riddle about the bear probably did not cause you to double up with laughter. Still it does illustrate three ways that authors create humor in stories. For one thing, you probably did not expect the paragraph to be like this. The first sentence seems to introduce a serious discussion of humor. Instead it introduces something unexpected: a bear riddle. One of the most common ways to be funny is through surprise. Surprise is particularly funny when you are prepared for something serious and what you get is not serious but silly. Can you remember an example of surprise used to create humor in the selections you have read in this unit?

The bear riddle involved a second element of humor: incongruity. Incongruity is the combination of things that just do not fit together. If you saw, for example, a very large, tall man walking down the street with a tiny little dog on a leash, you would probably find it hard *not* to laugh. The same would be true if you saw a very small child being pulled down the street by a very large dog. Both sights would be funny because the animals do not fit with the humans. A very small dog does not seem to be an appropriate pet for a very large man. A very large dog does not seem to be an appropriate pet for a very small child.

There is also a certain element of incongruity in the idea of a bear wearing shoes or *needing* shoes in the first place. Which of the selections you have read in this unit used incongruity to create humor?

The bear riddle also has a bearing on a third element of humor: word play. Word play involves words with multiple meanings or homophones—words that sound alike but have different meanings. Word play can also involve words that sound almost alike. The bear jokes play with the homophones *bear* and *bare.* How does word play work in this example?

> When they heard the storm warnings, the salad greens said, "A tomato is coming? Lettuce go to the celery!"

The author of "Inside the Giant Peach" uses these same elements to create humor. He, however, uses the elements of humor with great skill and talent, and the results are very funny. As you read "Inside the Giant Peach," try to identify the ways the author uses surprise, incongruity, and word play to create a humorous effect.

James
and the
Giant Peach

by Roald Dahl

190

Inside the Giant Peach

Fantasies often begin when the main character travels through some kind of doorway or opening from the real world into a strange and unusual place. This story is the beginning of a fantasy.

How does James enter the world of fantasy? Who does he find waiting for him when he gets there?

James, an orphan since he was four years old, lives with his two selfish aunts in a house high on a hilltop in England.

One day in the garden of his aunts' house, James meets a strange little man who gives him a package of magic green crystals. In his haste to hide his treasure, James stumbles and spills the crystals. They disappear into the roots of a peach tree. That night a giant peach appears in the garden. James is fascinated by the peach; it seems to draw him like a powerful magnet. When he discovers a hole in the side of the peach— the beginning of a tunnel—James crawls into the peach.

James crawled for several yards, and then suddenly—*bang*—the top of his head bumped into something extremely hard blocking his way. He glanced up. In front of him, there was a solid wall that seemed at first as though it were made of wood. He touched it with his fingers. It certainly felt like wood, except that it was very jagged and full of deep grooves.

"Good heavens!" he said. "I know what this is! I've come to the stone in the middle of the peach!"

Then he noticed that there was a small door cut into the face of the peach stone. He gave a push. It swung open. He crawled through it, and before he had time to glance up and see where he was, he heard a voice saying, "*Look who's here!*" And another one said, "We've been *waiting* for you!"

James stopped and stared at the speakers, his face white with horror.

He started to stand up, but his knees were shaking so much he

had to sit down again on the floor. He glanced behind him, thinking he could bolt back into the tunnel the way he had come, but the doorway had disappeared. There was now only a solid brown wall behind him.

James's large frightened eyes traveled slowly around the room.

The creatures, some sitting on chairs, others reclining on a sofa, were all watching him intently.

Creatures?

Or were they insects?

An insect is usually something rather small, is it not? A grasshopper, for example, is an insect.

So what would you call it if you saw a grasshopper as large as a dog? As large as a *large* dog. You could hardly call *that* an insect, could you?

There was an Old-Green-Grasshopper as large as a large dog sitting on a stool directly across the room from James now.

And next to the Old-Green-Grasshopper, there was an enormous Spider.

And next to the Spider, there was a giant Ladybug with nine black spots on her scarlet shell.

Each of these three was squatting upon a magnificent chair.

On a sofa nearby, reclining comfortably in curled-up positions, there was a Centipede and an Earthworm.

On the floor over in the far corner, there was something thick and white that looked as though it might be a Silkworm. But it was sleeping soundly and nobody was paying any attention to it.

Every one of these "creatures" was at least as big as James himself, and in the strange greenish light that shone down from somewhere in the ceiling, they were absolutely terrifying to behold.

"I'm hungry!" the Spider announced suddenly, staring hard at James.

"*I'm* famished!" the Old-Green-Grasshopper said.

"So am I!" the Ladybug cried.

The Centipede sat up a little straighter on the sofa. "*Everyone's* famished!" he said. "We need food!"

Four pairs of round black glassy eyes were all fixed upon James.

The Centipede made a wriggling movement with his body as though he were about to glide off the sofa—but he didn't.

There was a long pause—and a long silence.

The Spider (who happened to be a female spider) opened her mouth and ran a long black tongue delicately over her lips. "Aren't *you* hungry?" she asked suddenly, leaning forward and addressing herself to James.

Poor James was backed up against the far wall, shivering with fright and much too terrified to answer.

"What's the matter with you?" the Old-Green-Grasshopper asked. "You look positively ill!"

"He looks as though he's going to faint any second," the Centipede said.

"Oh, my goodness, the poor

thing!" the Ladybug cried. "I do believe he thinks that we are wanting *him* for dinner!"

There was a roar of laughter from all sides.

"Oh dear, oh dear!" they said. "What an awful thought!"

"You mustn't be frightened," the Ladybug said kindly. "We wouldn't *dream* of hurting you. You are one of *us* now, didn't you know that? You are one of the crew. We're all in the same boat."

"We've been waiting for you all day long," the Old-Green-Grasshopper said. "We thought you were never going to turn up. I'm glad you made it."

"So cheer up, my boy, cheer up!" the Centipede said. "And meanwhile I wish you'd come over here and give me a hand with these boots. It takes me *hours* to get them all off by myself."

James decided that this was most certainly not a time to be disagreeable, so he crossed the room to where the Centipede was sitting and knelt down beside him.

"Thank you so much," the Centipede said. "You are very kind."

"You have a lot of boots," James murmured.

"I have a lot of legs," the Centipede answered proudly. "And a lot of feet. One hundred, to be exact."

"*There* he goes again!" the Earthworm cried, speaking for the first time. "He simply cannot stop telling lies about his legs! He doesn't have anything *like* a hundred of them! He's only got forty-two! The trouble is that most people don't bother to count them. They just take his word. And anyway, there is nothing *marvelous*, you know, Centipede, about having a lot of legs."

"Poor fellow," the Centipede, said, whispering in James's ear. "He's blind. He can't see how splendid I look."

"In my opinion," the Earthworm said, "the *really* marvelous thing is to have no legs at all and to be able to walk just the same."

"You call that *walking*!" cried

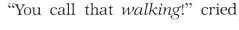

the Centipede. "You're a *slitherer*, that's all you are! You just *slither* along!"

"I glide," said the Earthworm primly.

"You are a slimy beast," answered the Centipede.

"I am *not* a slimy beast," the Earthworm said. "I am a useful and much loved creature. Ask any gardener you like. And as for you . . ."

"I am a pest!" the Centipede announced, grinning broadly and looking around the room for approval.

"He is *so* proud of that," the Ladybug said, smiling at James. "Though for the life of me I cannot understand why."

"I am the only pest in this room!" cried the Centipede, still grinning away. "Unless you count Old-Green-Grasshopper over there. But he is long past it now. He is too old to be a pest any more."

The Old-Green-Grasshopper turned his huge black eyes upon the Centipede and gave him a withering look. "Young fellow," he said, speaking in a deep, slow, scornful voice, "I have never been a pest in my life. I am a musician."

"Hear, hear!" said the Ladybug.

"James," the Centipede said. "Your name *is* James, isn't it?"

"Yes."

"Well, James, have you ever in your life seen such a marvelous colossal Centipede as me?"

195

"I certainly haven't," James answered. "How on earth did you get to be like that?"

"*Very* peculiar," the Centipede said. "*Very, very* peculiar indeed. Let me tell you what happened. I was messing about in the garden under the old peach tree, and suddenly a funny little green thing came wriggling past my nose. Bright green it was, and extraordinarily beautiful, and it looked like some kind of a tiny stone or crystal . . ."

"Oh, but I know what that was!" cried James.

"It happened to me, too!" said the Ladybug.

"And me!" Miss Spider said. "Suddenly there were little green things everywhere! The soil was full of them!"

"I actually swallowed one!" the Earthworm declared proudly.

"So did I!" the Ladybug said.

"I swallowed three!" the Centipede cried. "But who's telling this story anyway? Don't interrupt!"

"It's too late to tell stories now," the Old-Green-Grasshopper announced. "It's time to go to sleep."

"I refuse to sleep in my boots!" the Centipede cried. "How many more are there to come off, James?"

"I think I've done about twenty so far," James told him.

"Then that leaves eighty to go," the Centipede said.

"*Twenty-two*, not *eighty!*" shrieked the Earthworm. "He's lying again."

The Centipede roared with laughter.

"Stop pulling the Earthworm's leg," the Ladybug said.

This sent the Centipede into hysterics. "Pulling his *leg!*" he cried, wriggling with glee and pointing at the Earthworm. "Which leg am I pulling? You tell me that?"

James decided that he rather liked the Centipede. He was obviously a rascal, but what a change it was to hear somebody laughing once in a while. He had never heard Aunt Sponge or Aunt Spiker laughing aloud in all the time he had been with them.

"We really *must* get some sleep," the Old-Green-Grasshopper

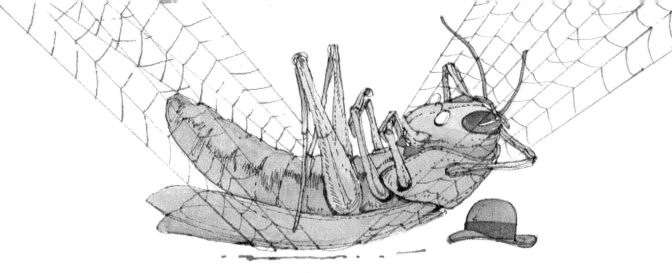

said. "We've got a tough day ahead of us tomorrow. So would you be kind enough, Miss Spider, to make the beds?"

A few minutes later, Miss Spider had made the first bed. It was hanging from the ceiling, suspended by a rope of threads at either end so that actually it looked more like a hammock than a bed. But it was a magnificent affair, and the stuff that it was made of shimmered like silk in the pale light.

"I do hope you'll find it comfortable," Miss Spider said to the Old-Green-Grasshopper. "I made it as soft and silky as I possibly could. I spun it with gossamer. That's a much better quality thread than the one I use for my own web."

"Thank you so much, my dear lady," the Old-Green-Grasshopper said, climbing into the hammock. "Ah, this is just what I needed. Good night, everybody. Good night."

Then Miss Spider spun the next hammock, and the Ladybug got in.

After that, she spun a long one for the Centipede, and an even longer one for the Earthworm.

"And how do you like *your* bed?" she said to James when it came to his turn. "Hard or soft?"

"I like it soft, thank you very much," James answered.

"For goodness' sake stop staring round the room and get on with my boots!" the Centipede said. "You and I are never going to get any sleep at this rate! And kindly line them up neatly in pairs as you take them off. Don't just throw them over your shoulder."

197

James worked away frantically on the Centipede's boots. Each one had laces that had to be untied and loosened before it could be pulled off, and to make matters worse, all the laces were tied up in the most terrible, complicated knots that had to be unpicked with fingernails. It was just awful. It took about two hours. And by the time James had pulled off the last boot of all and had lined them up in a row on the floor—twenty-one pairs altogether—the Centipede was fast asleep.

"Wake up, Centipede," whispered James, giving him a gentle dig in the stomach. "It's time for bed."

"Thank you, my dear child," the Centipede said, opening his eyes. Then he got down off the sofa and ambled across the room and crawled into his hammock. James got into his own hammock—and oh, how soft and comfortable it was compared with the hard bare boards that his aunts had always made him sleep upon at home.

"Lights out," said the Centipede drowsily.

Nothing happened.

"Turn out the light!" he called, raising his voice.

James glanced round the room, wondering which of the others he might be talking to, but they were all asleep. The Old-Green-Grasshopper was snoring loudly through his nose. The Ladybug was making whistling noises as she breathed, and the Earthworm was coiled up like a spring at one end of his hammock, wheezing and blowing through his open mouth. As for Miss Spider, she had made a lovely web for herself across one corner of the room, and James could see her crouching right in the very center of it, mumbling softly in her dreams.

"I said turn out the light!" shouted the Centipede angrily.

"Are you talking to me?" James asked him.

"Of course I'm not talking to you!" the Centipede answered.

"That crazy Glowworm has gone to sleep with her light on!"

For the first time since entering the room, James glanced up at the ceiling—and there he saw a most

extraordinary sight. Something that looked like a gigantic fly without wings (it was at least three feet long) was standing upside down upon its six legs in the middle of the ceiling, and the tail end of this creature seemed to be literally on fire. A brilliant greenish light as bright as the brightest electric bulb was shining out of its tail and lighting up the whole room.

"Is *that* a Glowworm?" asked

199

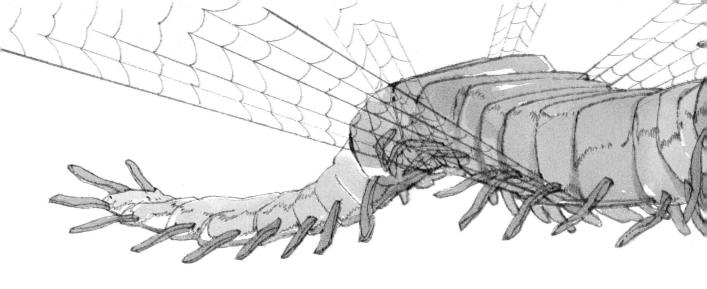

James, staring at the light. "It doesn't look like a worm of any sort to me."

"Of course it's a Glowworm," the Centipede answered. "At least that's what *she* calls herself. Although actually you are quite right. She isn't really a worm at all. Glowworms are never worms. They are simply lady fireflies without wings. Wake up!"

But the Glowworm didn't stir, so the Centipede reached out of his hammock and picked up one of his boots from the floor. "Put out that wretched light!" he shouted, hurling the boot up at the ceiling.

The Glowworm slowly opened one eye and stared at the Centipede.

"There is no need to be rude," she said coldly. "All in good time."

"Come on, come on, come on!" shouted the Centipede. "Or I'll put it out for you!"

"Oh, hello, James!" the Glowworm said, looking down and giving James a little wave and a smile. "I didn't see you come in. Welcome, my dear boy, welcome— and good night!"

Then *click*—and out went the light.

The insects had been waiting for James, and now that he has arrived the adventure can begin. To find out what is in store for James and his unusual companions, read the rest of the novel **James and the Giant Peach**, *by Roald Dahl.*

CHECK FOR UNDERSTANDING

1. How did James enter the world of fantasy?
2. Who did he find waiting for him when he got there?
3. What did James think at first might be served for dinner inside the peach?
4. What details in the story made it clear that James had nothing to fear from the creatures in the peach?
5. How did the insects become so large?
6. The Ladybug told James, "You are one of the crew. We're all in the same boat." Old-Green-Grasshopper said they were going to have a tough day tomorrow. What do you think will happen the next day?

WRITE ABOUT *"Inside the Giant Peach"*

The Centipede thought it was wonderfully funny when the Ladybug told him to stop pulling the Earthworm's leg. *To pull someone's leg* is an idiom that means to tease. There are other idioms that include the word *leg*. If you *shake a leg*, you hurry. If you are *on your last legs*, you are nearly exhausted. If you *don't have a leg to stand on*, you don't have good support for your argument or ideas. Write a short conversation among the insects that allows the Centipede to use one of these idioms when talking about the Earthworm.

THINK ABOUT IT

Think about the event or situation in each story that was not what it seemed to be.

- In "The Lost Umbrella," Kim and Mae must deal with a conflict between appearance and reality — or so they think.
- In "The Last of the Dragons," nobody behaves quite the way you would expect, but the dragon is a surprise to everyone.
- In "The Casserole Threat," Arthur draws a false conclusion that has some awkward consequences.
- In "The Snow in Chelm," the Elders go to great lengths to protect riches that never existed in the first place, while in "What Hershel's Father Did," the innkeepers go to great lengths to protect themselves from a horrible fate: that Hershel should go to bed hungry.
- In "Inside the Giant Peach," James realizes his fears about the unexpected creatures are unfounded.

In each of the stories, something is not what it seems to be and someone draws a false conclusion. Think about what each false conclusion reveals about the character who draws it. In what way do our own hopes and fears influence the way we see things?

WRITE ABOUT IT

Was there ever a time when you were *sure* you had something figured out, only to find that the situation was very different from what you had thought? If you are like most people, this has probably happened more than once. Think about the funniest experience you have had of something turning out to be "not what you think." Use that experience as the basis for a funny story.

READ ABOUT IT

Miss-Osbourne-the-Mop by Wilson Gage. Collins, 1963. Jody discovers that she has an unusual power: she can change a person or an object into something else.

The Diamond in the Window by Jane Langton. Harper & Row, Publishers, 1962. When Eleanor and Eddy attempt to solve the mystery of disappearing relatives in Concord, Massachusetts, things are not as they seem.

The Borrowers by Mary Norton. Harcourt Brace Jovanovich, 1952. This is the first book in the series about the Clocks, a family of little people no taller than a pencil. The Clocks live in old houses and secretly "borrow" whatever they need from human beings.

Freaky Friday by Mary Rodgers. Harper & Row, Publishers, 1972. It is not an ordinary Friday morning for Annabel: she discovers that she has changed into her mother overnight!

Stuart Little by E. B. White. Harper & Row, Publishers, 1945. Stuart, who strongly resembles a mouse, leaves New York and heads for Boston in search of his friend, the lovely bird Margolo.

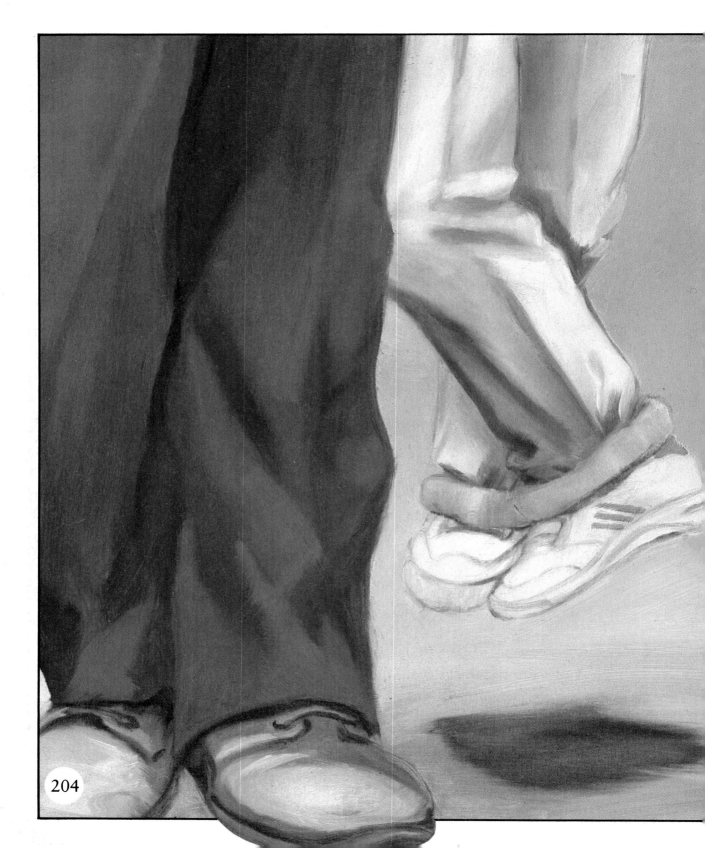

SOMEBODY SPECIAL

Everyone recognizes that there are people who are unique and special. At some time in life, everyone has met such a person. These people have qualities that set them apart from others. They have the ability to affect people's lives in a meaningful way—whether it is just the people closest to them or a great many people. Perhaps it is their courage or their determination that makes them special. Perhaps it is their pride in themselves or their joy in living.

Perhaps their simplicity and honesty make them easier to love than other people. The quality that makes someone special may be as special and unique as the person.

Each story in this unit introduces you to "somebody special." As you read each story, think about the qualities revealed by the special person or character's actions.

IDA EARLY

by ROBERT BURCH

Have you ever met a person you liked right away because that person seemed to have fun just doing ordinary things? Ida Early is that kind of person. When Ida knocked on their door one Saturday morning, the Suttons had never laid eyes on her before. Yet after only a few minutes, Mr. Sutton offers her a job.

What job does Mr. Sutton offer Ida? How does Ida manage to get her chores done?

Ida Early came over the mountains. Or else she came around them. Randall Sutton never was sure which. He just knew that early one Saturday morning in mid-July someone had rapped on the door, and when he opened it, there she stood.

"Howdy-do!" she said, flinging out her arms as if she expected him to rush into them. She looked for all the world like a telephone pole and seemed almost as tall. At the same time she reminded him of someone, but he couldn't remember who. Her face was plain, her complexion ruddy, and her hair light brown and stringy. She was not a real young person; Randall could tell that she was well out of her teens. Nor was she old, certainly not as old as his father, who was thirty-four. She wore a patchwork shirt, a baggy brown sweater, and overalls. The elbows of the sweater and the knees of the overalls had been reinforced with scraps of canvas. Her shoes were brogans—clod-hoppers, they were called—and a small buckeye dangled from one of the laces. A buckeye was said to bring good luck.

Randall didn't say anything, and his father, who had followed him to the door, only nodded. Ida Early stood there grinning. At the outset of the Depression, people had stopped occasionally to ask for a handout—food or old clothes. But times were a little better now, and there were seldom beggars at the door. And none of them ever stood grinning as if awaiting a special welcome. Finally Mr. Sutton asked, "Is there anything we can do for you?"

"Let me think," she said, brushing away a corn shuck from above her left ear. Then Randall knew who she reminded him of: she favored the scarecrow that he and his friend, J.C., had built last summer to keep birds out of the cantaloupe patch. That was it: she looked more like a scarecrow than a telephone pole.

After Ida had scratched her head, she smiled at Mr. Sutton. "If you insist on doing something for me," she said, "you could offer me a job."

Mr. Sutton smiled back at her. "Are you a lumberjack or a field hand?"

"Well," said Ida Early, "which would you be a-needing?"

"Neither. But it could be that we're wanting some help with the cooking and other chores around here."

"Well, then," said Ida, "this is your lucky day!" She waved Mr. Sutton and Randall aside so that she could enter. "I'm one of the best cooks in the Blue Ridges." The Suttons lived at the edge of the Blue Ridge Mountains—on the Georgia side—but Randall had never heard anybody speak of them as anything except "the mountains." Ida Early said, "Yes, siree, I'm one of the best cooks I know about. As a matter of fact, I'm noted in Georgia, Tennessee, and both Carolinas for my cooking."

Mr. Sutton said, "I'll have to see."

Ida looked around the hallway. "What have you got that you want cooked up?" she asked, rubbing her hands together. "Just let me at it!"

"I mean I'll have to see what Earnestine thinks."

"Is she your wife?"

"No, my sister. My wife died in spring."

"I'm sorry," said Ida. "I'm genuinely sorry. Is your sister looking after the family?"

208

Randall thought that "bossing the family" would be a better way of putting what Aunt Earnestine did.

"Yes," said his father, "but she's anxious to get back to her home in Atlanta. Let's talk to her." He led the way into the big room that was called the kitchen but was the dining and sitting room as well. There was a cookstove, cupboard, and icebox on one side, a table and chairs in the middle, and benches and more chairs over by the hearth.

When Mr. Sutton led Ida Early into the kitchen, Randall's sister and his twin brothers were still at the table, finishing their breakfast.

"Howdy, one and all!" said Ida, bowing to the three children.

"Good morning," said Ellen. The twins, Clay and Dewey, didn't say anything. They just stared. Ellen, being twelve, tried not to look too directly at Ida, but the twins, who were only five, seemed unable to look anywhere else. Randall's father went in search of Aunt Earnestine, leaving Ida standing in the middle of the room.

Mr. Sutton and Aunt Earnestine came into the room. Randall always thought of Aunt Earnestine as a battleship. She wasn't especially big, but she always looked as if she were ready for war. And she moved as if everybody should get out of the way. Randall always did; he considered himself a rowboat by comparison. Before Aunt Earnestine spoke to Ida Early, she ordered Ellen and Randall to get busy clearing the breakfast dishes from the table.

The grown-ups stood across the room, talking. Soon it had been decided that Ida would be given a job. "I can't pay much," said Mr. Sutton, "on account of times are still

not good, even if we do keep hearing that the Depression is easing up."

"I don't worry about the pay," said Ida, "if the job's interesting and there's plenty of work to do."

Aunt Earnestine said crossly, "There's plenty of work. You can start by cleaning the house."

Mr. Sutton said, "Maybe she'd like to sit down for a few minutes first and get acquainted with the children."

"She can get acquainted with them while she cleans the house," said Aunt Earnestine.

Ida Early stood back of one of the big rocking chairs. "Maybe I'll just rock a few minutes first," she said, taking off the baggy sweater that she wore. Then she held the sweater over her head, twirled it around twice, and let it go. It sailed to the corner, landing neatly on the hatrack.

Everyone laughed except Aunt Earnestine, who was horrified. "We *take* our garments across the room to hang them up!" she scolded.

"Of course you do!" said Ida. "It's not just everybody who can throw things and make 'em land in exactly the right spot." Then she grinned. "But I'll be happy to teach all of you the trick to it if I could have my sweater back." Dewey raced to get it for her.

Ida sat down in the rocker. "The secret of my good aim's in the wrist movement," she said. Then she announced, "And now, ladies and gentlemen, from a sitting position!" Before Aunt Earnestine could protest, Ida took the sweater, whirled it around, and threw it to the hatrack again. She told Aunt Earnestine with a little smile, "Think how many steps you could save in a day!"

"We'll be back before noon," said Aunt Earnestine a while later. "Do you think you can look after things here?"

"Oh, yes, ma'am," answered Ida Early. "It would pleasure me to look after things."

"We'll have stew for lunch," said Aunt Earnestine. "Do you think you could prepare it?"

Ida licked her lips and said enthusiastically, "Why, I'm a stew-making fool!"

But Aunt Earnestine frowned. "The beef is cut up and in the icebox. Brown it in the skillet before you put it in the pot to simmer. And you'll find vegetables in the pantry when it's time to add them."

Ida nodded.

"And just warm up the cornbread left from yesterday. Also, there's a bowl of turnip greens in the cupboard that can be heated."

After Mr. Sutton and Aunt Earnestine had driven away, Ida glanced at a tiddlywinks board on a shelf near the fireplace and said, "I don't suppose any of you would ever have guessed that once I was tiddlywinks champion of the whole wide world."

"I would," said Dewey. "I would have guessed it." And Clay said, "We like to play tiddlywinks."

"Do you really?" asked Ida. "Well, that's a happy fact to know! Why don't we just play a game of it right now?"

She sat down cross-legged in the middle of the room and the twins brought over the disks and the board, with its tiny cup in the center. While they were sorting the buttonlike disks according to color, Ida Early said, "Now let's see, do twins play separately, or should we add their scores together?"

Clay and Dewey looked at her as if they thought she was talking nonsense.

"I mean, wouldn't it be fair for anyone under the age of six to team up? Shouldn't the rest of us be willing to combine their scores?"

"Never!" said Randall. "Not unless you combine ours." He and Ellen spent a lot of their spare time trying to beat the twins at tiddlywinks. Occasionally one of them came out ahead of Clay, but no one had ever beaten Dewey. Randall had decided that either the twins had some special built-in talent for the game or else all the hours they had played it by themselves while he and Ellen were in school had turned them into near-perfect scorers.

Ellen asked Ida, "Are we going to begin a game before you start the stew?"

"Oh, that's right," said Ida, "the stew! I know what, why don't we take turns playing and cooking? Since you're the one who remembered the stew, I wouldn't feel right about not letting you begin it. Maybe you could find that meat and brown it in a little butter." Ellen looked as if she were about to object to being left out of the first game until Ida added, "Unless you think you might not be quite old enough to shoulder such a responsibility."

"I'm twelve," said Ellen. She went across to the icebox and took out the beef that Aunt Earnestine had cut up.

Dewey said, "You're company, Ida. You get to go first."

"Thank you kindly," she said, and pressed down on one of the yellow disks that had been given her. It landed

on the windowsill. Everyone laughed, and Ida acted upset. "We should have had a warm-up period!" she said. "We champion tiddlywinks players always have a warm-up period. But never mind, I'll catch up."

Randall played next, and his disk landed at the edge of the small board. "Better than the windowsill!" he said.

Clay was next, and when he snapped his disk he said, "Gingerbread!" The twins had picked up that idea from their father. He had told them that their aim would be more accurate if they thought of something pleasant while taking it. They themselves had decided that it might be even better if they said their "pleasant thought" aloud. Clay's disk landed on the board in the ring nearest the cup, scoring fifteen points for him.

Ida said, "Good for you!"

Dewey took the last turn. "Peanut butter!" he said softly as he snapped the disk. It landed with a *plink* in the tiny cup.

"Wow!" said Ida. "What luck!" Clay and Randall did not say anything; they might have said "Wow!" if Dewey had missed.

Ida landed her next disk within a few inches of the cup, and after two more turns she announced she would try Clay's and Dewey's system of having pleasant thoughts. She took careful aim and said loudly, "Feather bed!" She pressed down on the disk. It flew out the window.

"I shouldn't have thought of anything so fancy," she said. "It serves me right that the shot went wild." On her next try she shouted, "Straw mattress!" and the disk went into the cup. "See," she said, "didn't I tell you that it's best to be practical?"

Dewey won the game, and Clay came in second. Ida was third. "Randall, you're the loser," said Ida. "I guess that means Ellen gets to take your place." She called across the room, "How's the stew coming?"

"It's bubbling already."

"Fine!" said Ida. "You come join in this tiddlywinks game so Randall can have his chance to help over there." Before Randall could argue she turned to him. "You wouldn't mind finding a few potatoes, would you?" As he walked toward the pantry, she added, "Peel 'em clean and throw 'em in the pot!"

The next game was played while Randall peeled potatoes. Ellen was the loser, and Ida convinced her that she was to be treated to a rare opportunity: she could look for onions and carrots and put them in the stew. Randall was invited into the tiddlywinks game again.

Ida lost the next game, and she said, "It's probably my elbow that's holding me back. It hasn't been the same since I fell off a bucking mustang."

"What's a mustang?" asked Clay.

"A horse," said Randall.

"Did you really fall off one that was jumping up and down?" asked Dewey, and Clay said, "Tell us about it."

"It's too terrible to discuss," said Ida with a shudder. "Let's play tiddlywinks." She snapped down on one of the disks.

"Hey!" said Ellen, awaiting her turn to get back into the game. "You lost! It's my turn to play."

"That's right," said Ida, "and it must be my turn to cook. But it wouldn't be fair if you weren't allowed to season the stew, now would it? After all, you started the pot to perking."

A few minutes later Ellen was at the stove, putting salt and pepper in the stew, and when it was almost done, Randall was sent to see if the meat was tender. "Stick a fork in a chunk of it," called Ida, who had sat cross-legged on the floor all morning. "And while you're on your feet, see if you can locate those greens your aunt was talking about. Heat 'em in a boiler, and you might put the cornbread in the oven while you're at it. It'll soon be time to eat."

At noon Dewey remained champion tiddlywinks player. Ida Early had been second once, and Clay had been runner-up the other times. When the last game ended, Dewey said, "All right, everybody, pay up!" That was something else he had learned from his father. Mr. Sutton always said, "Pay up!" whenever he happened to win a game—as if a bet had been placed on it.

"I'll pay you with a hand shake," said Ellen, reaching across and pumping Dewey's hand up and down.

"I'll give you a love lick," said Ida, making a fist and giving Dewey a light tap on one arm.

"I'll give you a lick to grow on," said Randall, punching him on the other arm.

Dewey was laughing at the attention he was getting until Clay said, "And I'll give you a bite." He leaned over and bit his brother on the leg.

Dewey screamed, and he and Clay started fighting. Ellen and Randall yelled at the twins to stop. The noise was at its loudest when Mr. Sutton and Aunt Earnestine arrived home.

Finally everyone quieted down, and Aunt Earnestine said huffily, "I certainly hope the children haven't been carrying on like this all morning."

"No, ma'am," said Ida Early, winking at Randall. "I don't think they have. But to tell you the truth, I've been so busy cooking I've hardly had time to notice."

CHECK FOR UNDERSTANDING

1. What job did Mr. Sutton offer Ida?
2. Do you think Ida Early came to the Sutton house on purpose to ask for a job? Find clues in the story that support your answer.
3. How did Ida manage to get her chores done?
4. Ida decided that the loser at tiddlywinks must take the next turn cooking. Did she stick to that rule? Explain what happens.
5. In what ways are Ida and Aunt Earnestine different? In what way are they alike?
6. Do you think Ida will keep her job at the Sutton house? Give your reasons for thinking as you do.

WRITE ABOUT *"Ida Early"*

Pretend that you are Aunt Earnestine, and write a letter to a friend in Atlanta. In the letter you should tell your friend that your brother, Mr. Sutton, has found someone to help with the housekeeping and that you are planning to come home. You should also describe the person Mr. Sutton hired and give your opinion of her ability to run the household.

Cousin Carrée's CUBIC CUISINE

by X. J. KENNEDY

Carrée my cousin's
Long on tricks:
She shapes ground round
Into perfect bricks,

Six-sided roast-
Beef hash she slings.
Right-angled come
Her onion rings!

Because she carves
While she computes,
Her carrot sticks
Are real square roots.

She'll slice nice cubes
Of cool cucumber
And dice you fries
That roll a number,

Squeeze burger buns
To square and squeal:
"Ding-ding! come get
Your good square meal!"

219

VOCABULARY • LANGUAGE

Synonyms

Ida Early blames her poor tiddlywinks playing on the fact that her elbow has not been the same since she fell off a bucking mustang. When Clay asks what a mustang is, Randall tells him a mustang is a horse.

Mustang is just one of several different synonyms for *horse.* Ida might have been thrown by a *bronco* or a *cayuse* (kī yo͞os'). If she had been a better rider, she might have ridden off into the sunset on her *mount* or her *steed.* She might have galloped away on a *courser,* a *charger,* or a *palfrey.* Since Ida does not seem to have great *equestrian* skills, she might have been better off with a *nag* or a *plug.* Maybe she simply should have hitched up a *dobbin* or a *hack.*

All the words in italic type in the paragraph above are synonyms for *horse* except *equestrian. Equestrian* means "having to do with horsemanship." The paragraph gives twelve synonyms for *horse.* If you looked up *horse* in a **thesaurus** (thə sôr'əs)—a book that lists synonyms and antonyms for words—you would find even more synonyms for *horse.*

Have you ever wondered *why* there are synonyms? Have you ever wondered why our language has so many different words with the same basic meaning? There are actually two reasons why there are synonyms. Our list of *horse* words can help to explain both reasons.

If you looked up the *horse* words in a dictionary, you would find that each one names a slightly different kind of horse. If you were talking about a wild horse, you could use the word *bronco* or *mustang.* You would not, however, use *bronco* or *mustang* if you were talking about a fancy show horse. If you were talking about a saddle horse, you might call it a *mount* or a *steed.* But you would not use the word *mount* or *steed* if you were talking about a workhorse.

220

One reason for synonyms is that they help us say exactly what we mean. There are different words for *horse* because there are different kinds of horses. The synonyms for *horse* reflect differences in the type, the use, and even the quality of horses.

The *horse* words also reveal another reason why there are synonyms in English. The English language has the largest vocabulary of any language in the world. English has built its tremendous vocabulary by borrowing words from other languages. Take the *horse* words, for example. Of the twelve words, only four are purely English: *horse, steed, dobbin,* and *hack.* The rest of the words come from other languages. *Courser* and *equestrian* have Latin roots. *Mount* and *palfrey* come from French. *Nag* comes from Dutch. *Mustang* and *bronco* come from Spanish. *Cayuse* is an American Indian word.

For hundreds of years, English speakers have been adopting words from the languages of people they come in contact with. It began more than two thousand years ago, when Julius Caesar invaded the British Isles. Roman soldiers introduced Latin words into the native language. In 1066 the French-speaking Normans conquered England. During the time that the Normans ruled England, thousands of French words were added to the English language. Over the centuries, English-speaking people have explored all parts of the world. As they established colonies in North America and in other places, they continued to borrow words. These borrowed words have made the English language rich with synonyms. They have given English speakers a choice of ways to express ideas.

Here's a challenge. In "Ida Early" two different words for shoes are used: *brogans* and *clodhoppers.* How many synonyms for *shoe* and words for different kinds of shoes can you think of?

A Get-Well Gift

by BARBARA COHEN

Sometimes you can do something for a friend that you wouldn't do just for yourself. In this story, Sam Greene learns that this is true.

What does Sam want to do? Who helps Sam reach his goal?

Life was often difficult for Sam Greene. His father had died. His mother was always busy running the family's inn in New Jersey. His sister, Sara, cared only about books. There was no one for Sam to spend time with—no one, that is, until Davy came along. Sixty-year-old Davy was the new cook at the inn. He shared Sam's enthusiasm for baseball, the Brooklyn Dodgers, and Jackie Robinson. Davy and Sam spent many hours together talking baseball and going to the games at Ebbets Field. But now Davy was in the hospital recovering from a severe heart attack, and because he was not a family member, Sam was not permitted to visit him. Sam wanted to do something to show Davy how much he cared about him. He wanted to give Davy a special gift that would make him well again. Sam knew what the special gift would be. Getting it, however, would be a challenge for a boy who had trouble talking to strangers.

I had gone into the kitchen real early in the morning, before anyone else was up, and made myself a couple of egg-salad sandwiches. I had them and my money and the baseball in its little cardboard box. I walked the mile and a half to the bus station because there'd be no place to leave my bike if I rode there. I took the bus into New York City and I took the subway to Ebbets Field. I didn't have to ask anyone anything except the bus driver for a ticket to New York City and the man in the subway booth for change of a quarter. There was one thing I'd learned from Sara, and that was that if you know how to read you can do anything. Right in the middle of the subway was this big map of the subway system and Ebbets Field was marked right on it in large black letters. BMT, Brighton Local, downtown, get off at the station near Ebbets Field. I didn't even have to change trains.

You could see flags flying above the ball park when you climbed up out of the subway station. You had to walk three blocks and there you were. Inside it was as it always had been, as bright and green as ever, remote from the sooty streets that surrounded it, remote from all the world. In the excitement of being there, I almost forgot about Davy for a moment. I almost forgot why I had come. But then, when the Cubs' pitcher, Warren Hacker, began to warm up, I turned to Davy to ask him if he thought Shotton was going to give Jackie's sore heel a rest that day, but Davy wasn't there, and I remembered.

I thought maybe I'd better start trying right away. My chances were probably better during batting practice than they would be later. I took my ball out of its box and stashed the box underneath my bleacher seat. Then I walked around to the first-base side and climbed all the way down to the box seats right behind the dugout. I leaned over the rail. Billy Cox was trotting back to the dugout from home plate, where Erskine had been throwing to him.

I swallowed my heart, which seemed to be beating in my throat, and called out, "Billy, hey Billy," waving my ball as hard and high as I could. But I was scared, and

my voice wasn't very loud, and I don't think Billy Cox heard me. He disappeared into the dugout.

Marv Rackley came out of the dugout and then Carl Furillo. I called to them too, but they didn't seem to hear me either.

This method was getting me nowhere. I had to try something else before the game began and I'd really lost my chance. I looked around to see if there were any ushers nearby, but none was in sight. It was kind of early and the place hadn't really started to fill up yet. I guess the ushers were loafing around the refreshment stands.

I climbed up on the railing and then hoisted myself onto the roof of the dugout. That was something you could not do at many places besides Ebbets Field. That was one of the few advantages of such a small ball park. Of course, you know, you couldn't go to see Ebbets Field now if you wanted to. They tore it down and put an apartment building there.

I could have stood up and walked across the dugout roof to

the edge, but I figured if I did that an usher surely would see me. I sneaked across the roof on my belly until I came to the edge and then I leaned over.

It was really very nice in the dugout. I had always kind of pictured it as being literally dug out of the dirt, like a trench in a war. But it had regular walls and a floor and benches and a water cooler. Only trouble was, there were just a couple of guys in there—Eddie Miksis, and Billy Cox, whom I'd seen out on the field a few minutes before. I was disappointed. I had certainly hoped for Campy's signature, and Gil Hodges', and Pee Wee Reese's, and of course Jackie Robinson's. But I figured Davy would be thrilled with Miksis and Billy Cox, since their names on a ball would be more than he'd ever expected. And anyway a few more guys might come meandering in before I was through.

But no matter how hard I swallowed, my heart was still stuck in my throat. "Eddie," I called. "Eddie, Billy." Hardly any sound came out of my mouth at all.

And then all of a sudden I heard a voice calling real loud. Whoever it was didn't have any trouble letting the sound out of *his* mouth. "Hey you, kid, get down off that roof," the voice said. "What do you think you're doing?" I sat up and turned around. An angry usher was standing at the foot of the aisle, right by the railing, screaming at me. "Get yourself off that roof," he shouted. "Right now or I'll throw you out of the ball park."

I scrambled down fast as I could. Boy, was I a mess. My chino pants and striped jersey were absolutely covered with dust and grime from that roof. I guess my face and arms weren't any too clean either. I looked like a bum.

"I'm going to throw you out anyway," the usher said, "because you don't have a ticket."

I got real mad when I heard him say that. People had been throwing me out of places all week long and I was plenty sick of it. Especially since I certainly did have a ticket.

"You can't throw me out," I shouted back at him. "I've got as much right to be here as you have." I had suddenly found my voice. I was scared of the ball players, but this usher didn't frighten me one bit. I pulled my ticket stub out of my pocket.

"See?" I said, thrusting it into his face, "I certainly do have a ticket."

He made as if to take it out of my hand. I guess he wanted to look at it close, to make sure it was a stub from that day and not an old one I carried around in my pocket for emergencies. But I pulled my hand back.

"Oh, no, you don't," I said. "You can't take this ticket away from me. You won't give it back to me and then you'll throw me out because I don't have a ticket!"

"You nuts, kid?" he asked, shaking his head. "This is what I

get for working in Ebbets Field. Next year I'm applying for a job at the Polo Grounds."*

"Go, ahead," I said, "you traitor. Who needs you?" I turned away from him and leaned over the rail.

"I better not see you on that roof again," the usher said. "I'll have my eye out for you—and so will all the other ushers."

"Don't worry," I said.

Then I felt his hand on my shoulder. "As a matter of fact,

*The New York Giants, a rival team to the Brooklyn Dodgers, played at the Polo Grounds.

kid," he said, "I think I'll escort you to your seat where you belong. Up in the bleachers where you can't make any trouble!"

Well, right then and there the whole enterprise would have gone up in smoke if old Jackie Robinson himself had not come trotting out onto the field from the dugout that very second. "Hey, Jackie," I called, "Hey, Jackie," in a voice as loud as a thunderbolt. I mean there were two airplanes flying overhead right that minute and Jackie Robinson heard me anyway.

He glanced over in the direction he could tell my voice was coming from, and I began to wave frantically, still calling "Jackie, hey, Jackie."

He lifted up his hand, gave one wide wave, and smiled. "Hey, kid," he called, and continued on his way to the batting cage. In another instant he'd have been too busy with batting practice to pay any attention to me.

"Sign my ball," I screamed. "Sign my ball."

He seemed to hesitate briefly. I

took this as a good omen. "You have to," I went on frantically. "Please, please, you have to."

"He doesn't *have* to do anything," the usher said. "That's Jackie Robinson."

I went right on screaming.

"Come on, kid," the usher said, "we're getting out of here." He was a big hulking usher who must have weighed about eight hundred pounds, and he began pulling on me. Even though I gripped the cement with my sneakers and held onto the rail with my hand, he managed to pull

228

me loose. But he couldn't shut me up.

"Please, Jackie, please," I went right on screaming.

It worked. Or something worked. If not my screaming, then maybe the sight of that monster usher trying to pull me up the aisle and scrungy old me pulling against him for dear life.

"Let the kid go," Jackie Robinson said when he got to the railing. "All he wants is an autograph."

"He's a fresh kid," the usher said, but he let me go.

"Kids are supposed to be fresh," Jackie Robinson said.

I thrust my ball into Jackie Robinson's face. "Gee, thanks, Mr. Robinson," I said. "Sign it, please."

"You got a pen?" he asked. "A pen?" I could have kicked myself.

"A pen?" I'd forgotten a pen! I turned to the usher. "You got a pen?"

"If I had," the usher said triumphantly, "I certainly wouldn't lend it to you!"

"Oh, come on," Jackie Robinson said, "don't be so vindictive. What harm did the kid do, after all?"

"Well, as it happens, I don't have one," the usher replied smugly.

"Wait here," I said. "Wait right here, Mr. Robinson. I'll go find one."

Jackie Robinson laughed. "Sorry, kid, but I've got work to do. Another time, maybe."

"Please, Mr. Robinson," I said. "It's for my friend. My friend Davy."

"Well, let Davy come and get his own autographs," he said. "Why should you do his dirty work for him?"

"He can't come," I said. The words came rushing out of me, tumbling one on top of the other. I had to tell Jackie Robinson all about it, before he went away. "Davy can't come because he's sick. He had a heart attack."

"A heart attack?" Jackie Robinson asked. "A kid had a heart attack?"

"He's not a kid," I explained. "He's sixty years old. He's my

best friend. He's always loved the Dodgers, but lately he's loved them more than ever."

"How did this Davy get to be your best friend?" he asked.

So I told him. I told him everything, or as near to everything as I could tell in five minutes. I told him how Davy worked for my mother, and how I had no father, so it was Davy who took me to my first ball game. I told him how they wouldn't let me into the hospital to see Davy, and how we had always talked about catching a ball that was hit into the stands and getting it autographed.

Jackie listened silently, nodding every once in a while. When I was done at last, he said, "Well, now,

kid, I'll tell you what. You keep this ball you brought with you. Keep it to play with. And borrow a pen from someone. Come back to the dugout the minute, the very second, the game is over. I'll get you a real ball, one we played with, and I'll get all the guys to autograph it for you."

"Make sure it's one you hit," I said.

What nerve. I should have fainted dead away just because Jackie Robinson had deigned to speak to me. But here he was, making me an offer beyond my wildest dreams, and for me it wasn't enough. I had to have more. However, he didn't seem to care.

"OK," he said, "*if* I hit one." He had been in a little slump lately.

"You will," I said, "you will."

And he did. He broke the ball game wide open in the sixth inning when he hit a double to left field, scoring Rackley and Duke Snider. He scored himself when the Cubs pitcher, Warren Hacker, tried to pick him off second base. But Hacker overthrew, and Jackie, with that incredible speed he had, ran all the way home. Besides, he worked two double plays with Preacher Roe and Gil Hodges. On consecutive pitches, Carl Furillo and Billy Cox both hit home runs, shattering the 1930 Brooklyn home-run record of 122 for a season. The Dodgers scored six runs, and they scored them all in the sixth inning. They beat the Cubs, 6-1. They were hot, really hot, that day and that year.

But I really didn't watch the game as closely as I had all the others I'd been to see. I couldn't. My mind was on too many other things—on Jackie Robinson, on what was going to happen after the game was over, on that monster usher who I feared would find some way of spoiling things for me, but above all on Davy and the fact that he was missing all of the excitement.

And then I had to worry about getting hold of a pen. You could buy little pencils at the ball park for keeping box scores, but no pens. It was the first—and last—time in my life I walked into a ball park without something to write with. And I didn't see how I could borrow one from someone, since in all that mess of humanity I'd never find the person after the game to return it to him. Unless I took the guy's name and address and mailed it back to him later.

It didn't look to me like the guys in the bleachers where I was sitting had pens with them anyway. Most of them had on T-shirts, and T-shirts don't have pockets in them for pens. I decided to walk over to the seats along the first-base line to see if any of those fans looked more like pen owners.

I had to go in that direction anyway to make sure I was at the dugout the second the ball game ended. I took with me my ball in its box.

On my way over I ran into this guy hawking soft drinks, and I decided to buy one in order to wash down the two egg-salad sandwiches I had eaten during the third inning.

This guy had a pen in his pocket. As a matter of fact, he had two of them. "Look," I said to him, as I paid him for my soda, "could I borrow one of those pens?"

"Sure," he said, handing it to me after he had put my money into his change machine. He stood there, waiting, like he expected me to hand it back to him after I was done with it.

"Look," I said again, "maybe I could sort of buy it from you."

"Buy it from me? You mean the pen?"

"Yeah."

"What do you want the pen for?"

"I need it because Jackie Robinson promised me that after the game he and all the other guys would autograph a ball for me." Getting involved in all these explanations was really a pain in the neck.

"You don't say," the hawker remarked. I could tell he didn't believe me.

"It's true," I said. "Anyway, are you going to sell me your pen?"

"Sure. For a dollar."

I didn't have a dollar. Not any more. I'd have to try something else. I started to walk away.

"Oh, don't be silly, kid," he called to me. "Here, take the pen. Keep it." It was a nice pen. It was shaped like a bat, and on it, it said "Ebbets Field, Home of the Brooklyn Dodgers."

"Hey, mister, thanks," I said. "That's real nice of you." It seemed to me I ought to do something for him, so I added, "I think I'd like another soda." He sold me another soda, and between sipping first from one and then from the other and trying to watch the game, I made very slow progress down to the dugout. I got there just before the game ended in the top of the ninth. The Dodgers didn't have to come up to bat at all in that final inning, and I was only afraid that they'd all have disappeared into the clubhouse by the time I got there. I should have come down at the end of the eighth. But Jackie Robinson had said the end of the game. Although my nerve had grown by about seven thousand percent that day, I still didn't have enough to interrupt Jackie Robinson during a game.

I stood at the railing near the dugout, waiting, and sure enough, Jackie Robinson appeared around the corner of the building only a minute or two after Preacher Roe pitched that final out. All around me people were getting up to leave the ball park, but a lot of them stopped when they saw Jackie Robinson come to the rail to talk to me. Roy Campanella, Pee Wee Reese, and Gil Hodges were with him.

"Hi, kid," Jackie Robinson said. He was carrying a ball. It was covered with signatures. "Pee Wee here had a pen."

"And a good thing, too," Pee Wee said, "because most of the other guys left the field already."

"But these guys wanted to meet Davy's friend," Jackie Robinson said.

By that time, Preacher Roe had joined us at the railing. Jackie handed him the ball. "Hey, Preacher," he said, "got enough strength left in that arm to sign this ball for Davy's friend here?"

"Got a pen?" Preacher Roe asked.

I handed him the pen the hawker had given me. I was glad I hadn't gone through all the trouble of getting it for nothing.

"Not much room left on this ball," Roe said. He squirmed his signature into a little empty space beneath Duke Snider's, and then he handed me both the pen and the ball. Everybody was waving programs and pens in the faces of the ball players who stood by the railing. But before they signed any of them, they all shook my hand. So did Jackie Robinson. I stood there, clutching Davy's ball and watching while those guys signed the programs of the other fans. Finally, though, they'd had enough. They smiled and waved

their hands and walked away, five big men in white uniforms, etched sharply against the bright green grass. Jackie Robinson was the last one into the dugout and before he disappeared around the corner, he turned and waved to me.

I waved back. "Thank you, Jackie Robinson," I called. "Thanks for everything." He nodded and smiled. I guess he heard me. I'm glad I remembered my manners before it was too late.

When everyone was gone, I looked down at the ball in my hands. Right between the rows of red seaming, Jackie Robinson had written, above his own signature, "For Davy. Get well soon." Then all the others had put their names around that.

CHECK FOR UNDERSTANDING

1. What did Sam want to do?
2. At first when Sam yelled to the ball players, no one heard him. What happened to help Sam find his voice?
3. Who helped Sam reach his goal?
4. What did Sam tell Jackie Robinson that made him offer to get the whole team to sign a game ball?
5. What do Jackie Robinson's actions tell you about this character?
6. If Sam had remembered to bring a pen, do you think things would have worked out the same way? Explain your answer.

WRITE ABOUT *"A Get-Well Gift"*

Pretend that you are Jackie Robinson and that you are talking to a reporter. The reporter saw you and the other players give the autographed ball to Sam and has asked you about it. Describe what happened the way you think Jackie Robinson might have described it.

The Real
Jackie Robinson

In "A Get-Well Gift," the character Jackie Robinson played a special part in Sam Greene's life. In real life, Jackie Robinson played a special part in the history of baseball. Read this article to learn about the real Jackie Robinson.

Jackie Robinson was born in 1919. As a child he loved all kinds of sports—mostly because he was good at them. When he was a student at U.C.L.A., he excelled in four sports. He was the first person in the school's history to win letters in football, baseball, track, and basketball.

In 1945 Jackie Robinson began his career in professional baseball. The major league teams did not hire black players, so Jackie joined the Kansas City Monarchs of the Negro American League.

Playing for the Monarchs wasn't a happy experience. The team spent the season traveling around the country. Sometimes the players could not find hotels that admitted blacks. Often they had to eat meals outside or on their bus because blacks were not allowed to sit at tables in restaurants. After one season, Jackie was ready to quit professional baseball.

Jackie didn't know that a man named Branch Rickey had been following his career with interest. Rickey had just been named president of the Brooklyn Dodgers. It had long been Rickey's dream to end racial discrimination in major league baseball. In his new position he had the chance to do it.

Rickey called Jackie Robinson to New York. At their first meeting,

237

Rickey asked Jackie if he would like to become the first black player in the major leagues. Then he fired question after question at Jackie. What would Jackie do if a pitcher threw at his head? What would he do if players deliberately used their spikes on him? What would he do if players called him names? Before Jackie could answer, Rickey said, "I'm looking for a ballplayer with enough guts *not* to fight back."

By the time the meeting was over, Jackie had become a member of the Dodger organization.

Jackie played the 1946 season with the Montreal Royals, the farm club of the Brooklyn Dodgers. A year later, he was moved up to the Dodgers.

Jackie's first year as a Dodger was difficult. Everything Rickey had warned Jackie about happened, and worse. Some of the other Dodgers made it clear that they did not want Jackie on the team. Angry letters poured in to the Dodger offices.

No matter what happened, Jackie did not fight back. He knew there was more at stake than his own career. Instead of fighting back, he played even harder. By the end of his first season, he led the team in stolen bases and was named "Rookie of the Year" by a national newspaper. More important, his teammates had come to accept him. They took his side when other teams jeered him.

Jackie's greatest triumph came in 1949. It was his best year in baseball. The Dodgers won the National League Pennant for the second time in three years, and Jackie became the first black player to play on the National League All-Star team. Best of all, Jackie was chosen, out of all the players in baseball, to receive the Most Valuable Player Award, the highest award in baseball.

CHECK FOR UNDERSTANDING

1. What kind of player did Branch Rickey tell Jackie he was looking for?
2. Why was there more at stake than Jackie's own career when he first started playing for the Dodgers?

In "A Get-Well Gift," Sam Greene went to Ebbets Field to get the autographs of the Dodger players.

How can someone get the autograph of a ballplayer without actually meeting the player? How would someone get Jackie Robinson's autograph today?

Collecting Autographs

by HERMAN M. DARVICK

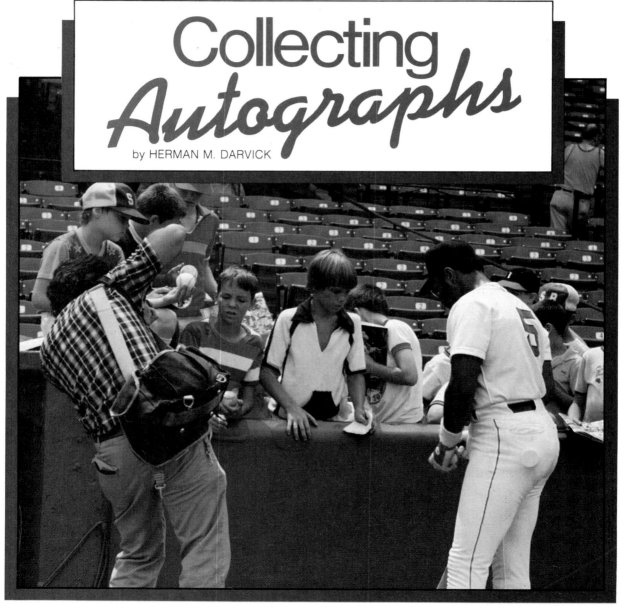

What Is a Philographer?

"The baseball game had been over for an hour," recalls Richard Goldberg. "We were waiting outside Yankee Stadium—my father and I and about a hundred other people. I held my scorecard in one hand, a pen in the other. 'There he is!' screamed a girl behind me. It was Reggie Jackson, the great Yankee outfielder. How I wanted his autograph—he was my hero! Luckily, I was near the front of the crowd. He only signed three scorecards, and mine was one of them. Then he drove off in his car. I could hardly read what he wrote, but I didn't care. I had Reggie's autograph."

Richard didn't know it then, but he had become a philographer (fi log′ rə fər), an autograph collector. The word was invented by Charles Hamilton, one of the leading authorities on autographs. It has become part of the language of collectors and dealers. Philography is one of the world's oldest hobbies. Two thousand years ago, a great Roman statesman named Cicero collected letters written by famous people living in Rome. One of his most prized possessions was a letter written to him by Emperor Julius Caesar. No one knows where that letter is today, but if it were ever found it would be worth over two million dollars!

How to Become a Philographer

How can you become a philographer? Collect autographs in whatever interests you. If you're a baseball fan, your collection could include names like Dave Winfield and Steve Garvey. Just write to them in care of their teams. It's better to write them during the baseball season, but anytime during the year is fine. You can add the names of such former superstars as Willie Mays, Mickey Mantle, and Joe DiMaggio to

your collection. Write to them in care of the National Baseball Hall of Fame. If you would like to expand your collection to include baseball greats such as Babe Ruth, Jackie Robinson, Lou Gehrig, Ty Cobb, and Roberto Clemente (all of whom are no longer living), you will have to either buy these autographs from dealers or trade with other collectors.

If you are lucky enough to meet

a baseball player in person, you can ask him to sign a baseball for you. Signed baseballs, footballs, and basketballs are one way of assembling autograph collections for easy display. Seven-year-old Lee Mattes and his younger brother Keith got eleven tennis autographs on a racket cover when their parents took them to a tennis tournament in Flushing, New York.

Autographs of actors and actresses are also very popular to collect. If you enjoy watching a certain show on television, start a collection of the autographs of the show's stars. Movie stars answer autograph requests through the mail. Once again, you would have to buy or trade for autographs of stars who are no longer alive.

The most popular area of all to collect is presidents of the United States. It is difficult to get the autograph of the current president of the United States because he is so busy. However, former presidents usually answer all requests. Herbert Hoover, president from 1929 to 1933, and Harry S Truman, president from 1945 to 1953, always answered collectors' letters. Letters written by them after they left the White House are very common. In fact, Herbert Hoover was once asked by an eleven-year-old boy for three autographs. Hoover sent them and asked the boy why he wanted three. "Because it takes two of yours to trade for one of Babe Ruth's" was the honest reply.

Write to every congressman, congresswoman, and governor in the news. Keep writing to them as they become important. Almost all presidents of the United States were in Congress or were governors before they were elected president. So if you got someone's autograph before that person became president, it would become very valuable after that person moved to the White House.

A handwritten letter of the current president of the United States is worth at least one thousand dollars. It does not matter if it was written before the presidential election. You could trade that handwritten letter for an autograph of George Washington or Abraham Lincoln.

There are many other areas in

Abraham Lincoln.

G Washington

which to collect. Some of these are: authors, scientists, astronauts, aviators, Supreme Court justices, kings and queens, artists, military leaders, Nobel prize winners, world leaders, singers, vice-presidents, black leaders, musicians, religious leaders, Cabinet members, and composers. Or you can collect autographs of famous people born in your state. If you write to the department of tourism at your state capital, they will send you a list.

One of the most interesting collecting areas is astronauts. Since Alán Shepard's flight in *Freedom* 7 in 1961, the United States has launched many teams of astronauts into space. In addition, there are dozens of new astronauts who have not as yet gone into space.

Seymour M. Kessler has one of the best astronaut collections in the world. He advises young collectors to write to the new astronauts. "Show your interest in America's space program and especially in the astronaut. You may be surprised with the nice letter you will receive in return," says Mr. Kessler.

Yogi Berra

Wally Schirra

John Hancock

CHECK FOR UNDERSTANDING

1. How can someone get the autograph of a ballplayer without actually meeting the player?
2. How would someone get Jackie Robinson's autograph today?
3. Why do you think so many people enjoy collecting autographs?

Joe DiMaggio

COMPREHENSION

Predicting Outcomes

What is the point of predicting outcomes? If you know what is going to happen at the end of a story, why bother reading it?

Reading a story or a book can be a little like taking a trip. When you start out on a trip, you know exactly where you are going and you usually have a pretty good idea of what you will find when you get there. Knowing where you are going and what you can expect does not keep you from making the trip. Your predictions and expectations are probably what made you decide to take the trip in the first place. You take the trip for the pleasure of the experience.

When you select a book or story to read on your own, you have really made a prediction. When you decide to read a certain story or book, you are predicting that it is something you will enjoy. You use different kinds of information to make this kind of a prediction. You may have read and enjoyed another story or book by the same author. A friend may have told you the story or book was good. It may be a story or book about a subject that interests you. You may even have been attracted by the book's cover or the pictures that illustrate a story.

As you read the story, you go on predicting. Predicting involves you in the story. In a way, predicting is like setting a purpose for reading. When you make a prediction about what will happen, you continue reading to find out whether or not your prediction was correct.

One of the skills of *writing* is knowing just how many clues to give the reader and how many to leave out. One of the skills of *reading* is recognizing the clues. When you read "A Get-Well Gift," you were probably pretty sure from the beginning of the story that Sam would manage to get some autographs on the baseball for his friend Davy. But you probably could not predict *how* he would get them or how many he would get.

244

Another prediction you could probably make as you read the story was that an usher would catch Sam on the roof of the dugout. The author gives you a couple of clues that this will happen. Before he climbs out on the roof Sam says:

> I looked around to see if there were any ushers nearby, but none was in sight. . . . I guess the ushers were loafing around the refreshment stands.

After Sam is on the roof he mentions the ushers again: "I could have stood up and walked across the dugout roof to the edge, but I figured if I did that an usher surely would see me." Sam's concern about the ushers helps the reader predict that before Sam manages to get the attention of the players in the dugout, an usher will see him and make him come down.

Another prediction you probably made as you were reading the story was that Jackie Robinson would play an important role. Sam mentions Jackie Robinson twice before Jackie actually makes an appearance in the story. When he does appear, the reader gets a clear clue that Jackie will help Sam reach his goal.

> Well, right then and there the whole enterprise would have gone up in smoke if old Jackie Robinson himself had not come trotting out onto the field from the dugout that very second.

Can you remember another prediction you made while you were reading "A Get-Well Gift"? What was it? What clues in the story helped you make it? Did your prediction turn out to be true?

My Vietnamese Grandmother

by HUYNH QUANG NHUONG

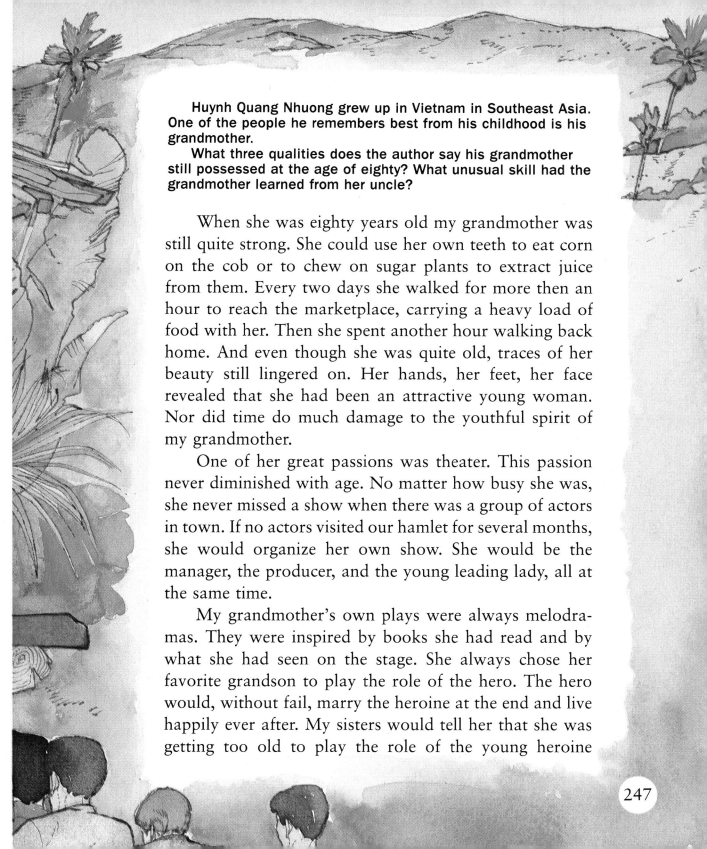

Huynh Quang Nhuong grew up in Vietnam in Southeast Asia. One of the people he remembers best from his childhood is his grandmother.

What three qualities does the author say his grandmother still possessed at the age of eighty? What unusual skill had the grandmother learned from her uncle?

When she was eighty years old my grandmother was still quite strong. She could use her own teeth to eat corn on the cob or to chew on sugar plants to extract juice from them. Every two days she walked for more then an hour to reach the marketplace, carrying a heavy load of food with her. Then she spent another hour walking back home. And even though she was quite old, traces of her beauty still lingered on. Her hands, her feet, her face revealed that she had been an attractive young woman. Nor did time do much damage to the youthful spirit of my grandmother.

One of her great passions was theater. This passion never diminished with age. No matter how busy she was, she never missed a show when there was a group of actors in town. If no actors visited our hamlet for several months, she would organize her own show. She would be the manager, the producer, and the young leading lady, all at the same time.

My grandmother's own plays were always melodramas. They were inspired by books she had read and by what she had seen on the stage. She always chose her favorite grandson to play the role of the hero. The hero would, without fail, marry the heroine at the end and live happily ever after. My sisters would tell her that she was getting too old to play the role of the young heroine

247

anymore. My grandmother merely replied: "Anybody can play this role if she's young at heart."

My grandmother had married a man whom she loved with all her heart. But he was totally different from her. My grandfather was very shy. He never laughed loudly and always spoke very softly. And physically he was not as strong as my grandmother. But he excused his lack of physical strength by saying that he was a "scholar."

About three months after their marriage, my grandparents were in a restaurant. A rascal began to insult my grandfather because he looked weak and had a pretty wife. At first he just made insulting remarks, such as, "Hey! Wet chicken! This is no place for a weakling!"

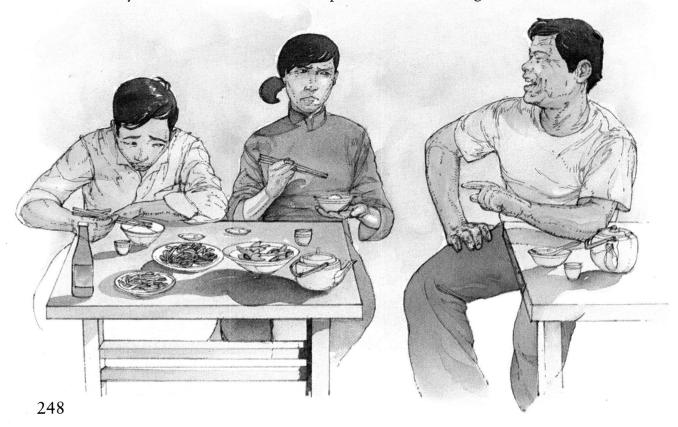

My grandfather wanted to leave the restaurant even though he and my grandmother had not yet finished their meal. But my grandmother pulled his shirt sleeve and signaled him to remain seated. She continued to eat and looked as if nothing had happened.

Tired of yelling insults without any result, the rascal got up from his table. He moved over to my grandparents' table and grabbed my grandfather's chopsticks. My grandmother immediately wrested the chopsticks from him and struck the rascal on the cheekbone with her elbow. The blow was so quick and powerful that he lost his balance and fell on the floor. Instead of finishing him off, as any street fighter would do, my grandmother let the rascal recover from the blow. But as soon as he got up again, he kicked over the table between him and my grandmother. Food and drink flew all over the place. Before he could do anything else, my grandmother kicked him on the chin. The kick was so swift that my grandfather didn't even see it. He only heard a heavy thud. Then saw the rascal tumble backward and collapse on the ground.

All the onlookers were surprised and delighted, especially the owner of the restaurant. The rascal was one of the best karate fighters of our area. He came to this restaurant every day and left without paying for his food or drink. The owner was too afraid to confront him.

The rascal's friends tried to revive him. Everyone else surrounded my grandmother. They asked her who had taught her karate. She said, "Who else? My husband!"

After the fight at the restaurant people assumed that my grandfather knew karate very well. They thought he refused to use it for fear of killing someone. In reality, my grandmother had received special training in karate from my great-great uncle from the time she was eight years old.

Anyway, after that incident, my grandfather never had to worry again. Anytime he had some business downtown, people treated him very well. And whenever anyone happened to bump into him on the street, they bowed to my grandfather in a very respectful way.

One morning my grandmother wanted me to go outside with her. We climbed a little hill that looked over the whole area. When we got to the top, she looked at the rice field below, the mountain on the horizon, and especially at the river. As a young girl, she had often brought her herd of water buffaloes to the river to drink. She swam there with the other children of the village. Then we visited the graveyard where her husband and some of her children were buried. She touched her husband's tombstone and said, "Dear, I will join you soon." And then we walked back to the garden. She gazed at the fruit trees her husband had planted. He had planted a new one for each time she had given birth to a child. Finally, before we left the garden, my sister joined us. The two of them fed a few ducks swimming in the pond.

That evening my grandmother did not eat much of her dinner. After dinner she combed her hair and put on her best dress. We thought that she was going to go out again. Instead she went to her bedroom. She told us that she didn't want to be disturbed.

The family dog seemed to sense something was amiss. He kept looking anxiously at everybody and whined from

time to time. At midnight my mother went to my grand-mother's room. She found that she had died. Her eyes were shut, as if she were sleeping normally.

It took me a long time to get used to the reality that my grandmother had passed away. Wherever I was, in the house, in the garden, out in the fields, her face always appeared so clearly to me. And even now, many years later, I still have the feeling that my last conversation with her has happened only a few day before.

CHECK FOR UNDERSTANDING

1. What three qualities does the author say his grand-mother still possessed at the age of eighty?
2. What role did the grandmother always play in her own shows? What did she say when she was told she was too old for that role?
3. What unusual skill had the grandmother learned from her uncle?
4. Why did the grandmother tell the people in the restaurant that she had learned this skill from her husband?
5. For what qualities do you think the author admired his grandmother most?

The Daring Doctor of Brazoria

by JANELLE D. SCOTT

Dr. Sofie Herzog (1848-1925)

Today there is nothing unusual about a woman becoming a doctor. A hundred years ago, however, things were different. Medicine was not considered a "proper" profession for a woman. That didn't stop Sofie Herzog. Her taste for adventure and her confidence in her own ability led her to practice medicine in a rugged town in southeast Texas.

What was Sofie's original reason for studying medicine? How did Sofie show that she was confident in her own ability as a doctor?

She was a daring doctor in a gun-fighter's town. She galloped across Texas trails. She hopped railroad cars to reach her patients. She treated bandits for gunshot wounds. And she made a necklace out of the bullets she removed from them.

She was Sofie Herzog, the mother of fourteen children. She became the unlikely town doctor in the coastal community of Brazoria, Texas, in the 1890s. She was one of only a handful of Texas's women doctors at the time. But few of them were as daring as "Dr. Sofie."

She shocked townspeople by wearing short hair and a man's hat. She rode astride her horse, instead of sidesaddle the way most ladies did. But over a thirty-year career, she endeared herself to the people of Brazoria. They came to admire her medical skill and her tender devotion to the sick and wounded.

Sofie was born in Austria in 1848. She was the daughter of a fa-mous surgeon. At fourteen she married a young surgeon. During their twenty-six-year marriage, the couple had fourteen children, including two sets of twins. The Herzogs lived in Vienna, the medical center of the world in the nineteenth century.

Around 1870 Sofie decided to study medicine. She could then assist her husband. She attended a Viennese university and observed world-famous surgeons at work. At home, she discussed the latest methods and medical ideas with her husband.

In 1886 her husband accepted a job in New York. The Herzogs said good-by to their native land and started a new life in America. Sofie's husband had high hopes for a brilliant career in the United States. But only a few years after they arrived, Dr. Herzog died.

Sofie was just past forty years old. She was alone in a strange country with children to support. What

could she do? The only profession she knew was medicine. But in America, there was great prejudice and suspicion against women doctors.

Medicine was considered an "unladylike" occupation. A woman doctor had to examine unclothed bodies. Many people thought this was shocking. At that time only the very poorest women worked. Middle-class women were considered too delicate to face the hardship and dangers of the outside world. Most professions and careers were closed to women.

Sofie thought that was nonsense. So Sofie decided to do what *she* thought was right. She didn't care what anyone else said. After all, she was a trained physician. So she set up her medical practice in New York. She soon earned an excellent reputation and had many patients.

One day Sofie's youngest daughter told Sofie that she was getting married. She was going to Texas with her new husband.

Texas! Everyone knew it was a land of adventure. It had an untamed wilderness filled with opportunities. Sofie decided she wanted to go to Texas, too. After all, her children were beginning to build their own lives now. They really didn't need her to look after them anymore.

Sofie was forty-five years old and ready for a new adventure. She packed her medical instruments and supplies and headed for Texas! Sofie knew a life in Texas would be very different from life in Vienna or New York. Compared to those cities, life in Brazoria, Texas, would be primitive. But that didn't bother her. Sofie was ready for a change and a challenge.

People in Brazoria were very curious about their new woman doctor. The ladies of Brazoria peered out of their lace-curtained windows to look at the newly arrived Dr. Herzog.

They shook their heads and muttered their disapproval. They saw an attractive woman with lively dark eyes. But she had *short* curly hair. The women were shocked. No woman in Brazoria had short hair! They all wore their long hair pinned up modestly on top of their heads—the way they thought all ladies should.

Sofie was not bothered by gossip and wagging tongues. She went about the business of setting up a medical practice.

If Sofie wanted adventure, challenges, and a new type of medical practice, she found it in Brazoria. Most of her cases in those early years were gunshot victims. Bandits plagued the citizens of Brazoria County. Political battles were often fought with six-shooters.

Sofie became an expert at removing bullets. Her skill as a surgeon soon became well known. She treated outlaws, saloon brawlers, and feuding settlers. The lively town excited Sofie. It needed her skills. It began to value her services. Sofie had found a home.

Brazoria County was at the mouth of the Brazos River near the Gulf of Mexico. It was still a primitive area with few roads. After a rain, its trails became muddy. They could be traveled only on horseback. Some of Sofie's patients lived along swampy river bottoms, among snakes and other wild animals. It was difficult to get through with her wagon. Sofie wanted to be able to get to her patients when they needed her. So she bought a beautiful horse for transportation. She ordered a dressmaker to make her a divided skirt.

Wearing a man's hat and her divided skirt, Sofie rode through the town astride her horse. The ladies were shocked once again. No "respectable" woman rode a horse like that! The proper way was side-

saddle—modestly and slowly. But Sofie wanted to get where she was going fast. She galloped past the women on their porches, leaving them speechless. Sofie had no time for false modesty when patients needed her.

Sofie, like most small town doctors, practiced all kinds of medicine. She delivered babies and treated a variety of illnesses. She liked to mix her own medicines for her patients, and she experimented with new methods of treatment.

In 1905 the St. Louis, Brownsville, and Mexico Railroad Company began laying track in Brazoria County. The growing number of workers increased Sofie's business. Time and again they were hurt in the serious accidents that happen when a railroad is built in an untamed land.

Many of these accident calls came to Sofie. She jumped on her horse and followed the faint trails into the woods to the construction site. Soon, the workers sang her praises. They had complete confidence in this brave woman doctor.

In 1907 Sofie applied for the job of chief surgeon to the railroad. Railroad workers and local officials gave Dr. Herzog glowing recommendations. She was hired at once.

But there was one problem. No one had told the railroad directors that Dr. Herzog was a woman! When the officials back East found this out, they withdrew their job offer. Being a railroad doctor was no job for a woman, they believed. It was rugged work, with long hours and many emergencies. They sent Sofie a letter, explaining their misunderstanding. They said they were certain she would give up the job.

Of course, Sofie did no such thing.

"I'll keep this job so long as I give satisfaction," she wrote back. "If I fail, then you can fire me."

Sofie never gave them a reason to fire her. She rode the train back and forth from Brazoria to Brownsville, treating sick and injured people along the way. Sometimes she rode in box cars, on hand cars, on engines. She rode on anything that would get her quickly to the scene of the emergency.

Townspeople got used to the sight of "Dr. Sofie" whizzing by on a handcar with a railroad employee pumping at top speed. People said, "Sofie clutched her hat with one hand and her doctor's bag with the other."

When the first chugging automobiles appeared on the streets of Brazoria, Sofie just had to have one. By now, Sofie was an elderly woman. People must have thought she was very foolish to take a chance on driving the noisy, snorting early model cars. Sofie once again did as she pleased. She took a few driving lessons from the man who sold her the car. Then she began making her rounds in her Ford "runabout."

When she was sixty-five, Sofie married again. Her husband was Marion Huntington. He was the seventy-year-old owner of a plantation between Freeport and Brazoria. She moved into his home and traveled seven miles over rough roads to her office every day for eleven years.

Sofie practiced medicine until 1925—the year of her death. She was seventy-six years old. She had given thirty years of her life to the people of Brazoria County and the railroad workers up and down the Gulf Coast. She had used her medical talents in a place that badly needed skilled doctors.

When she died, Sofie was

honored for being one of the few women ever to serve as a railroad company surgeon. Her "professional skill and tenderness endeared her to all the Gulf Coast work force. The good she did lives after her," a newspaper article reported.

She was a woman who handled a rough job in a rugged place and did it exceptionally well. Like all women struggling to break into the professions at the time, she had to overcome ridicule and social disdain. But her abilities and courage eventually earned her the grateful respect of the community.

CHECK FOR UNDERSTANDING

1. What was Sofie's original reason for studying medicine?
2. Why did Sofie move to Brazoria, Texas?
3. What did the directors of the St. Louis, Brownsville, and Mexico Railroad do when they found out that Dr. Herzog was a woman?
4. How did Sofie show that she was confident in her own ability as a doctor?
5. Dr. Sofie Herzog and Jackie Robinson faced similar problems in their professions. In what ways were their responses to the problem alike?
6. Would Sofie have achieved the same kind of success in her career if she had stayed New York instead of going to Texas? Explain your answer.

WRITE ABOUT *"The Daring Doctor of Brazoria"*

Pretend you are a reporter for the local Brazoria newspaper. It is 1893, and your assignment is to interview the woman doctor who just arrived from New York City. Think about the kinds of things your readers would like to know about the new doctor. Then write five questions that you will use in your interview.

USING AN ENCYCLOPEDIA

Which two Presidents of the United States were father and son? When did a human being first go up in the air in a machine? Did Benedict Arnold ever do anything of which America could be proud? What country had the earliest form of soccer? What are the two Sioux words that make up the name *Minnesota*?

Chances are you don't know the answers to some of these questions. But what if you needed to have the answers? Where would you look?

The answers to these questions can be found in an encyclopedia. An encyclopedia contains general information about many different subjects. An encyclopedia has articles on all the important places, events, people, ideas, discoveries, and machines in the world. But encyclopedias have more than articles. They also have maps of states, countries, and oceans. They have graphs, charts, diagrams, photographs, and illustrations. To unlock the secrets of an encyclopedia, you need to know how the information is organized.

Every article in the encyclopedia is listed by topic. The topic is printed in large, dark letters at the beginning of the article. The topic may be a general one, like SPACE TRAVEL. It may be the name of an important person. When the topic is a person's name, the last name always appears first. The topic may also be a specific place, religion, historical period, group of people, or sport.

To find an article in the encyclopedia, you first need to identify the topic to look for. Usually, the question you want answered will lead you to the right topic. For example, the first question in the lesson asks about a father and son who were both Presidents. To find the answer you might look for the topic U.S. GOVERNMENT. You also might find the information if you look for the topic PRESIDENTS OF THE U.S.

Finding one article on a particular topic will give you ideas for other topics that are related. Suppose, for example, you were writing a report on well-known American poets. You know that Gwendolyn Brooks is a well-known poet, so you look up her name in the encyclopedia. In the article on Gwendolyn Brooks, you find that she won a Pulitzer Prize in 1950. To find the names of other well-known American poets, you look up PULITZER PRIZE in the encyclopedia.

Encyclopedias also have a system called *cross-referencing*. With this system, an article will suggest related topics you can look up to get more information. For example, an article on the star, Orion, might have a note that says *See ASTRONOMY*. That tells you that more information on Orion can be found in the article on astronomy.

Look back to the questions at the beginning of the lesson. What topic would you look up to find the information that would help you answer each question?

STUDY SKILLS

How to Find an Article

Once you have decided on a topic to look up, you need to know how to find the topic listed in the encyclopedia. Most encyclopedias are made up of several volumes. The first thing you must do is decide which volume to look in. The picture on this page shows the volumes of an encyclopedia. Each volume has a number and one or more letters on its spine. The letters are called *guide letters*. They indicate the beginning letters of all the topics discussed in that volume. Topics that begin with *A* will be found in Volume 1, the volume marked "A." Articles with titles that begin with *B* will be found in Volume 2, the volume marked "B."

Look at the volumes of the encyclopedia shown in the picture. What is the number of the volume you would look in to find information on each of these topics?

baseball	Great Smoky Mountains
Cicero	Vietnam
karate	Jackie Robinson
Marie Curie	Elizabeth Blackwell

The idea for the footpath was proposed in 1921 by the forester and regional planner Benton MacKaye. The trail was completed in 1937. The Appalachian Trail Conference, in Washington, D.C., is the headquarters for organizations interested in trail activities. *Frank Ahnert*

appeal (ə pēl′), in law, a formal request to a higher court, or court of appeal, to review the decision of a lower court. The term also applies to the review itself. An appeal may be made by a person, called the appellant, who seeks to have the original decision in his case reversed or modified. An appeal may be granted if the appellant files a notice of appeal within a specified time, and if he shows good reason why the case should be reviewed.

In its review the court of appeal decides whether any error has been made by the lower court, or whether the evidence justifies a reexamination of the case. It considers a wrong interpretation of evidence to be an error of fact and improper legal procedure to be an error of law. In appeals after the verdict of a trial jury, the court of appeal will consider only errors of law. If it finds an error, it may reverse the decision of the lower court and order a new trial or grant a judgment in favor of the appellant.

Appeals occur in both civil and criminal cases. Most persons convicted of a crime have an absolute right to appeal, and when a death sentence has been pronounced the appeal is automatic. Both state and federal court systems in the United States have courts of appeal. Each state has one court of last resort, usually called the supreme court, and many have intermediate courts of appeal. If an issue of federal constitutional law is involved, the decision of the highest state court may be appealed to the U.S. Supreme Court. *Herbert Peterfreund*

appendicitis (ə pen′də sī′tis), an inflammation of the appendix, usually caused by an obstruction within the organ, and sometimes accompanied by bacterial infection. The obstructed appendix swells and fills with exudate, or pus. If the appendix ruptures, the pus spills into the surrounding abdominal cavity and may cause peritonitis, a serious infection of the membrane that lines the abdominal cavity.

Appendicitis most frequently occurs among adolescents and young adults. The first symptom is often a cramping pain in the mid-abdomen. The pain is intermittent and may be accompanied by nausea and vomiting. It shifts after a few hours to the lower right part of the abdomen and becomes constant. The muscles in the abdomen contract, and the area is painful to pressure. The patient's white-blood-cell count often increases, and he may have a slight fever.

Treatment is the surgical removal of the inflamed appendix. The operation, called an appendectomy, is among the most common major surgical procedures. Because laxatives may cause rupture of the appendix, they must never be used to treat abdominal pains without consulting a doctor. *Louis J. Vorhaus, M.D.*

appendix (ə pen′diks), also called vermiform appendix, a worm-shaped abdominal structure. It is closed at one end, and attached by its open end to the cecum, the beginning of the large intestine. The human appendix, which seems to have no function in modern man, is normally about 2 to 3 inches (5–7 cm) long and one-third inch (8 mm) in diameter. It is located in the lower right abdomen, pointing down toward the pelvis although its position varies with the location of the cecum.

Only man and the anthropoid apes have a vermiform appendix. Most other mammals have a similar organ, but not a true appendix. In these mammals, the organ is usually much longer than the human appendix and probably plays a role in the animal's digestion. Many scientists believe that the human appendix at one time served a useful purpose which, through evolution, has gradually been lost. *See also* APPENDICITIS. *Louis J. Vorhaus, M.D.*

Appert, Nicolas (à per′, nē kō lä′), *French chef and inventor. Born Châlons-sur-Marne, France, Nov. 17, 1749. Died near Paris, France, June 2, 1841.*

Appert invented a process for preserving foods by sterilizing them with heat and sealing them in containers. In Appert's process, food was placed in glass bottles which were then loosely stoppered and immersed in hot water. After being heated, the bottles were removed from the water and sealed tightly. If the seal was not broken until just before the food was eaten, there was usually no spoilage. Later Appert and others found that food preservation was best accomplished at temperatures above the boiling point of water.

Appert's method, which is essentially the same as that used in modern home canning, was adopted by Napoleon for use by the French navy. *Everett Mendelsohn*

Appia, Adolphe (à pyà′, à dôlf′), *Swiss stage designer. Born Geneva, Switzerland, Sept. 1, 1862. Died Nyon, Switzerland, Feb. 29, 1928.*

Appia pioneered in the development of stage designs that suggest the atmosphere of a play rather than its realistic setting. He designed simple, massive sets and was particularly concerned with the dramatic effects of lighting. Some of his best work was for Richard Wagner's operas *Tristan und Isolde*, *Das Rheingold*, *Die Walküre*, and *Parsifal*. *A. M. Nagler*

Appian Way (ap′i ən), or Via Appia, a famous Roman road in southern Italy that connected Rome with Brundisium on the Adriatic Sea. The highway was one of the first great long-distance Roman roads and was the principal highway between Rome and the Adriatic ports for travel to Greece and the East.

The road was named for Appius Claudius Caecus, who ordered its construction in 312 B.C. It originally linked Rome with Capua, 105 miles (170 km) to the southeast. By the mid-3d century B.C. it had been extended to the cities of Beneventum (now Benevento), Tarentum (now Taranto), and Brundisium (now Brindisi). The complete road was more than 350 miles (560 km) long and about 15 feet (4.5 meters) wide. Originally, the Appian Way was probably surfaced with gravel, but parts were later paved with large blocks of stone. Although the road was built mainly for military purposes, it also served as a highway.

Much of the ancient road no longer exists. Some sections, however, are still in use, and elsewhere modern roads follow part of the route. Many ancient Roman monuments still line the section of the Appian Way leading out of Rome. *Norman J. G. Pounds*

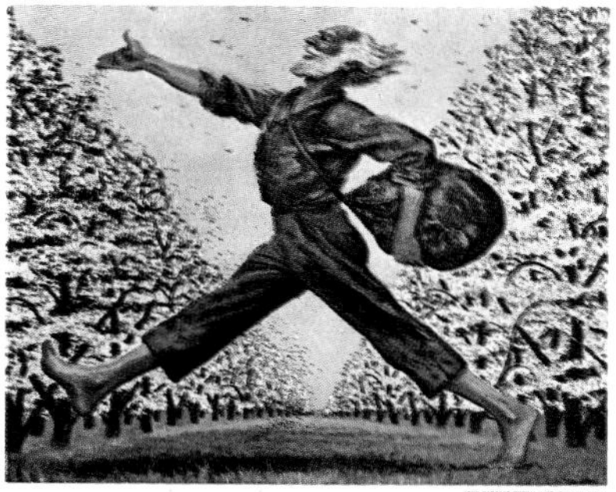

JOHN HANCOCK MUTUAL LIFE INSURANCE CO.

Johnny Appleseed roamed throughout the Ohio river valley during the early 1800's planting apple seeds and saplings. Johnny Appleseed, whose real name was John Chapman, is believed to have planted more than 35 apple nurseries in 19 counties. Today, in North America, apples are the major fruit crop in Canada and the United States. Apples are also widely cultivated in parts of Europe.

apple (ap′əl), any of a group of trees that are closely related to the pear tree and that bear edible round fruit, called apples. Apples are the best-known and most widely cultivated of all fruits. They are scientifically classified as pome fruits, because their edible portion probably develops from the pome stem rather than from the ovary of the original flower.

There are about 25 species of apple trees, but thousands of varieties have been developed by crossbreeding the trees. Most of the cultivated varieties have been developed from two species of wild apples: the common apple (*Malus pumila*), which is native to southwestern Asia, and the closely related Siberian crab apple (*M. baccata*), which is native to Siberia, Manchuria, and northern China.

Apples are fleshy, crisp, and flavorful. Because they contain more than 80 percent water, they are relatively low in calories. A large raw apple, for example, contains only about 100 calories. The chief nutrients found in apples are fructose and sucrose, natural fruit sugars. Apples also contain fair amounts of vitamin A and vitamin C (ascorbic acid), as well as the minerals calcium, phosphorus, and iron.

Cultivated Varieties. There are more than 7,500 varieties of apple trees, but only about 50 varieties are grown for their fruit. Most commercially cultivated apples were developed from the common apple, but some are crosses between the common apple and the crab apple. The varieties developed from the crab apple are usually raised only in home orchards or as ornamental trees.

The common apple is a round-topped tree that may grow more than 40 feet (12 meters) tall. It has fuzzy, sawtoothed leaves and bears clusters of large pink or white blossoms. The round or oval-shaped fruits range from 2 to 4 inches (5–10 cm) in diameter and are green, yellow, or red or various shades of these colors.

The crab apple has a more slender, wiry structure than the common apple tree. It is usually slightly shorter, has less downy leaves, and bears clusters of pink, white, or red blossoms that are often very fragrant. Its fruits range from pea-size to 2 inches (5 cm) in diameter and may be various shades of green, yellow, or red. Because they are sour and hard, crab apples are usually cooked before being eaten.

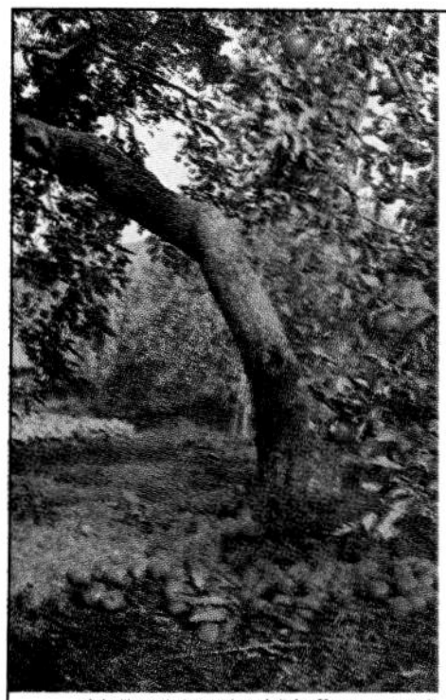

A healthy apple tree produces fruit for 60 years or more. It usually begins to bear from 3 to 10 years after planting.

The particular variety of apple cultivated in any area depends upon the climate, soil conditions, and market demand. In the United States, the most popular varieties are Delicious, McIntosh, Winesap, Rome Beauty, Jonathan, Golden Delicious, Stayman, York Imperial, Newtown Pippin, Cortland, Rhode Island Greening, and Northern Spy. The most popular varieties in Canada are Delicious, McIntosh, Melba, Oldenberg, and Wealthy.

Planting and Cultivation. Apples grow best in a temperate climate and in soil that is deep, fairly rich, and well drained. Because their blossoms may be easily killed by frost, the trees are usually planted on rolling, sloping land rather than in low pockets where cold air collects. Many orchards are located on the elevations of river valleys. The hills above lakes are also popular orchard sites.

Almost all apple trees are raised by grafting the stem or bud of a desired variety of apple to a strong apple tree seedling, called a rootstock. The apples borne by the mature tree will be similar to the apples borne by the tree from which the stem or bud was taken, but the size of the tree will be determined by the rootstock. Some rootstocks develop into very small, or dwarf, trees, and others grow into semidwarf or larger trees. Because most varieties require cross-pollination to produce a sizable crop, commercial apple growers usually raise more than one variety of apple in an orchard.

The trees from the nursery are transplanted to rows in the orchard when they are one to two years old. They are usually spaced so that there are about 25 trees per acre. Sometimes the spaces between the apple trees are planted with a number of "fillers," such as additional apple, peach, or other quick-maturing fruit trees that will provide a harvest while the "permanent" trees are maturing. After about 20 years, the fillers are removed so that they will not appropriate needed water and sunlight.

Where cultivation between the rows is practiced, a cover crop, such as oats or rye, is planted in orchards in late summer to help prevent erosion, to hold snow, and to protect the trees against freezing. In the spring, the cover crop is disked in to decay and enrich the soil. In many areas, orchards are operated under the sod-mulch system. The grass is mowed, and a sizable amount of hay, straw, or other material is spread as a mulch under the branches. Nitrates and other commercial fertilizers, as well as boron, magnesium, and other needed elements, may also be applied around the base of the trees in order to increase their growth and vigor.

Apple trees usually begin to bear fruit from three to ten years after planting, depending upon their variety and location. However, some quick-maturing varieties, which are often grown on East Malling IX rootstock, will bear fruit a year or two after they are planted. A healthy, well-tended apple tree will produce fruit for 60 or more years.

Pruning. Mature trees are pruned, usually in early spring before the buds open, to remove dead and diseased wood and to keep the trees 20 feet (6 meters) or less in height. Pruning also permits more sunlight to enter the trees and makes it easier to spray the apples and to pick them.

In the espalier system of pruning, widely used in France, apple trees are trimmed and trained to grow horizontally against walls or on trellises. In American orchards, young trees are usually pruned to create the modified leader, a tree with a fairly low central trunk and main branches spaced evenly and pointing in different directions.

Disease and Pest Control. Apples are attacked by a wide variety of insect pests and fungus diseases. For this reason, spraying against insects and diseases is the most important single operation in commercial apple production and accounts for 25 to 50 percent of the total cost of running an orchard.

Chewing insects, such as the codling moth, tent caterpillar, plum circulio, red-banded leaf roller, and apple maggot, are usually controlled by spraying the trees with poisons that act inside the insect's stomach. Sucking insects, such as aphids, scales, red bugs, and leafhoppers are fought with contact insecticides, which kill the insects on contact by suffocating, burning, or paralyzing them. In the United States, information on specific types of insecticides to control pests that attack apples may be obtained from state universities and the U.S. Department of Agriculture.

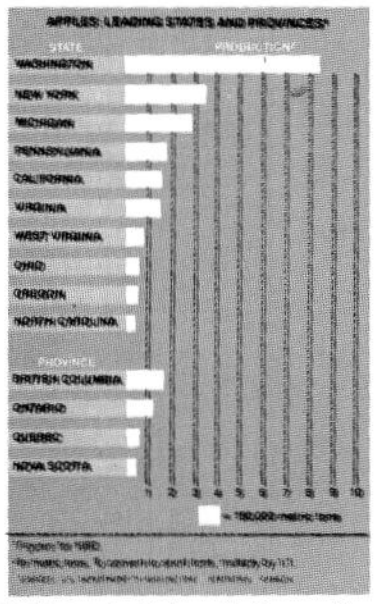

Fungus diseases, such as apple scab, apple rust, or black rot, are combated by spraying the trees with fungicides, most of which contain sulfur or copper. In recent years, certain new organic repellents have been developed which enter the leaf tissue and are circulated by the sap to fight the fungus from inside the leaf.

Since the various insects and fungus diseases attack the trees at different times throughout the season, the grower must use the proper chemicals at the proper times in order to protect his orchard. With the approach of the harvest season, the grower must also time the application of sprays in order to avoid chemical residues on the fruits when they are ready for marketing.

Harvesting and Storage. The probable size of a harvest can be determined soon after the flowers bloom. A mature tree may have as many as 100,000 flowers. If all these flowers developed into full-sized fruits, the tree might theoretically produce 800 bushels (28,000 liters) of apples, or 20 times more than its branches could possibly support.

Actually, however, only 2 to 4 percent of the blossoms "set" into fruit. The others never develop because of a limited supply of food and water, injury from frost, disease, lack of pollination, or other natural causes. The tree also thins itself by dropping some young apples early in the growing season. This natural thinning is called "June drop."

Some varieties of trees, including the Golden Delicious and the Wealthy, tend to produce large quantities of apples in spite of the June drop. If all of these apples are allowed to develop to maturity, the result will be a large crop of very small apples. Therefore, the apples are further thinned out by applications of dinitro or hormone sprays.

Apples are harvested by hand and taken to a nearby packing shed. With the aid of mechanical conveyors, the grading crew sorts the apples by size and quality, washes them, and packs them into crates, trays, or cartons. Apples that are unsuitable for marketing whole are usually pressed to produce apple juice and cider.

Some varieties of apples can be stored from three to eight months if they are cooled quickly and then placed in a storage area with a temperature of 30° F. or 31° F. (−1° C. or −0.56° C.) and a humidity of 88 to 90 percent. Both the temperature and humidity must be carefully controlled throughout the storage time to prevent apples from shriveling or spoiling.

In some varieties of apples, including the McIntosh and Delicious, the storage life can be increased by a process known as controlled-atmosphere storage. In this process, the apples are stored in a cool, gastight room in which the air contains more carbon dioxide and less oxygen than is found in the normal atmosphere. Through regulation of the carbon dioxide-oxygen balance in the room, the ripening process can be slowed down and the apples preserved in good condition for longer periods of time.

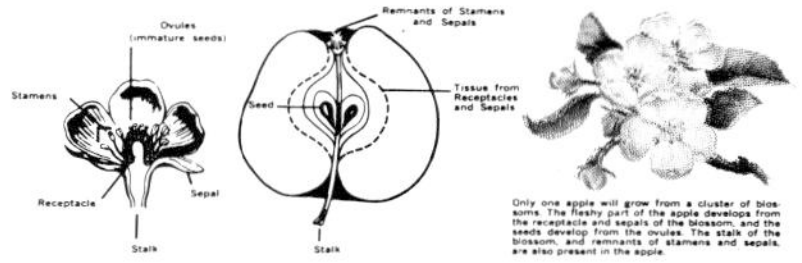

Only one apple will grow from a cluster of blossoms. The fleshy part of the apple develops from the receptacle and sepals of the blossom, and the seeds develop from the ovules. The stalk of the blossom, and remnants of stamens and sepals, are also present in the apple.

Inside each volume, articles are arranged in alphabetical order according to their topics. At the top of each pair of pages there are *guide words.* The guide words in an encyclopedia are similar to the guide words in a dictionary or glossary. The guide word on the left-hand page indicates the first topic discussed on the two pages. The guide word on the right-hand page tells you the last topic discussed on the pages. By looking at the guide words, you can tell whether the topic you want is talked about on the pages.

Look at these guide words.

NAPOLEON III   NAUTILUS

Now look at this list of topics. Which topics would you find discussed on pages that had these guide words?

Ogden Nash   Naples
Nantucket   Nashville
Navajo Indians narwhal
navigation   national parks

Using What You Have Learned

Although Benedict Arnold ended up a traitor, he was once considered a brave patriot. During the Revolutionary War, he fought with Ethan Allen at Fort Ticonderoga, and he was praised for his courage in two other battles. Imagine that you are going to write a report about Benedict Arnold. You are particularly interested in the things Benedict Arnold did *before* he betrayed his country and you want to find out what caused him to betray his country. What topics would you look up in the encyclopedia if you were writing this report?

List at least three topics you would look up to find information for your report. When you have listed the topics, refer again to the picture of the encyclopedia and write the number of the volume in which you would find each topic discussed.

Another famous American Patriot was accused of treason during the Revolutionary War. This man fought beside Benedict Arnold. He was accused of trying to make Vermont a British province. He was, however, cleared of the charges.

Imagine that you needed to find out the name of this person. What topics would you look up to find information that would help you identify this person? Write three topics that you think would be good choices. Then, using the picture of the encyclopedia, indicate in which volume each topic would be discussed.

Expanding Your Skills

The patriot accused of treason was Ethan Allen. Suppose you wanted to write a report comparing the lives of Ethan Allen and Benedict Arnold. Decide on five topics that you could look up in an encyclopedia that would give you information to help you write your report. Then go to the library and look up each topic. Read the articles that discuss each topic. Make notes on the information in the article and write down any related topics mentioned at the end of each article.

CHARLIE

by BETSY BYARS

When you want something badly enough, you keep trying—
no matter how tired you get, no matter how hopeless the
situation may seem. This story describes Sara's search for her
younger brother, Charlie, who is lost in the woods.

How does Sara finally discover that Charlie is nearby? In
what ways does Sara's knowledge of Charlie help her find him?

One day swans suddenly appear on the lake near Sara's house. Sara has better things to do, but she finally agrees to take Charlie, her mentally retarded younger brother, to see the swans. Charlie is fascinated by the birds' silent beauty.

Later that night, he sets off alone to see the swans again. Frightened by the dark and by dogs' barking, Charlie loses his way in the woods.

The next morning, when it is discovered that Charlie is missing, a search party is formed to look for him. Sara is sure that Charlie tried to go back to the lake. With her friend Joe, she begins a search of her own, trying to follow the path she thinks Charlie must have taken.

"Charlie! Charlie!"

The only answer was the call of a bird in the branches overhead, one long tremulous whistle.

"He's not even within hearing distance," Sara said.

For the past hour she and Joe Melby had been walking deeper and deeper into the forest without pause, and now the trees were so thick that only small spots of sunlight found their way through the heavy foliage.

"Charlie, oh, Charlie!"

She waited, looking down at the ground.

Joe said, "You want to rest for a while?"

Sara shook her head. She suddenly wanted to see her brother so badly that her throat began to close. It was a tight feeling she got sometimes when she wanted something, like the time she had had the measles and had wanted to see her father so much she couldn't even swallow. Now she thought that if she had a whole glass of ice water—and she was thirsty—she probably would not be able to drink a single drop.

"If you can make it a little farther, there's a place at the top of the hill where the strip mining is, and you can see the whole valley from there."

"I can make it."

"Well, we can rest first if—"

"I can make it."

She suddenly felt a little better. She thought that if she could stand up there on top of the hill and look down and see, somewhere in that huge green valley, a small plump figure in blue pajamas, she would ask for nothing more in life. She thought of the valley as a relief map where everything would be shiny and smooth, and her brother would be right where she could spot him at once. Her cry, "There he is!" would ring like a bell over the valley and everyone would hear her and know that Charlie had been found.

Her progress up the hill seemed slower and slower. It was like the time she had won the slow bicycle race, a race in which she had to go as slow as possible without letting a foot touch the ground, and she had gone slower and slower, all the while feeling a strong compulsion to speed ahead and cross the finish line first. At the end of the race it had been she and T.R. Peters, and they had paused just before the finish line, balancing motionless on their bicycles. The time had seemed endless, and then T.R. lost his balance and his foot touched the ground and Sara was the winner.

She slipped on some dry leaves, went down on her knees, straightened, and paused to catch her breath.

"Are you all right?"

"Yes, I just slipped."

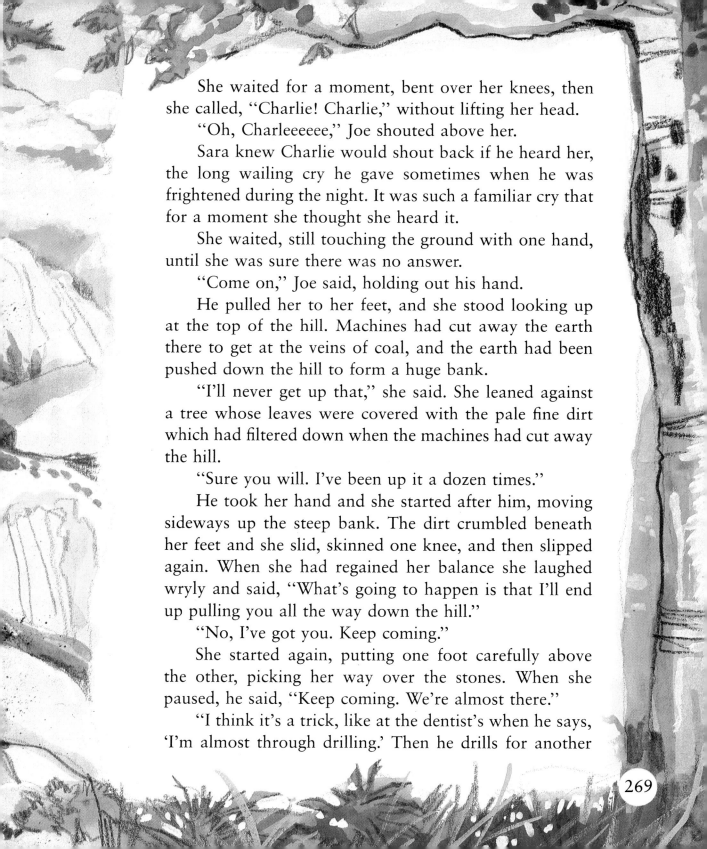

She waited for a moment, bent over her knees, then she called, "Charlie! Charlie," without lifting her head.

"Oh, Charleeeeee," Joe shouted above her.

Sara knew Charlie would shout back if he heard her, the long wailing cry he gave sometimes when he was frightened during the night. It was such a familiar cry that for a moment she thought she heard it.

She waited, still touching the ground with one hand, until she was sure there was no answer.

"Come on," Joe said, holding out his hand.

He pulled her to her feet, and she stood looking up at the top of the hill. Machines had cut away the earth there to get at the veins of coal, and the earth had been pushed down the hill to form a huge bank.

"I'll never get up that," she said. She leaned against a tree whose leaves were covered with the pale fine dirt which had filtered down when the machines had cut away the hill.

"Sure you will. I've been up it a dozen times."

He took her hand and she started after him, moving sideways up the steep bank. The dirt crumbled beneath her feet and she slid, skinned one knee, and then slipped again. When she had regained her balance she laughed wryly and said, "What's going to happen is that I'll end up pulling you all the way down the hill."

"No, I've got you. Keep coming."

She started again, putting one foot carefully above the other, picking her way over the stones. When she paused, he said, "Keep coming. We're almost there."

"I think it's a trick, like at the dentist's when he says, 'I'm almost through drilling.' Then he drills for another

hour and says, 'Now, I'm really almost through drilling,' and he keeps on and then says, 'There's just one more spot, and then I'll be practically really through.' "

"We must go to the same dentist."

"I don't think I can make it. There's no skin at all left on the sides of my legs."

"Well, we're really almost practically there now, in the words of your dentist."

She fell across the top of the dirt bank on her stomach, rested for a moment, and then turned and looked down the valley.

She could not speak for a moment. There lay the whole valley in a way she had never imagined it, a tiny finger of civilization set in a sweeping expanse of dark forest. The black treetops seemed to crowd against the yards, the houses, the roads, giving the impression that at any moment the trees would close over the houses like waves and leave nothing but an unbroken line of black-green leaves waving in the sunlight.

Up the valley she could see the intersection where they shopped, the drugstore, the gas station where her mother had once won a set of twenty-four stemmed glasses, the grocery store, the lot where the yellow school buses were parked for the summer. She could look over the valley and see another hill where white cows were all grouped together by a fence and beyond that another hill and then another.

She looked back at the valley and she saw the lake, and for the first time since she had stood up on the hill, she remembered Charlie.

Raising her hand to her mouth, she called, "Charlie! Charlie! Charlie!" There was a faint echo that seemed to waver in her ears.

"Charlie, oh, Charlie!" Her voice was so loud it seemed to ram into the valley.

Sara waited. She looked down at the forest, and everything was so quiet it seemed to her that the whole valley, the whole world was waiting with her.

"Charlie, hey, Charlie!" Joe shouted.

"Charleeeeee!" She made the sound of it last a long time. "Can you hear meeeeee?"

With her eyes she followed the trail she knew he must have taken—the house, the Akers' vacant lot, the old pasture, the forest. The forest that seemed powerful enough to engulf a whole valley, she thought with a sinking feeling, could certainly swallow up a young boy.

"Charlie! Charlie! Charlie!" There was a waver in the last syllable that betrayed how near she was to tears.

"Charlie, oh, Charlie." She waited. There was not a sound anywhere. "Charlie, where are you?"

"Hey, Charlie!" Joe shouted.

They waited in the same dense silence. A cloud passed in front of the sun, and a breeze began to blow through the trees. Then there was silence again.

"Listen, just because you can't hear him doesn't mean anything. He could be—"

"Wait a minute." She looked down the valley. A sudden wind blew dust into her face, and she lifted her hand to shield her eyes.

"I thought I heard something. Charlie! Answer me right this minute."

She waited, one hand to her eyes, her whole body motionless, concentrating on her brother. Then she stiffened. She thought again she had heard something—Charlie's long, high wail. Charlie could sound sadder than anyone when he cried.

She called, then stopped abruptly and listened. She looked at Joe, and he shook his head slowly.

She looked away. A bird rose from the trees below and flew toward the hills in the distance. She waited until she could see it no longer, and then slowly, still listening for the call that didn't come, she sank to the ground and sat with her head bent over her knees.

Beside her, Joe scuffed his foot in the dust and sent a cascade of rocks and dirt down the bank. When the sound of it faded, he began to call, "Charlie, hey, Charlie," again and again.

273

Charlie awoke, but he lay for a moment without opening his eyes. He did not remember where he was, but he had a certain dread of seeing it.

There were great parts of his life that were lost to Charlie, blank spaces that he could never fill in. He would find himself in a strange place and not know how he got there. Like the time Sara had been hit in the nose with a baseball at the ice cream store, and the blood and the sight of Sara kneeling on the ground in helpless pain had frightened him so much that he had turned and run without direction, in a frenzy, dashing headlong up the street, blind to cars and people.

By chance Mr. Weicek had seen him, put him in the car, and driven him home, and Aunt Willie had put him to bed, but later he remembered none of this. He had only awakened in bed and looked at the crumpled bit of ice cream cone still clenched in his hand and wondered about it.

His whole life had been built on a strict routine, and as long as this routine was kept up, he felt safe and well. The same foods, the same bed, the same furniture in the same place, the same seat on the school bus, the same class procedure were all important to him. But always there could be the unexpected, the dreadful surprise that would topple his carefully constructed life in an instant.

The first thing he became aware of was the twigs pressing into his face, and he put his hand under his cheek. Still he did not open his eyes. Pictures began to drift into his mind. He saw Aunt Willie's cigar box, which was filled with old jewelry and buttons and knick-knacks, and he found that he could remember every item in that box—

the string of white beads without a clasp, the old earrings, the tiny book with souvenir fold-out pictures of New York, the plastic decorations from cakes, the turtle made of seashells. Every item was so real that he opened his eyes and was surprised to see, instead of the glittering contents of the box, the dull and unfamiliar forest.

He raised his head and immediately felt the aching of his body. Slowly he sat up and looked down at his hands. His fingernails were black with earth, two of them broken below the quick, and he got up slowly and sat on the log behind him and inspected his fingers more closely.

Then he sat up straight. His hands dropped to his lap. His head cocked to the side like a bird listening. Slowly he straightened until he was standing. At his side his fingers twitched at the empty air as if to grasp something. He took a step forward, still with his head to the side. He remained absolutely still.

Then he began to cry out in a hoarse excited voice, again and again, screaming now, because he had just heard someone far away calling his name.

At the top of the hill, Sara got slowly to her feet and stood looking down at the forest. She pushed the hair back from her forehead and moistened her lips. The wind dried them as she waited.

Joe started to say something, but she reached out one hand and took his arm to stop him. Scarcely daring to believe her ears, she stepped closer to the edge of the bank. Now she heard it unmistakably—the sharp repeated cry—and she knew it was Charlie.

"Charlie!" she shouted with all her might.

She paused and listened, and his cries were louder, and she knew he was not far away after all, just down the slope, in the direction of the ravine.

"It's Charlie, it's Charlie!"

A wild joy overtook her, and she jumped up and down on the bare earth, and she felt that she could crush the hill just by jumping if she wanted.

She sat and scooted down the bank, sending earth and pebbles in a cascade before her. She landed on the soft ground, ran a few steps, lost her balance, caught hold of the first tree trunk she could find, and swung around till she stopped.

She let out another whoop of pure joy, turned and ran down the hill in great strides, the wind in her face, her hands grabbing one tree trunk after another for support. She felt like a wild creature who had traveled through the forest this way for a lifetime. Nothing could stop her now.

At the edge of the ravine, she paused and stood gasping for breath. Her heart was beating so fast it pounded in her ears, and her throat was dry. She leaned against a tree, resting her cheek against the rough bark.

She thought for a minute she was going to faint, a thing she had never done before, not even when she broke her nose. She hadn't even believed people really did faint until this minute when she clung to the tree because her legs were as useless as rubber bands.

There was a ringing in her ears and another sound, a wailing siren-like cry that was painfully familiar.

"Charlie?"

Charlie's crying, like the sound of a cricket, seemed everywhere and nowhere.

She walked along the edge of the ravine, circling the large boulders and trees. Then she looked down into the ravine where the shadows lay, and she felt as if something had turned over inside her because she saw Charlie.

He was standing in his torn pajamas, face turned upward, hands raised, shouting with all his might. His eyes were shut tight. His face was streaked with dirt and tears. His pajama jacket hung in shreds about his scratched chest.

He opened his eyes, and as he saw Sara, a strange expression came over his face, an expression of wonder and joy and disbelief, and Sara knew that if she lived to be a hundred, no one would ever look at her quite that way again.

She paused, looked down at him, and then, sliding on the seat of her pants, went down the bank and took him in her arms.

"Oh, Charlie."

His arms gripped her like steel.

"Oh, Charlie."

She could feel his fingers digging into her back as he clutched her shirt. "It's all right now, Charlie, I'm here and we're going home." His face was buried in her shirt, and she patted his head and said again, "It's all right now. Everything's fine."

CHECK FOR UNDERSTANDING

1. What did Sara imagine the valley would look like from the top of the hill? What did she hope she would see?
2. What did the valley actually look like from the top of the hill?
3. How did Sara finally discover that Charlie was nearby?
4. At the beginning of the story, Sara said, "He's not even within hearing distance." Was she correct? Explain why Charlie didn't hear Sara and Joe calling.
5. In what ways did Sara's knowledge of her brother help her find him?
6. In what ways did Joe help Sara find Charlie?

WRITE ABOUT *"Charlie"*

The story "Charlie" is written in third-person point of view, but the information the narrator gives is not limited to what can be observed. Throughout the story, the narrator tells the reader what Sara is thinking and feeling. Select two paragraphs from the end of the story and rewrite them in first-person point of view. Use the pronouns *I* and *my* in place of *she* and *her* and retell what happened as if Sara herself were telling the story.

The Medicine Bag

by VIRGINIA DRIVING HAWK SNEVE

Martin's great-grandfather, Joe Iron Shell, lives on a Sioux reservation in South Dakota. Martin's family visits him on the reservation every summer. Then one day Grandpa pays an unexpected visit to Martin's home in Iowa.

How does Martin feel when Grandpa arrives? What was the purpose of Grandpa's visit?

My kid sister Cheryl and I always bragged about our Sioux grandpa, Joe Iron Shell. Our friends, who had always lived in the city and only knew about Indians from movies and TV, were impressed by our stories. Maybe we exaggerated and made Grandpa and the reservation sound glamorous, but when we'd return home to Iowa after our yearly summer visit to Grandpa, we always had some exciting tale to tell.

We never showed our friends Grandpa's picture. Not that we were ashamed of him, but because we knew that the glamorous tales we told didn't go with the real thing. Our friends would have laughed at the picture, because Grandpa wasn't tall and stately like TV Indians. His hair wasn't in braids but hung in stringy, gray strands on his neck, and he was old. He was our great-grandfather, and he didn't live in a tepee, but all by himself in a part log, part tar-paper shack on the Rosebud Reservation in South Dakota. So when Grandpa came to visit us, I was so ashamed and embarrassed I could've died.

There are a lot of yippy poodles and other fancy little dogs in our neighborhood, but they usually barked singly at the mail carrier from the safety of their own yards. Now it sounded as if a whole pack of mutts was barking together in one place.

I got up and walked to the curb to see what the commotion was. About a block away I saw a crowd of little kids yelling, with the dogs yipping and growling around someone who was walking down the middle of the street.

I watched the group as it slowly came closer and saw that in the center of the strange procession was a man wearing a tall black hat. He'd pause now and then to peer at something in his hand and then at the houses on either side of the street. I felt cold and hot at the same time as I recognized the man. "Oh, no!" I whispered. "It's Grandpa!"

I stood on the curb, unable to move even though I wanted to run and hide. Then I got mad when I saw how the yippy dogs were growling and nipping at the old man's baggy pant legs and how wearily he poked them away with his cane. "Stupid mutts," I said as I ran to rescue Grandpa.

"Grandpa," I said and felt pretty dumb when my voice cracked. I reached for his beat-up old tin suitcase, which was tied shut with a rope. But he set it down right in the street and shook my hand.

"*Hau, Takoza,* Grandchild," he greeted me formally in Sioux.

All I could do was stand there with the whole neighborhood watching and shake the hand of the leather-brown old man. I saw how his gray hair straggled from under his big black hat, which had a drooping feather in its crown. His rumpled black suit hung like a sack over his stooped frame. As he shook my hand, his coat fell open to expose a bright-red, satin shirt with a beaded bolo tie under the collar. His getup wasn't out of place on the reservation, but it sure was here, and I wanted to sink right through the pavement.

"Hi," I muttered with my head down. I tried to pull my hand away when I felt his bony hand trembling, and looked up to see fatigue in his face. I felt like crying. I couldn't think of anything to say, so I picked up Grandpa's suitcase, took his arm, and guided him up the driveway to our house.

Mom was standing on the steps. I don't know how long she'd been watching, but her hand was over her mouth, and she looked as if she couldn't believe what she saw. Then she ran to us.

"Grandpa," she gasped. "How in the world did you get here?"

She checked her move to embrace Grandpa, and I remembered that such a display of affection is unseemly to the Sioux and would embarrass him.

"*Hau,* Marie," he said as he shook Mom's hand. She smiled and took his other arm.

As we supported him up the steps the door banged open, and Cheryl came bursting out of the house. She was all smiles and was so obviously glad to see Grandpa that I was ashamed of how I felt.

"Grandpa!" she yelled happily. "You came to see us!"

Grandpa smiled, and Mom and I let go of him as he stretched out his arms to my ten-year-old sister, who was still young enough to be hugged.

"*Wicincala*, little girl," he greeted her and then collapsed.

He had fainted. Mom and I carried him into her sewing room, where we had a spare bed.

After we had Grandpa on the bed, Mom stood there helplessly patting his shoulder.

"Shouldn't we call the doctor, Mom?" I suggested, since she didn't seem to know what to do.

"Yes," she agreed with a sigh. "You make Grandpa comfortable, Martin."

I reluctantly moved to the bed. I knew Grandpa wouldn't want to have Mom undress him, but I didn't want to, either. He was so skinny and frail that his coat slipped off easily. When I loosened his tie and opened his shirt collar, I felt a small leather pouch that hung from a thong around his neck. I left it alone and moved to remove his boots. The scuffed old cowboy boots were tight, and he moaned as I put pressure on his legs to jerk them off.

I put the boots on the floor and saw why they fit so tight. Each one was stuffed with money. I looked at the bills that lined the boots and started to ask about them, but Grandpa's eyes were closed again.

Mom came back with a basin of water. "The doctor thinks Grandpa is suffering from heat exhaustion," she explained as she bathed Grandpa's face. Mom gave a big sigh, "*Oh hinh*, Martin. How do you suppose he got here?"

We found out after the doctor's visit. Grandpa was angrily sitting up in bed while Mom tried to feed him some soup.

"Tonight you let Marie feed you, Grandpa," spoke my dad, who had gotten home from work just as the doctor was leaving. "You're not really sick," he said as he gently pushed Grandpa back against the pillows. "The doctor said you just got too tired and hot after your long trip."

Grandpa relaxed, and between sips of soup, he told us of his journey. Soon after our visit to him, Grandpa decided that he would like to see where his only living descendants lived and what our home was like. Besides, he admitted sheepishly, he was lonesome after we left.

I knew everybody felt as guilty as I did—especially Mom. Mom was all Grandpa had left. So even after she married my dad, who's a white man and teaches in the college in our city, and after Cheryl and I were born, Mom made sure that every summer we spent a week with Grandpa.

I never thought that Grandpa would be lonely after our visits, and none of us noticed how old and weak he had become. But Grandpa knew, and so he came to us. He had ridden on buses for two and a half days. When he arrived in the city, tired and stiff from sitting for so long, he set out, walking, to find us.

He had stopped to rest on the steps of some building downtown, and a police officer found him. The officer, according to Grandpa, was a good man who took him to the bus stop and waited until the bus came and told the driver to let Grandpa out at Bell View Drive. After Grandpa got off the bus, he started walking again. But he couldn't see the house numbers on the other side when he walked on the sidewalk, so he walked in the middle of the street. That's when all the little kids and dogs followed him.

I knew everybody felt as bad as I did. Yet I was proud of this eighty-six-year-old man, who had never been away from the reservation, for having the courage to travel so far alone.

"You found the money in my boots?" he asked Mom.

"Martin did," she answered and roused herself to scold. "Grandpa, you shouldn't have carried so much money. What if someone had stolen it from you?"

Grandpa laughed. "I would've known if anyone tried to take the boots off my feet. The money is what I've saved for a long time—a hundred dollars—for my funeral. But you take it now to buy groceries so that I won't be a burden to you while I am here."

"That won't be necessary, Grandpa," Dad said. "We are honored to have you with us, and you will never be a burden. I am only sorry that we never thought to bring you home with us this summer and spare you the discomfort of a long trip."

Grandpa was pleased. "Thank you," he answered. "But do not feel bad that you didn't bring me with you, for I would not have come then. It was not time." He said this in such a way that no one could argue with him. To Grandpa and the Sioux, he once told me, a thing would be done when it was the right time to do it, and that's the way it was.

"Also," Grandpa went on, looking at me, "I have come because it is soon time for Martin to have the medicine bag."

We all knew what that meant. Grandpa thought he was going to die, and he had to follow the tra-dition of his family to pass the medicine bag, along with its history, to the oldest male child.

I didn't know what to say. I had the same hot and cold feeling that I had when I first saw Grandpa in the street. The medicine bag was the dirty leather pouch I had found around his neck. "I could never wear such a thing," I almost said aloud. I thought of having my friends see it in gym class, at the swimming pool, and could imagine the smart things they would say. But I just swallowed hard and took a step toward the bed. I knew I would have to take it.

But Grandpa was tired. "Not now, Martin," he said, waving his hand in dismissal, "it is not time. Now I will sleep."

So that's how Grandpa came to be with us for two months. My friends kept asking to come see the old man, but I put them off. I told myself that I didn't want them laughing at Grandpa. But even as I made excuses I knew it wasn't Grandpa that I was afraid they'd laugh at.

Nothing bothered Cheryl about bringing her friends to see Grandpa. Every day after school started there'd be a crew of happy little girls or round-eyed little boys crowded around the old man on the patio, where he'd gotten in the habit of sitting every afternoon.

Grandpa would smile in his gentle way and patiently answer their questions, or he'd tell them stories of brave warriors, ghosts, animals, and the kids listened in awed silence. Those little guys thought Grandpa was great.

Finally, one day after school, my friends came home with me because nothing I said stopped them. "We're going to see the great Indian of Bell View Drive," said Hank, who was supposed to be my best friend. "My brother has seen him three times, so he ought to be well enough to see us."

When we got to my house Grandpa was sitting on the patio. He had on his red shirt, but today he also wore a fringed leather vest that was decorated with beads. Instead of his usual cowboy boots he had solidly beaded moccasins on his feet that stuck out of his black trousers. Of course, he had his old black hat on—he was seldom without it. But it had been brushed and the feather in the beaded headband was proudly erect, its tip a brighter white. His hair lay in silver strands over the red shirt collar. I stared just as my friends did, and I heard one of them murmur, "Wow!"

Grandpa looked up, and when his eyes met mine they twinkled as if he were laughing inside. He nodded to me and my face got all hot. I could tell that he had known all along I was afraid he'd embarrass me in front of my friends.

"*Hau, hoksilas,* boys," he greeted and held out his hand.

My buddies passed in a single file and shook his hand as I introduced them. They were so polite I almost laughed. "How, there, Grandpa," and even a "How-do-you-do, sir."

"You look fine, Grandpa," I said as the guys sat on the lawn chairs or on the patio floor.

"*Hanh,* yes," he agreed. "When I woke up this morning, it

seemed the right time to dress in the good clothes. I knew that my grandson would be bringing his friends."

"You guys want some lemonade or something?" I offered. No one answered. They were listening to Grandpa as he started telling how he'd killed the deer from which his vest was made.

Grandpa did most of the talk-ing while my friends were there. I was proud of him and amazed at how respectfully quiet my buddies were. Mom had to chase them home at supper time. As they left they shook Grandpa's hand again and said to me: "Martin, he's really great!"

"Yeah, man! Don't blame you for keeping him to yourself."

"Can we come back?"

But after they left, Mom said, "No more visitors for a while, Martin. Grandpa won't admit it, but his strength hasn't returned. He likes having company, but it tires him."

That evening Grandpa called me to his room before he went to sleep. "Tomorrow," he said, "when you come home, it will be time to give you the medicine bag."

I felt a hard squeeze from where my heart is supposed to be and was scared, but I answered, "OK, Grandpa."

All night I had weird dreams about thunder and lightning on a high hill. From a distance I heard the slow beat of a drum. When I woke up in the morning, I felt as if I hadn't slept at all. At school it seemed as if the day would never end, and when it finally did, I ran home.

Grandpa was in his room, sitting on the bed. The shades were down, and the place was dim and cool. I sat on the floor in front of Grandpa, but he didn't even look at me. After what seemed a long time, he spoke.

"What you will hear today is only for your ears. What you will receive is only for your hands." He fell silent, and I felt shivers down my back.

"My father in his early manhood," Grandpa began, "made a vision quest to find a spirit guide for his life. You cannot understand how it was in that time, when the great Teton Sioux were first made to stay on the reservation. There was a strong need for guidance from *Wakantanka,* the Great Spirit. But too many of the young men were filled with despair and hatred. They thought it was hopeless to search for a vision when the glorious life was gone and only the hated confines of a reservation lay ahead. But my father held to the old ways.

"He carefully prepared for his quest with a purifying sweat bath, and then he went alone to a high butte top to fast and pray. After three days he received his sacred dream—in which he found, after long searching, the white man's iron. He did not understand his vision of finding something belonging to the white people, for in that time they were the enemy. When he came down from the butte to cleanse himself at the stream below, he found the remains of a campfire and the broken shell of an iron kettle. This was a sign that reinforced his dream. He took a piece of the iron for his medicine bag, which he had made of elk skin years before to prepare for his quest.

"He returned to his village, where he told his dream to the wise old men of the tribe. They gave him the name *Iron Shell,* but neither did they understand the meaning of the dream. This first Iron Shell kept the piece of iron with him at all times and believed it gave him protection from the evils of those unhappy days.

"Then a terrible thing happened to Iron Shell. He and several other young men were taken from their homes by the soldiers and sent far away to a white man's boarding school. He was angry and lonesome for his parents and the young girl he had wed before he was taken away. At first Iron Shell resisted the teachers' attempts to change him, and he did not try to learn. One day it was his turn to work in the school's blacksmith shop. As he walked into the place, he knew that his medicine had brought him there to learn and work with the white man's iron.

"Iron Shell became a blacksmith and worked at the trade when he returned to the reservation. All of his life he treasured the medicine bag. When he was old and I was a man, he gave it to me, for no one made the vision quest anymore."

Grandpa quit talking, and I stared in disbelief as he covered his face with his hands. His shoulders were shaking with quiet sobs, and I looked away until he began to speak again.

"I kept the bag until my son, your mother's father, was a man and had to leave us to fight in the war across the ocean. I gave him the bag, for I believed it would protect him in battle, but he did not take it with him. He was afraid that he would lose it. He died in a faraway place."

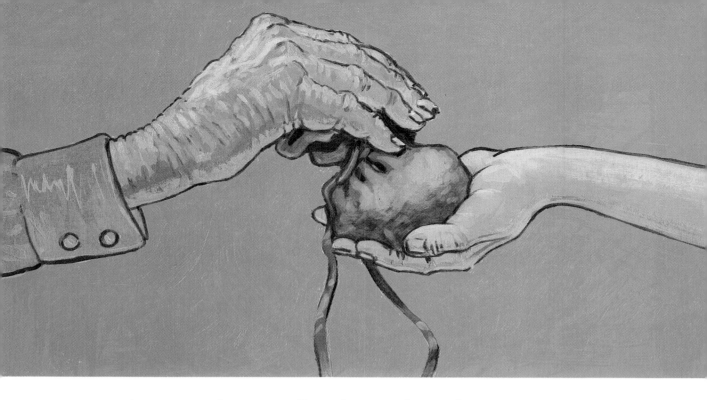

Again Grandpa was still, and I felt his grief around me.

He unbuttoned his shirt, pulled out the leather pouch, and lifted it over his head. He held it in his hand, turning it over and over as if memorizing how it looked.

"In the bag," he said as he opened it and removed two objects, "is the broken shell of the iron kettle, a pebble from the butte, and a piece of the sacred sage." He held the pouch upside down and dust drifted down.

"After the bag is yours, you must put a piece of prairie sage within and never open it again until you pass it on to your son." He replaced the pebble and the piece of iron, and tied the bag.

I stood up, somehow knowing I should. Grandpa slowly rose from the bed and stood upright in front of me, holding the bag before my face. I closed my eyes and waited for him to slip it over my head. But he spoke.

"No, you need not wear it." He placed the soft leather bag in my right hand and closed my other hand over it. "It would not be right to wear it in this time and place where no one will understand it. Put it safely away until you are again on the reservation. Wear it then, when you replace the sacred sage."

Grandpa turned and sat again on the bed. Wearily he leaned his head against the pillow. "Go," he said, "I will sleep now."

"Thank you, Grandpa," I said softly and left with the bag in my hands.

That night Mom and Dad took Grandpa to the hospital. Two weeks later I stood alone on the lonely prairie of the reservation and put the sacred sage in my medicine bag.

CHECK FOR UNDERSTANDING
1. How did Martin feel when Grandpa arrived? Why did he feel this way?
2. What was the purpose of Grandpa's visit?
3. What was Martin's real reason for not wanting his friends to meet Grandpa?
4. How did Martin's feelings change when his friends actually did meet Grandpa? Why?
5. When Martin puts the sacred sage in the medicine bag, what is he really doing?

WRITE ABOUT *"The Medicine Bag"*
Imagine that you are Martin's friend Hank. Write an article for your school newspaper describing Joe Iron Shell, your visit with him, and your reaction to him.

Birdfoot's Grampa

by JOSEPH BRUCHAC

The Old Man
must have stopped our car
two dozen times to climb out
and gather into his hands
the small toads blinded
by our lights and leaping
like live drops of rain.

The rain was falling,
a mist around his white hair,
and I kept saying,
"You can't save them all,
accept it, get in,
we've got places to go."

But, leathery hands full
of wet brown life,
knee-deep in the summer
roadside grass,
he just smiled and said,
"They have places to go, too."

293

Theme

Have you ever had one of those magical days when everything went just right? Maybe you were late for the bus, but it waited for you. On a day like this, it almost seems as if the day has been planned for your benefit. Everything that happens seems to follow a design.

Although events in life aren't often like this, events in stories are. The events in a story always follow a design made up by the author. This design leads the reader to one idea that the author wants the reader to understand. This one idea is called the *theme.* The theme is usually the idea that made the author want to write the story in the first place. Not only stories, but poems, novels, and plays also have themes.

Since a theme is the idea *behind* a story, play, or poem, it almost never appears as part of the story itself. Instead, the theme is the overall idea the reader gets from the details of the story. The way a character looks and talks helps the reader understand the theme. The things that happen in a story help make the theme clear. The special images the writer uses contribute to the reader's understanding of the theme.

Think of the first story you read in this unit, "Ida Early." What would you say is the theme of "Ida Early"? Read the three possible themes below, and decide for yourself which one is developed by the characters, events, and language of the story.

> Strangers can turn out to be better friends than relatives.
>
> A person with a joyful attitude spreads that feeling to others even when doing things that aren't usually fun.

Every member of a family should take part in jobs for the good of the whole family.

What about the first theme? Is the story about Ida Early as a stranger? Are all the events in the story designed to show only the difference between strict Aunt Earnestine and fun-loving Ida? Since Aunt Earnestine disappears for a big part of the story, the answer is probably no.

The third choice is not the best one either. If this were all the story were about, Ida would not be such an interesting person with such a big role in the story. There would be no reason for Ida and the children to play tiddlywinks, either.

The best statement of the theme is the second. Ida Early is a joyful person, and she is always present in the story. The way Ida looks, the things she says and does, all help the reader understand what it is like to be around a joyful person like her.

As you read the next selection, "The Night Traveler," think about the things you learn about the characters. Think about the events that happen in the selection. What theme is introduced in the selection? How do you think the theme might be developed in the rest of the book?

Zeely

by Virginia Hamilton

The Night Traveler

Elizabeth and John Perry are spending the summer on their Uncle Ross's farm. When their parents said good-bye to them, Elizabeth's father told her, "And now, I leave it all to you." To Elizabeth that meant it was up to her to make the summer something special. She begins by giving John and herself new names. She will be Miss Geeder Perry, and John will be Toeboy.

What does Geeder decide to do the first night on the farm? What does Geeder think she sees that night?

•

The first day at the farm, Geeder and Toeboy looked over the hogs in Uncle Ross's west field. These were no ordinary animals, but prize razorback hogs owned by a Mr. Nat Tayber and his daughter, who rented the land from Uncle Ross.

"Look at the size of the hogs!" Toeboy said.

"They're big all right," Geeder said, "and they're mean. I wouldn't get too close to them even if I had to."

They leaned on the fence, looking in at the hogs. The hogs wallowed around, eating and rutting in the earth with their snouts. Often they came close to the fence but veered away as they caught the scent of Geeder and Toeboy.

"Let's go," said Geeder. "I don't believe they like us here."

They fed a bit of corn to Uncle Ross's two hundred leghorn chickens. They could feed them as much corn as they liked, Uncle Ross had said. And they could gather up eggs whenever they had a mind to.

"Well, it's the truth. I can do whatever I want," Geeder said to herself. Still, not one thing had taken place that fit with her father's words *"And now, I leave it all to you."*

That was why, when evening came, Geeder decided to spread sheets and blankets out on the front lawn. She and Toeboy would sleep outside, and maybe they would see a comet.

Toeboy liked looking up into the sky, as long as Geeder was talking. The sound of her voice made the night less strange, and he felt safe. He had made his bed partly beneath a sprawling lilac bush close to the house. Geeder had made hers near the high hedge that shielded the house from the road. Toeboy felt so good that he decided to get up and make his bed next to Geeder's.

"I think I'll come over there," he called to her.

"Better not," she said. "Just better stay where you are."

"But I want to sleep by the hedge, too," he said.

"I know one thing," Geeder said. "Late at night in the country, night travelers walk along dark roads."

"What?"

"Night travelers," Geeder said again, "and they usually come up when you're just about to sleep."

"What kind of things are they?" asked Toeboy. He dug his legs deeper among the branches of the lilac bush.

"I'll tell you this," Geeder said.

"If you see one, you'd better close your eyes fast and dive as far under the covers as you can go. They don't like kids watching them. In fact, they don't like anybody watching them!"

Toeboy stayed uneasily beneath the lilac bush. He was glad to be so near the house, for if he heard any sound, he could race inside. He did not mind at all seeing half stars and a half-moon through the lilac leaves.

Geeder turned around to see what Toeboy was doing and saw that he had pulled most of his bedding all the way under the lilac shrub. That nearly made her laugh out loud. She had made up the

whole thing about the night travelers. She was only trying to frighten Toeboy—not for any really mean reason, but just because he was little and was easy to scare. As far as she knew, nobody walked late at night along this dark road.

But maybe ghosts do, she thought. A chill passed up her spine, and she closed her eyes tight for an instant to make it go away.

"Toeboy," she called, "are you still awake?"

"I'm awake," he said. "I don't want to sleep yet." He lay fingering the cool leaves of the lilac.

"Then I'll tell you all about stars," said Geeder, "since you're so wide awake."

Geeder talked about the stars and the night. She knew Toeboy had gone to sleep when he no longer asked her anything or chuckled about what she said.

A long time passed. Geeder dozed and awoke with a start. The grass beyond the tip of her toes was wet with dew. She pulled the blankets more tightly around her,

tucking her feet safely inside. She had closed her eyes again when she heard a rustling sound on Leadback Road.

Some old animal, she thought. The sound grew louder and she could not think what it was. Suddenly, what she had told Toeboy flashed through her mind.

Night travelers! She dove under the covers.

"But something's happening!" she told herself, poking her head out again.

It took all her courage to crawl out of the covers and the few feet over the wet grass up to the hedge. She trembled with fear but peeked through the hedge in spite of it. What she saw made her bend low, hugging the ground for protection. Truthfully, she wasn't sure what she saw. The branches of the hedge didn't allow much of a view.

Something tall and white was moving down the road. It didn't quite touch the ground. Geeder could hear no sound of footsteps. She couldn't see its head or arms. Beside it and moving with it was something that squeaked omi-

nously. The white, very long figure made a rustling sound when she held her breath. It passed by toward town.

Geeder watched, moving her head ever so slowly until she could no longer see it. After waiting for what seemed hours, quaking at each sound and murmur of the night, she crept back to bed, pulling the covers over her eyes. She lay, cold and scared, unable to think and afraid even to clear her dry throat. This way, she fell asleep. She woke in the morning, refreshed but stiff in every muscle.

Geeder lay for a moment, watching mist arise from the pink, sweet clover that sprinkled the lawn. The air smelled clean and fresh and was not yet hot from the sun.

"I've got to decide," she whispered. In the stillness, the sound of her own voice startled her. She turned carefully around to see if Toeboy had stirred. The tangled bedding deep in the lilac bush did not move.

"If I tell Toeboy about the night traveler," she whispered, "he

might not want to sleep outside any more. Just think of it! Not more than a few hours ago, an awful, spooky thing walked by here!"

Geeder wasn't at all sure she wanted to sleep outside again, herself.

"Goodness knows what a night traveler will do if it sees you watching! Maybe I'd better tell Uncle Ross. . . . Maybe I shouldn't."

Geeder knew it would take her a while to figure out what course to take. Almost any minute now, the people Uncle Ross rented land to would come down the road.

Uncle Ross had said they came every morning as soon as the sun was well up in the sky. It was just about that time, and watching them would be something to do.

When her dew-soaked blankets grew warm from the sun, Geeder whistled for Toeboy as softly as she could. Turning around, she saw one eye peek out from the lilac bush.

"Wake up, Toeboy!" she whispered loudly. "I think I hear them coming!"

Toeboy leaped up before he looked where he was going and hit his head against a branch. Leaves spilled dew all over him.

He was wet and still half asleep when Geeder yanked him to the ground before they could be seen.

They knelt low by the hedge. Trying not to move or blink an eye, they watched Mr. Tayber and his daughter come into view along

Leadback Road. What they saw was no ordinary sight. They watched, spellbound, for nothing in the world could have prepared them for the sight of Miss Zeely Tayber.

Zeely Tayber was more than six and a half feet tall, thin, and deeply dark as a pole of Ceylon ebony. She wore a long smock that reached to her ankles. Her arms, hands, and feet were bare, and her thin, oblong head didn't seem to fit quite right on her shoulders.

She had very high cheekbones and her eyes seemed to turn inward on themselves. Geeder couldn't say what expression she saw on Zeely's face. She knew only that it was calm, that it had pride in it, and that the face was the most beautiful she had ever seen.

Zeely's long fingers looked exactly like bean pods left a long time in the sun.

Geeder wanted to make sure Toeboy noticed Zeely's hands, but the Taybers were too close, and she was afraid they would hear her.

Mr. Tayber and Zeely carried feed pails, which made a grating sound. It was the only sound on the road besides that of Mr. Tayber's heavy footsteps. Zeely made no sound at all.

You would think she would, thought Geeder, she was so long and tall.

Geeder and Toeboy stayed quiet as the Taybers passed, and the Taybers gave no sign that they saw them hiding there. Uncle Ross had said that they were not known to speak much, even to one another. They had not lived in Crystal always, as Uncle Ross had.

Geeder and Toeboy watched the Taybers until they went out of sight. It was then that Toeboy said, "Let's go watch them in the field."

"No," said Geeder quietly, "no, Toeboy." She could not possibly have made him understand how stunned she had been at seeing Miss Zeely Tayber for the first time. Never in her life had she seen anyone quite like her.

Later on, as they fed the chickens, Geeder talked to Toeboy

303

about the arrival of the Taybers in Crystal.

"They must have come early one morning," she told him. "They might have come from the west, but I suspect they came from Tallahassee. They brought all their wild animals with them in a wagon train, and they bought that house they live in from Mr. Crawley."

"How could they come in a wagon train?" Toeboy wanted to know.

Geeder was thinking and didn't answer him.

"Mr. Tayber came down the road to see about using some of the west field," Geeder said. "Uncle Ross was to get a third of the profit from the sale of the best razorback hogs."

"But why would Uncle Ross rent land to strangers?" Toeboy asked. "And what is a 'a third of the profit'?"

"Oh, goodness, Toeboy!" Geeder said. "I don't know what 'a third of the profit' would be. And if Uncle Ross waited until he got to know the Taybers the way you know ordinary people, he'd wait forever. Listen." She stood very close to Toeboy, as though the chickens might hear and she didn't want them to. "All of Crystal knows only a few things about the Taybers."

"What things?" Toeboy asked.

"Well, they know that Zeely Tayber is awfully tall for a girl. Even Nat Tayber is very tall," Geeder said, "but not too tall for a grown man."

"What else do they know?" asked Toeboy.

"The Taybers like to be left alone," Geeder said, counting off on her fingers. "Zeely's mother is dead. Both Nat and Zeely have thin noses and very high cheekbones."

"Maybe the Taybers are Indians," Toeboy said.

Geeder had to laugh. "The Taybers are black people," she said, "just like you and me and Uncle Ross. But they are different from any people I've ever seen. We don't know what kind of person Zeely is." Geeder's voice was full of the awe she felt for her. "But you know what I think? I think we've found a new people that nobody's ever heard of!"

All that morning, Geeder talked to Toeboy about Zeely. When they sat down for lunch with Uncle Ross, Toeboy was surprised by the off-handed way Geeder asked, "How long have those Tayber people been around this town?"

"Oh, it's been about a year and a half now," Uncle Ross said.

"That's a long time," Geeder said. "I guess you've gotten to know Mr. Tayber and his girl real well in all that time."

Uncle Ross smiled. "No," he said, "I wouldn't say that. The Taybers aren't easy to know, although they are speaking-polite to most folks."

"What would you say then?" asked Toeboy.

"What would I say when?" Uncle Ross replied.

Geeder wished Toeboy would just keep quiet. "He means to say that if you don't know them well, then what way *do* you know them?" she asked. "And why don't you know them well when they're in the west field every day working over those animals?"

Uncle Ross took a careful look at Toeboy and a much longer look at Geeder.

"Toeboy means to say all that?" he said to Geeder. "Well, I mean to say what I did say. Mr. Tayber and his daughter live to themselves. They stay aloof from the whole town." He paused. "One day, the town had no thought of them. The next day, there they were, hammering and putting storm windows in that old house once owned by Jacob Crawley."

"Just like that?" Geeder said, snapping her fingers.

"No, not exactly like that," Uncle Ross said. "Now that I think about it, there had been time . . . room . . . for people like them among us. It's like it took them a long time to get here. The first time we see them, they are taking care to fix up that house. Strangers. And they stay on taking their time, still strangers. That's all right, the way I see it."

"Strangers," Geeder said. But that was all she said. She asked no more questions.

But by nightfall, Geeder was ready to talk about Zeely Tayber once more. As she and Toeboy lay in their beds on the lawn, she began.

"You would like to think a lady like Zeely would have all kinds of friends," Geeder said. "I mean, being so tall and being so pretty. But there she goes with just old Mr. Tayber. She hardly even talks to *him*."

"He doesn't talk much to her, either," Toeboy said.

"That's because both Zeely and Mr. Tayber are different," Geeder said, "with ways about them none of us can understand."

Toeboy lay beneath the lilac bush, hugging the covers around himself. He listened to the rise and fall of Geeder's voice and was lulled into a deep sleep.

Geeder stopped talking. She was watching the stars when there grew in her mind a lovely picture. . . . It was daytime, with sunlight spilling over Uncle Ross's farm. She sat in shade on a grassy slope beside Leadback Road. Miss Zeely Tayber came gliding down the road. Her face and arms were shiny from heat and walking so long in the sun. She came right up to Geeder. She had been looking for her.

"Geeder, have you waited long?" Miss Zeely said. *"I would dearly love a drink of water from the pump room."*

Geeder brought Miss Zeely a drink of water in a tall glass, and a silk handkerchief. Miss Zeely sat beside Geeder, sipping the water. She wiped her face with the handkerchief and dried her hands. When she had finished, she folded the hanky and placed it in Geeder's palm.

"Geeder Perry," said Miss Zeely, *"I don't know what I would do without you."*

Geeder pretended she hadn't done anything at all. . . .

"Miss Zeely Tayber," she whispered to the stars, "oh, Miss Zeely!"

Her hand touched something cool and heavy beside her. Uncle Ross's flashlight! She had taken it from his workroom. She meant to shine the light on the night traveler just as it passed by the house.

Suddenly alert and watchful, she listened to the silence around her.

"If the night traveler tries to bother me, I'll throw the flashlight at it," she muttered. "And if that doesn't stop it, I'll scream and wake up the whole town!"

But Geeder was tricked by the fresh night air into falling asleep. Many times she roused herself but did not awaken. Once she said in her sleep, "Is that you? Is that you coming?" It seemed that a voice came through the hedge, murmuring, "Yes, child, now sleep." It was her mother's voice. She slept more calmly then. She dreamed of home and people she knew there. In the morning, she was mad as a bull at having fallen asleep and had no recollection of the dream.

❧

Who is Zeely Tayber?

Geeder is convinced that she is no ordinary woman. She makes up her mind to find out Zeely's real identity.

To find out what Geeder discovers about Zeely and about herself, read the rest of the novel **Zeely,** *by Virginia Hamilton.*

CHECK FOR UNDERSTANDING

1. What did Geeder decide to do the first night on the farm?
2. What special thing did Geeder think they might see that night?
3. Why did Geeder make up the story about the night travelers?
4. What did Geeder think she saw that night? Who did she really see?
5. Why is Geeder fascinated by Zeely?

WRITE ABOUT *"The Night Traveler"*

In "The Night Traveler," Geeder makes up stories about Nat Tayber and Zeely. For example, she tells Toeboy that they came from Tallahassee in a wagon train. If Geeder knew that the "night traveler" was Zeely, what kind of story might she make up to explain why Zeely walks down the road alone at night? Write the story as Geeder might tell it.

THINK ABOUT IT

Think about the special qualities of the people you met in this unit.

- Ida Early, who doesn't take *no* for an answer and finds a way to make everything fun
- Jackie Robinson, whose fame does not prevent him from being touched by a small act of love
- The Vietnamese grandmother, who has lived her life with such dignity that death does not frighten her
- Sofie Herzog, whose confidence in her own ability stood up against other people's fears and misgivings
- Charlie, who has a gift for being loved
- Joe Iron Shell, who is wiser than his grandson realizes and who gives Martin the wisdom of his heritage
- Zeely, who, surrounded by mystery, inspires Geeder's imagination

Think about the characters and the people who are "somebody special" in each story. Is each one special and unique because of what he or she is? Or is each one special because of the effect he or she has on others?

WRITE ABOUT IT

Who do you know who is special? How is that person special? Write a description of someone who is not famous, or even well-known in your community. Write about someone whose "specialness" is inside and only discovered through really knowing that person.

READ ABOUT IT

Professor Diggins' Dragons by Felice Holman. Macmillan
   Publishing Co., 1974. Professor Diggins' students fight
   "dragons," but they are not at all like medieval monsters.

The Hot & Cold Summer by Johanna Hurwitz. William Morrow &
   Co., 1984. Everyone tells Rory and Derek that they will like
   Bolivia, a neighbor's niece who will be visiting all summer.
   Rory and Derek know better; after all, Bolivia is a *girl*.

Bridge to Terabithia by Katherine Paterson. Thomas Y. Crowell
   Co., 1977. Even though Jesse's new neighbor, Leslie Burke,
   beats him in a footrace, the two become friends. They
   share an imaginary kingdom called Terabithia.

Soup & Me by Robert Newton Peck. Alfred A. Knopf, 1975.
   These humorous adventures of Rob and his best friend,
   Soup, in Vermont include chasing a runaway pumpkin and
   blazing a trail through Mrs. Stetson's marigolds.

The Best Bad Thing by Yoshiko Uchida. Atheneum Publishers,
   1983. Rinko is prepared for a terrible August in 1935 when
   her mother asks her to spend the month with Mrs. Hata, an
   eccentric friend, in Oakland, California.

4

GROWING TOGETHER

Have you ever thought of an animal as a teacher? Humans usually think of themselves as the ones who teach animals, but often it is the other way around. Humans can often learn a great deal from animals—particularly about themselves.

The animals in this unit range from a tiny, short-tempered chickaree squirrel to a stubborn and willful horse. The animals are different; the experiences humans have with animals are different. But in each story, a human learns something new and grows in self-knowledge and understanding.

A Day to Remember

by WALT MOREY

People sometimes refuse to try something because they are afraid they cannot do it. David, the main character in this story, has this problem. David learns a valuable lesson in courage from his dog, Scrub.

What does Scrub teach David? How does the dog do this?

It had been fifteen weeks since David Martin broke his leg. The cast had been removed, but David still used his crutches. The leg was weak, and David was afraid he would fall and break it again.

One day, Scotty, an old family friend, brought a homeless dog to the Martins' cabin. The dog had been attacked by a pack of dogs. It was badly injured, and one of its hind legs was broken. David's mother helped Scotty stitch up the wounds and set the broken leg.

Scotty told David that the dog's leg would heal in three weeks. According to Scotty, it takes a human six times longer to heal than a dog. So David and the dog should both be able to walk in three weeks. "It won't be easy for either of you," Scotty warned. "It's going to be painful and hard. But this dog's going to walk again. So can you."

For the first time since he was a very small pup, Scrub was not half-starved and constantly on the prowl for something to steal. Now twice a day there was all the food he could eat. He soon forgot about dodging rocks and clubs and avoiding the pack of dogs. Instead of curling up to sleep beneath a bush, in some old building, or an abandoned mine shaft, Scrub had his own blanket in a corner of the kitchen. The room was always warm, the people spoke quietly, kindly, and delicious mouthwatering odors kept his black nose twitching.

At first, he avoided the dogs staked out around the cabin. But when they paid no attention to him, he finally hobbled over to visit. Noble, the big white leader, welcomed him with much sniffing and a waving plume. In turn, the rest of the team accepted him.

Scrub was the first pet David ever had. He talked to the dog in a low, intimate voice while he scratched the thick fur of his forehead and patted the deepening chest until it boomed like a drum. "You're going to have a

bigger chest than Noble in a few months," he'd say. At such times Scrub would lower his head and push it against the boy as a way of inviting more patting and scratching. "I like you, too," David said. "We make a good team."

Scrub expected to go everywhere with David and share in all his activities. The two were outside so much that David's mother often had to hunt for them to come to meals. This pleased both parents, for David had been morose and listless since the accident. Now his voice would ring out across the clearing a dozen times a day, and he and Scrub would be off on some business of their own, the boy on his crutches, the dog hobbling beside, carefully holding his splinted leg above the ground.

They returned often to the river bank. It was about as far as they could hobble, taking their time, resting often. They would lie side by side in the grass and listen to the river. Often the dog's big head was on the boy's

good knee. David would bare his leg to the warm sun and gently massage the weakened muscles. Scrub would doze and then try to lick the sore spots between the splints.

David spent hours fishing with the flies Scotty had tied. He became quite expert and kept the table well supplied with trout. His excitement when he hooked a fish was immense. He shouted and laughed. He played the fish expertly, finally lifting it in a clean pull to land flopping in the grass.

Scrub shared the excitement. He stood beside David and barked encouragement. The moment the fish landed, he grabbed it and carried it to David with the air of having caught it himself. David would pat him and say, "We caught him, didn't we? I don't know what I'd do without your help." Scrub would wave his tail and lift his lips in a grin, to show that he understood they had caught the fish together.

There came a day when they made it from the cabin to the river without stopping to rest. David smiled at Scrub and said, "You're doing fine." Scrub shoved his head against David, and the boy patted his sides. "You're gaining weight. I can hardly feel your ribs. You're going to look great."

David could almost see the daily change in Scrub. The dog was growing stronger, his lean sides were filling out, and the sheen was coming to his wolf-gray coat.

"He's beginning to look fine, don't you think, Mom?" he asked his mother one morning.

"With what he eats he should," she said. "That dog out-eats the three of us morning and night."

"He never had a good meal before he came here," David explained. "He's making up for lost time."

"Lost time!" His father's eyes were twinkling. "That dog's making up for time before he was born."

But no one begrudged Scrub a bite.

David was counting the days until he could walk, but each day he cared more about the changes in Scrub and himself.

A coat of tan was covering his own pale skin. His strength had improved. He was sure he could hobble to town and back now. His leg muscles no longer hurt when he massaged them or when he exercised the leg. The pains he'd known at night were gone. One day he noticed that Scrub was touching his splinted leg lightly to the ground and making stepping motions with it. He tried, too, and felt only a momentary weakness and pain. From then on he put his foot down lightly, just as Scrub was doing. It was another memorable day.

The changes on the river made him most aware of the passage of time. He didn't always fish when they hobbled out there. Often he lay on the bank, with Scrub close beside him, watched the water, and let the good warm sun beat down on him. He saw the baby ducks and geese change from downy fluff-balls to small birds sprouting their first feathers. The adult birds molted, lost their primaries, and were unable to fly. They would remain earthbound until they grew new primaries for the long flight south this fall. The river level dropped, leaving a stretch of barren beach which was no hiding place for the pair of prowling foxes. A moose and calf came almost daily to the river. The calf was now sure-footed and waded into the water to feed with its mother. The lazy summer days slipped away.

The morning of the twenty-first day David said nothing to his parents. He had been unable to sleep for thinking of this day. After breakfast, his mother asked, "What are you and Scrub doing today?"

"Guess we'll go fishing."

"Good. We haven't had fish for several days. You planning anything else?"

"No." She had never asked before what he planned to do with his day. He waited, curious. She continued moving about the kitchen clearing up the breakfast dishes. "Be sure and get back for lunch," she said finally.

"I will." He hobbled outside, got the fish pole, and, with Scrub beside him, headed for the river. He was glad his parents had forgotten this was the day. He wanted to be alone with Scrub to do this his own way. If he failed, he didn't want them to see.

David lowered himself carefully in his favorite spot on the river bank and leaned the fish pole against a rock. He had no intention of fishing today. Scrub lay down beside him. The ducks and geese were busy about their business against the far shore. Their faint gabbling was the only sound this still morning. A small breeze barely stirred the leaves. He guessed the moose and her calf wouldn't come until later in the day. But David was not interested in the ducks and geese or thinking about the moose. Finally he patted Scrub's big head and said, "Scotty told us this would be the day. I guess there's no use waiting any longer. You first."

David began loosening the splints. His fingers trembled. "It's going to hurt like sixty," he said. "But here goes." He carefully unwound the binding and took the splints off. "There you are. You can try it any time." He watched the dog intently.

Scrub smelled his leg and licked the broken spot. He rose, still on three legs, and took a couple of hobbling steps. Then he seemed to realize that the bandages and splints were gone. He put the paw on the ground and immediately lifted it. For a moment he balanced there, then carefully lowered the foot again. He hobbled off a few feet, then turned and came back and lay down. That small exertion seemed to have exhausted him.

David knew what the dog was going through. Scotty had been wrong. The leg was not healed. Scrub was aware of this and quit just as David had been forced to do.

But soon the dog was up again. He limped a few steps and stopped. But he didn't lie down. He began walking again and limped a circle around David, head down, ears flattened to his head. He wandered off and returned. David could see, or he imagined, the dog was putting more weight on the leg. The limp seemed a little less pronounced. Scrub walked farther between stops.

David's fists were clenched. What had Scotty said? "He'll endure pain. He does what nature tells him he has to do to walk again." Scotty had been right! Scrub's leg was healed! The dog was proving it with every step. David called Scrub to him and patted his head. He held the big head between his hands and shook him lovingly. "You made it! You made it!" Scrub wagged his tail and lifted his lips in a grin. David drew a deep breath. "Scotty said when you walked I could. Well, here goes!"

David got carefully to his feet and balanced on the crutches. His palms were wet. He was shaking and for a moment could not stop. This was the day he'd waited so long for, and now he was afraid. He straightened his leg gingerly, put his foot flat on the ground, and bore down with weight. He dropped the crutches and stood. Pain was a knife that made him lift the foot as Scrub had done. Maybe if he tried to walk. He got off three quick steps, then the weakened leg folded. He sprawled full-length, wrenching the muscles of the leg as he fell. David rolled over and sat up holding the leg with both hands. He wasn't crying. But he couldn't stop tears from squeezing between his shut lids. Then he felt Scrub's warm tongue licking his cheek. David put his arms around the furry neck and held the dog close until the worst of the pain had passed. Then he got up and tried again.

He balanced on the good leg and brought his weight down carefully on the bad one. The pain was no worse. He knew then that his task, too, was to endure the pain. David managed a grin at Scrub and said, "You're not the only one who can walk." He picked out a big rock as target a few steps away—and made it. Next he limped a circle around the rock, close enough so that he could grab it if he started to fall. He didn't.

David leaned against the rock and rested a couple of minutes. Then he picked up the crutches, limped to the

edge of the bank, and hurled them into the river. "Come on," he said triumphantly to Scrub, "let's go home."

It was not the proud, heads-up, joyous return David had visualized. It was slow and painful, and they had to stop several times to rest. The dog made better time than the boy. But he slowed his pace, and they traveled together. They went through the trees and across the clearing to the cabin. When David stepped through the door, his mother and father were in the kitchen. He had planned to say something exciting and dramatic, but all he could think of was the great distance they'd come, and he said, "We made it. We both made it."

CHECK FOR UNDERSTANDING

1. How did David and Scrub change in the course of the story?
2. Why was David glad that his mother seemed to have forgotten that it was an important day?
3. What do you think David's thoughts were as he walked to the river bank?
4. What did Scrub teach David?
5. How did the dog do this?
6. What do you think David's parents said and did when David and Scrub got back to the cabin?

WRITE ABOUT *"A Day To Remember"*

Scotty had predicted that when Scrub's leg was healed David's leg would be healed, too. Pretend that you are David. Write a letter to Scotty describing what happened when you and Scrub both started walking again on your injured legs.

VOCABULARY · LANGUAGE

Idioms

When David Martin loosened the splints on Scrub's leg, he warned the dog "It's going to hurt like sixty." Have you ever heard anyone use the expression *hurt like sixty*? What do you think it means?

Like sixty is an idiom used in some parts of the United States. An *idiom* is a group of words, or an expression that has a special meaning. The meaning of an idiom is quite different from the literal meaning of the words that make up the idiom. For example, the idiom *to raise the roof* does not mean "to lift the roof." When you raise the roof you complain loudly. In the same way, something that is *out of this world* is not drifting around in outer space. If something is out of this world, it is wonderful, terrific, fantastic. *Raise the roof* and *out of this world* are idioms.

When you read a story, you can usually figure out the meaning of an idiom by seeing how it is used. Clues in the sentence and in the passage will help you to figure out the meaning. In "A Day to Remember," for example, David was nervous when he and Scrub were getting ready to find out if their broken legs were really healed.

> Finally he patted Scrub's big head and said, "Scotty told us this would be the day. I guess there's no use waiting any longer. You first."
>
> David began loosening the splints. His fingers trembled. "It's going to hurt like sixty," he said. "But here goes." He carefully unwound the binding and took the splints off.

You can figure out from this passage that *like sixty* means "very much" or "a great deal."

324

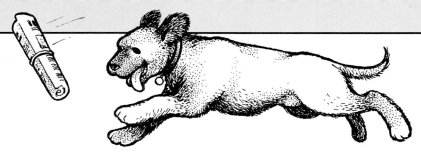

Actually, the idiom *like sixty* goes back to the days of the horse and wagon. It meant "going at sixty miles an hour" or "at a very great speed." In horse-and-buggy days, going sixty miles an hour—a mile a minute!—seemed an impossibly fast speed. So anything that went like sixty went incredibly fast. The exact meaning of this idiom has changed somewhat over the years. But it is still used to indicate something extraordinary or extreme.

Sometimes, you can find the meaning of an unfamiliar idiom by looking up a *key word* in the idiom in the dictionary. Idioms are usually listed in **bold face,** or dark type, at the end of the entry for a key word.

Look up the word *dog* in the dictionary. At the end of the entry, you will probably find the idioms **go to the dogs** and **put on the dog.** Here are their meanings.

go to the dogs	to weaken or become worse; to fall apart
put on the dog	to dress in one's fanciest clothes; to act wealthy or important

You might say that a restaurant that no longer serves really tasty food has *gone to the dogs.* How would you use the idiom *put on the dog* in a sentence?

Look up the word *leg* in a dictionary. What idioms are listed at the end of the entry for *leg*? How would you use each of the idioms in a sentence?

As you read the story "The Comeback Dog," see if you can find examples of idioms.

The death of a pet is a difficult experience. Many people who lose pets think they will never want another pet. Sometimes when people do get another pet, the new pet is a painful disappointment. In this story, Daniel adopts a new dog, but things don't work out exactly as Daniel expected.

Why is Daniel disappointed with the new dog? Why does Daniel change his mind about the dog?

The Comeback Dog

by JANE RESH THOMAS

After his dog Captain died, Daniel thought he would never want another dog. But one day he discovered a dog hiding in a culvert near his home. The dog was battered and nearly dead from starvation and the cold. Daniel took the dog home, determined to nurse her back to health.

Daniel slept on the couch by the stove that night. He forced himself to awaken when the clock chimed the hours. Since Lady seemed more alert, he had gradually increased her ration of broth with each feeding, so that both of them could sleep for longer intervals.

At three o'clock, he woke in confusion. The fire shone through the isinglass windows in the stove door and reflected on the opposite wall in moving red shapes and shadows that terrified him. He leaped off the couch, thinking that he was in his own bed and the room was afire.

Behind the stove, Lady whined. In an instant, Daniel awoke completely, remembering where he was and why.

"Yes," he said, "you can have all the broth you want. Hold on a minute, dog. I'll warm it for you. It gets thick when it's cold."

Returning with the warm broth, he found her no longer outstretched on her side, but lying with her chin between her paws. She pushed the medicine dropper away with her nose and snuffed the side of the bowl in Daniel's hand.

"I'm not fast enough for you?" Daniel held the soup bowl under the dog's nose. She lapped and slurped the broth until she had licked the bowl dry. Then she pricked her ears and looked expectantly at Daniel.

He laughed. "For a dead dog, you sure are hungry!"

He pushed the lace curtains aside to look out at the blizzard that had shrieked around the house since dinner. Snow still fell so thickly that all he could see of the yard lamp was a glowing swirl. The wind had dropped, and the snow was coming down in big soft flakes. Spruce trees and hedges planted as windbreaks partially protected the farmyard. Elsewhere, snowdrifts had closed country roads by now, buried fences and mailboxes, and filled ditches.

Daniel thought with satisfaction—as if he had planned and organized the snowstorm himself—that the school bus would be kept away from his house for several days. That would be long enough for him to get Lady back on her feet.

He imagined himself teaching her to herd the cows as Captain used to do, running across the meadow on cold spring mornings with his breath visible in gusts. In his mind, Daniel saw her playing Captain's old games. She would bring him sticks to throw and bark at him until he cooperated. She would sleep under his covers on winter nights. She would lie with her chin on his foot while he did his homework.

Then he looked at the skinny dog that lay by the stove, already sleeping again. Her big feet and starved legs were like clubs. Her coat was so sparse he could see her knobby spine and her ribs.

Even if she lives, he thought, she may not stay here. I didn't want a new dog. Maybe she doesn't want a new boy. Maybe she'll go back home where she belongs.

•

The snow blocked the road to school for three days. By the time the county plow cleared a path for the milk truck and the mail on Tuesday afternoon, Daniel thought he had shoveled a ton of snow.

On Wednesday, Daniel and his father came into the house together for breakfast. They had fed and watered the chickens, gathered the eggs, and milked the cows before the sun rose.

"They say the roads are open. School today," said Pa.

"Did you hear that, dog? School will be a vacation from all this work." Daniel dropped down on his knees beside the stove, where Lady was watching them out of the corner of her eye, her ears laid back.

As he lunged happily toward her, Lady bared her teeth and snarled. She jumped to her feet and crawled under the couch. She cowered in the darkest corner, shivering and watchful.

"What's the matter with her?" said Daniel.

"Something more than starvation ails that dog," said Mama.

"Looks like she's taken some beatings from somebody," said Pa. "Sometimes people's meanness ruins dogs. She may never be any good."

"I'll train her," said Daniel. "Now that we've caught up on the work, I'll take her outdoors after school. I'll throw sticks for her."

"You'd better put her on a leash," said Pa. "If you don't control her until this place seems like home, she'll run."

●

In the weeks that followed, Lady looked healthier every day. With Doc's advice, Daniel gradually changed her diet from liquids to bland foods to meat. After her appetite returned, she was constantly hungry. The weight she gained was visible. Her eyes were bright. Her coat began to shine.

When Daniel thought no one was looking, he tried to train her. He dragged her out from her place under the couch and held her head between his knees while he stroked her silky hair. He forced her to lie under the table while he did his homework, and jabbed her with the toe of his boot when she inched away. He shut her in his room at night and held her in his bed with his arm locked around her neck. He even tried to make her lick his hand.

But inevitably his grip relaxed when he fell asleep. In the morning, he found her in the closet, squeezed under the low shelf, or far under the bed, with fluffs of dust caught in her whiskers and eyebrows.

Lady never snarled at Daniel again, but she wouldn't wag her tail either. She merely submitted.

One day after school, when Daniel found her under the couch as usual, he lost all patience. As he grabbed her hair and yanked at her, she yelped and whined.

"What's the matter with you?" he said. "I'm the one who fed you when you were half dead."

"You can't squeeze blood out of a turnip, Daniel," said his mother quietly at the kitchen door.

"What's that supposed to mean?"

"You can't get love by force, if she's not willing."

Daniel let Lady go, and she crawled back under the couch.

"She's not a bit like Captain," he said. "He followed me everywhere. I had to lock him up to get rid of him."

His mother knelt beside him and put her arm around him. "Every dog has ways of its own," she said.

"She let me touch her when she was sick because she couldn't get away." He wiped his eyes on his flannel sleeve. "Now she won't come near me."

His mother nodded.

"Maybe she thought I didn't want another dog. Maybe it's my fault she doesn't like me."

His mother patted his head.

"She's worse than nothing!" Daniel cried. "I wish she had died that first day. I wish I'd never found her!"

•

The last week of March brought robins and weather so warm the family worked outdoors without jackets. The remaining snow melted suddenly. The runoff overflowed the creek and flooded the fields near the house. Within a few days, the water receded, and warm winds and sun dried the ground.

After the chores were done and breakfast was over on Saturday morning, Daniel's father said, "Take this morning off, Daniel. You and Lady can check all the fences around the west meadow, while I muck out the barn."

His father watched as the boy pulled Lady from under the couch, fastened the choke-chain around her neck, and snapped the leash onto the ring. The chain ran through a larger ring, like a slipknot, so that tension on the leash would tighten the chain around the dog's neck.

Daniel pulled on the leash. Lady sat back. She stubbornly stiffened her front legs and leaned in the opposite direction. Daniel jerked the leash. She coughed and gagged as the chain pinched her windpipe.

"A choke-chain can be a brutal thing, Daniel," said his father, in a voice so soft it was almost a whisper.

"Oh, you know I won't hurt the dumb dog," Daniel said. He put his head down so his father couldn't see the redness in his hot cheeks as he pushed Lady across the dining room, through the kitchen, and out the back door.

They walked side by side across the yard, past the windmill and the chicken coop, but they were not companions. Lady skulked along, close to the ground, watching Daniel, leaning as far as she could against the leash.

"You don't trust me one bit, do you, dog?" Daniel said. "I saved you, but now you can't wait for the thinnest chance to get away."

As they crossed the lane between the farmyard and the fields, Daniel picked up a short stick, thinking Lady might chase it. She shied away so fearfully she fell over on her side, whimpering, and pawing at the ground as if she wished she could crawl into the earth. She rolled on her back, with her feet in the air in a gesture of surrender.

Furious, Daniel threw the stick with all his strength over last year's chopped-off cornstalks. He slipped the choke-chain off Lady's neck and ran as fast as he could across the soft earth. Looking back, he saw Lady creeping on her belly down a corn row, watching him distrustfully over her shoulder.

"Go, then! Starve to death!" he shouted. "I never wanted you anyway!"

When he certainly could not have caught her even if he had tried, she bolted. With her tail curled under, between her legs, she dashed for the woods at the far end of the field. In a moment, Daniel lost sight of her as she plunged into the creek bed, still filled with cottony morning fog.

The creek divided the cornfield. Its banks were now two or three feet above the water. As Daniel approached it, with a sick feeling in his stomach and tears dripping from his chin, he bent

333

automatically to pick up a field stone. Although he and his father had carried off wagonloads of rocks from that field, every spring the frost had heaved up more.

Looking down, he noticed the claw of a dead crayfish and nearby another. The claws were everywhere. They were no longer the clay-green color of the living animal, but blue as could be, with red edges on the pincers.

Daniel was amazed by their number and their beauty. He knew that the flood had washed them out of the creek, but they might have been carved purposely for miniature decorations and polished by hand. Daniel imagined the multitudes of creatures living unnoticed in the creek. He filled the pockets of his windbreaker and jeans with the claws. In the distance, he could see Lady where she sat at the edge of the woods, watching him. He watched back until she fled into the brush. She was gone for good now, he was sure.

He walked back to the flower garden at the side of the house. There he and his father and mother had taken turns breaking the frozen ground with a pickax, to bury Captain among the hybrid iris and rambler roses. He carefully coiled the choke-chain and the leash on the bare earth and put the crayfish in a mound beside them. Then, trying not to look towards the woods, where nothing lively moved, he walked quickly out to the barn to help his father clean the stalls.

Every day for a week Daniel pressed his cheek against the cool glass and watched from the school bus window until his eyes hurt. He searched the countryside for a glimpse of white fur. Every evening, as he sat in the pool of warm lamplight at the dining-room table, trying to think about math problems, he listened for Lady, scratching like Captain to come in.

He woke up once in the middle of the night, thinking he had heard her bark. When he opened the back door, a startled raccoon ran for cover across the moonlit yard. He knew that no coon would come near if a dog were about. Daniel picked up a stick of kindling and threw it into the darkness after the coon.

Back in bed, he shivered under blankets that had chilled while he was off fooling himself, looking for Lady. He wouldn't be tricked again by wishful thinking, he told himself. She was gone, and good riddance. He would forget her.

After that, when he caught himself with his mind wandering, looking out the bus window, searching the fields, he made himself open his books and study his homework. "There are six kinds of simple machines," he read. He shut his eyes and tried to list them without looking at the book. "The wheel, the lever, the inclined plane. . . ." But he couldn't concentrate. His thoughts returned to Lady. He worried that she might be trapped in some culvert just down the road from his house. She might have gone back to the place where somebody beat her.

Then, one chilly morning nineteen days after Lady had run off, Daniel went to the barn with his father to do the chores before school. Violins were playing a love song on the radio that ran all day to soothe the cows so they would give more milk.

The door creaked open. A shaft of sunshine lit a pile of hay in the corner, and there crouched Lady. Daniel saw that her nose

335

and lips and even one eyelid bristled with broken white needles.

"Look at her!" said Daniel. "What a mess."

"She's tangled with a porcupine," said Pa. When he reached for her, she snarled. "She wants nothing to do with me."

"She can cure herself then," said Daniel. He pulled down the bill of the green and yellow cap the machinery dealer had given him, until it all but covered his eyes.

"For heaven's sake, Daniel, what do you want of that dog?" said Pa. "You've been grieving for nearly three weeks because she ran away. Now you're mad because she's come back."

Lady struggled to her feet and limped to Daniel's side. She raised her ragamuffin head high, erect and stately as a show dog. She looked at him imploringly with her uninjured eye.

Daniel turned his back on her and kicked a pail so hard it bounced and banged halfway across the barn. It rolled into the straw and bumped a cow in the shins. The cow jumped back, surprisingly nimble, but with her head fastened in the stanchion, she couldn't go far. The whole herd shifted, frightened by the noise.

"Daniel, stop and look at yourself." Pa rarely spoke so sharply. "No matter how you feel, I won't have you disturbing the cows."

"I didn't mean to kick it so hard," said Daniel.

As he retrieved the bucket and patted the insulted cow on the nose, Lady followed him. He tried not to look at her, but she whined and nudged him and stood on his foot.

"It's now or never, son," said Pa. "She's yours if you want her."

Tears spilled down Daniel's cheeks. He knelt beside her, put his arms around her shoulders, and whispered in her ear, "Of course I'll help."

"Hold on, and I'll get the pliers," said Pa.

Daniel sat on a crate with the dog's head in his lap. "You're a good dog," he whispered, as he gripped the porcupine quills close to the skin with the narrow-nosed pliers. Then he drew them out one by one. "Good Lady. We're halfway done."

Her whole face was swollen and infected. She trembled in his lap, moaning and watching his every move with her good eye, but she sat still. When Daniel had pulled out all of the quills, first from her eyelid and then from her muzzle, he took a deep, shuddering breath. His hands were shaking.

"Look her over carefully," said Pa. "Your grandfather claimed that porcupine needles move into an animal's body. He said they might kill a bear if they lodged in a place the bear couldn't reach."

Together Daniel and Pa gently made the dog lie down. She lay patiently still as they combed through her hair with their fingers and inspected every part of her body.

"Look at her paws," said Daniel. "Sores all over the pads of her feet."

"She must have tried to clean her face and pierced her paws with

the needles," said Pa. "But she could pull those out with her teeth."

"I don't know how she could walk," said Daniel.

The door swung open as Mama came into the barn, hugging herself in a heavy knitted sweater. "What's happened? Breakfast is getting cold," she said, squinting in the dim light of the barn. "Why, it's Lady!"

"She's come back," said Daniel.

His mother saw the porcupine needles at Daniel's feet and the pliers in his hand and Lady's hurt face. "I begin to doubt that dog's sense," she said. "Bring the old pincushion up to the house. We'll put some salve on her face."

Lady wouldn't let Pa pick her up. She cringed and clung to Daniel.

"It's a good thing we weren't quick to get rid of her bed," said Mama.

"Look how bedraggled she is," said Daniel. "We'll have to start just about fresh, fattening her up again. What a pain in the neck you are, dog."

He turned away from her and walked into the morning sunshine. "I can't carry you," he said, "and I got rid of the leash. You'll have to make it on your own power."

Slowly Lady followed the boy through the barn door and limped across the yard. The windmill swung and squeaked in the rising breeze. The tulips Daniel had planted along the sidewalk last fall had broken through the ground. The yellow cups bobbed on stiff stems. The air was alive with a robin's song.

Footsore and stiff and muddy as on the day Daniel had first seen her, the dog wagged her tail and licked his hand.

Overcome by the morning, he took off his cap and skimmed it into the branches of the oak he climbed in summer. "Lady's come back on her own," he said to the birds.

He bent and kissed the dog on her hot, dry nose. "Maybe this time," he said, "you'll stay."

CHECK FOR UNDERSTANDING

1. Why was Daniel disappointed with the new dog?
2. What was Daniel's mother really saying to Daniel when she said "You can't squeeze blood out of a turnip"?
3. Why did Daniel take the choke-chain off Lady's neck in the cornfield?
4. What happened to Lady that caused her come back?
5. Why does Daniel change his mind about Lady?
6. Do you think Lady will run away again? Explain your answer.

WRITE ABOUT *"The Comeback Dog"*

When Daniel found Lady in the culvert, he might have tried to locate Lady's owner by placing an ad in the Lost and Found section of the local newspaper. Write the ad as Daniel might have written it, describing Lady and explaining how she was found.

GONE

by DAVID McCORD

I've looked behind the shed
And under every bed:
I think he must be dead.

What reason for alarm?
He doesn't know the farm.
I *knew* he'd come to harm!

He was a city one
Who never had begun
To think the city fun.

Now where could he have got?
He doesn't know a lot.
I haven't heard a shot.

That old abandoned well,
I thought. Perhaps he fell?
He didn't. I could tell.

Perhaps he found a scent:
A rabbit. Off he went.
He'll come back home all spent.

Groundhogs, they say, can fight;
And raccoons will at night.
He'd not know one by sight!

I've called and called his name.
I'll never be the same.
I blame myself . . . I blame . . .

All *he* knows is the park;
And now it's growing dark.
A bark? *You hear a bark?*

Little Bit, the Chickaree Squirrel

by ESTHER KELLNER

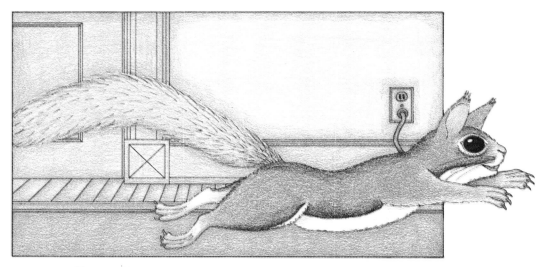

Esther Kellner, the author of this story, has cared for many kinds of wild animals. In this story, she describes life with Little Bit, a chickaree squirrel.
How did Little Bit come to live at the Kellners' house? Why did Little Bit refuse to go when the Kellners tried to release him?

One day a woman telephoned me and said she had found a baby squirrel. She wanted me to come and look at it and tell her how to take care of it. I was much surprised by the call because it was now October, which is much later than squirrels are usually born. When I saw the tiny creature, I was even more surprised. It was a baby chickaree.

She had not known that baby animals must be kept warmly covered and had laid it in an open box. It was almost dead from cold and hunger. She had found it on the sidewalk the evening before. No doubt it had fallen

342

from its nest onto the grass and leaves and had crawled out to the sidewalk searching for its mother. We tried to find the nest or the mother, but saw no sign of either one.

When I told her the baby would have to be fed every three hours, she asked me to adopt him. She worked in an office and could not take care of him. So I covered him warmly and brought him home. My daughter, Jamie, named him Little Bit.

We decided that he was about a month old, since his eyes were open. He was still so tiny we hardly dared hold him for fear of hurting him. At the time he weighed only an ounce. Even after he was fully grown, he weighed only four ounces and could stand on all four feet on the palm of Jamie's small hand. His own hands (or front feet) were about as large as the head of a kitchen match.

We examined him carefully, wondering at his beauty. His eyes were large, round, and shiny black, each rimmed in white. His coat was a dark reddish color, smooth and gleaming like a polished table. His underparts were snow white, divided from the reddish top by a sharp black line. His

small tail was flat, like a yellowish feather edged in black. One of the most interesting things about him was his ears. They were long and stood straight up, with little tufts of fur growing around them. The ears themselves were transparent. When you held him up to the light, tiny veins like the veins on a leaf could be seen running through them.

Though he was very weak, he flew into a temper and complained loudly when we handled him. Chickarees

343

complain about everything. He complained when we fed him, covered him, looked at him.

His mouth was too tiny for a bottle. We fed him with a medicine dropper while he was on the formula. At first we gave him only a few drops, since he needed very little to fill his tummy. He ate every three hours and slept a great deal afterward. During this time we kept him covered. As he gained strength, he would sit up in his blankets to see what was going on. We then started offering him one teaspoon of formula at each feeding. He did not always take all of it. Unlike most squir-

rels, he never seemed to want more than was good for him.

A pet squirrel will choose for himself the person he wants to belong to, no matter who may be his rescuer. And in a short time we could see that Little Bit had chosen Jamie. He soon looked to her as his mother. When he wanted food or attention, he would whistle for her to come. *Whist! Whist! Whist!* When he heard a strange noise or saw a strange visitor, he would give a shrill alarm cry, *brrrrrrr!*, which sounded somewhat like the call of a locust.

He never "talked" to me. But when Jamie fed him or played with him, he made little contented sounds— *mm . . . mmm . . . mm.* And sometimes when he was pleased, he made a high-pitched sound something like a thin whine. *Mmmmmmmmmmmmm!*

As soon as he was old enough to be taken off his milk formula, we started to feed him a cereal mixture. It made him furious when it stuck to his chin. He liked the cereal, but hated being sticky. He flew into a regular tantrum if a drop fell on him. Jamie would wash the stickiness off his face with a wet cottonball, which made him scream and kick with rage. But he never tried to bite her. No woods animal bites its mother except in play.

At this time Little Bit was so small that he held to Jamie's hand by wrapping his arms and legs around her first finger. His tantrums were very funny. He would glare at us. His little ears would bristle. The furry tufts on his jaws would stick out. And he would squall angry protests in his own language.

I would ask, "What do you suppose he is saying?"

And Jamie would answer, "I think he means: *Stop getting me all gooey, or I'll leave home!*"

When he was about six weeks old, we brought an empty birdcage from the attic and put him in that. This seemed to make him happy. It was circular in shape, and he could race around it as much as he pleased. Jamie added animal blankets. He shaped these into a burrow where he hid when things got too noisy for him, which was often. Even the sound of high heels passing by annoyed him.

A week or so later Jamie started taking him out of the cage to play. He would spring to her shoulder, then race around and around her, as a squirrel

races around the trunk of a tree. It was a sort of hide-and-seek, catch-me-if-you-can game. He would suddenly appear at her ear. When she saw him, he would cry, "*Whist!*" Then he would run around to her other side and pop up under her arm, all the time with a grin on his little face.

As he grew older and stronger, he learned to leap to the floor. Then he would run around the room at such a high speed that he was only a streak. This worried Jamie. She was afraid he might disappear into some little niche where she couldn't find him.

Of all the animals we have sheltered, he was the most "touchy." Of course, because he was tiny and pretty and appealing, everyone wanted to see him. But he didn't want strangers looking at him. When they came near he would cover his eyes and make whimpering sounds.

We knew that every living thing has to have a "safety zone" around it, a certain amount of space which he needs to make him feel comfortable. Jamie began to feel that Little Bit's

After he discovered that he could run, he began to take long leaps, very long for an animal his size. He was beautiful in flight, with his flat tail spread out to balance him and his arms as stiff as a dancer's. He would sail from Jamie's arm to the bookcase, back to her shoulder and then to her desk, all the time crying out, "Whist! Whist! Whist!"

Once he leaped into an open desk drawer among pencils, erasers, paper clips, and other things. He ran all the way through it and fell out the space at the back. He tumbled to the floor and bounced up in a rage. *Brrrrrr!* As if to say, "Why did you let that happen to me?"

346

"safety zone" was larger than the bird-cage. So she moved him to a parakeet flight cage, which was large and roomy. This made him happy. He ran around and around it, whistling his delight.

We built "furniture" for the new cage, apple and maple twigs that formed ladders and resting places up and down the walls. One branch was hung loosely from the top so that Little Bit could swing on it.

People who came to our house always wanted to see our animals. In spite of our warnings, they were always poking a finger into their cages. This frightened the animals. To any creature as tiny as Little Bit, somebody's forefinger looked as large as a python. He felt that he had to defend himself. Chickarees are very brave and bold. They have been known to attack a fox, even a grown man. So when a woman poked her finger at Little Bit one day, he bit it. His tiny teeth were finer than sewing machine needles and could bite about as fast as a sewing machine sews.

When he was fully grown, Jamie put him in a little basket (the kind used for party favors) and weighed him on

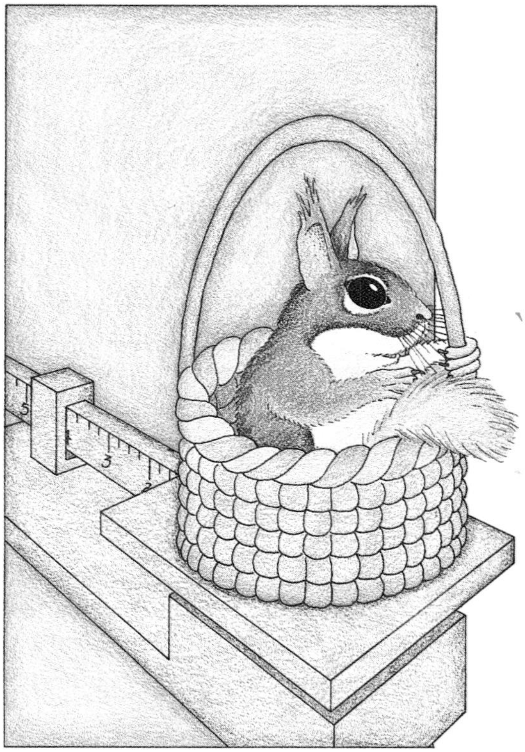

my postal scales. Four ounces. He looked strong and healthy. He had always been very lively, but suddenly he became ill.

I heard him whimpering and called Jamie. When she reached into the cage, he crawled into the palm of her hand and lay there making a sobbing sound. We didn't know what was wrong with him. It was impossible for a veterinarian to examine him, even Dr. Siebert, who had visited him many times. He wouldn't let anyone touch him but Jamie.

For days he was quiet. He was so quiet that his little nails had no chance to be worn down and became very long. One night Jamie found him huddled on top of his covers. His eyes were full of pain. He had caught one long nail in his blanket and almost torn it off. We treated it with a spray-on antiseptic. It soon healed, but he was still weak and ill.

Dr. Siebert reminded us that baby animals raised by humans usually have a vitamin lack because they have been deprived too early of their mother's milk. He suggested giving Little Bit the vitamin drops we used for the other animals. Jamie diluted this with water and poured it into his water dish. Because he would eat almost anything that was sweet, she added a bit of honey. His little tongue soon lapped up this remedy.

In a few days he was better. In three weeks he was much better. In a month he was running as fast as ever, insulting our visitors as sharply as usual, and going *whist!* when he wanted Jamie.

He was a fine little "watch squirrel." No sound, however soft, escaped his perky ears. His cage was near the patio door. When the curtains were closed at night, he could not see outside. Yet in the middle of the night, he might sound an alarm, *brrrrrr!* Jamie or I would look out and see a possum walking across the patio. How he could have heard this soft-walking animal was hard to understand! On summer nights a possum has passed right by me, and I heard him only because he blundered in some dry leaves.

Little Bit was a great hoarder. It is the nature of these animals to have what is called a midden. This is something like an apartment where they live and store all their belongings. In the

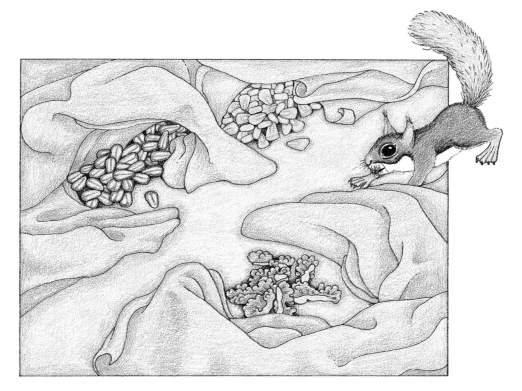

wild they may have a midden in their nest and one or two middens on the ground.

For his first midden, Jamie gave Little Bit a short piece of drapery material. It was old and soft. He spent several days getting it shaped just right. He tugged it here and there, working very hard. He made a number of tunnels in the cloth by patting them into place with his tiny hands. Until the midden was finished and filled, he was too busy to play. But once it was done, he wanted Jamie to see it and called to her in a bossy manner, "Whist! Whist!"

When she put her hand in the cage and examined the midden, he did not seem to mind. I'm sure he would have flown into a rage if anyone else had touched it.

There was a "front hall" where nothing was stored. ("A place to leave your coat and boots, I guess," Jamie said.) There was a tiny room holding walnut pieces. Beyond that was a room full of sunflower seeds and then a small bedroom. All these came off a central tunnel, or "hallway." Beyond the bedroom was a room full of shelled corn. Everything was neatly arranged and in its proper place.

While Jamie examined it, Little Bit ran along beside her hand making excited clicking sounds. We didn't always know what the animal sounds meant. Sometimes we had to use our imaginations. "I think," said Jamie, "he's so proud of the midden he wants to show it to me. He's afraid I'm going to miss something."

As her hand was lying in the "front hall," Little Bit seized a piece of tissue and began packing it around her wrist. He was bustling, "talking" all the time, as if he thought she had come to stay and was trying to store her, too.

Little Bit often stored some of the food he didn't eat, and when grapes or bits of apple started to spoil, the midden had to be cleaned out. That didn't please Little Bit at all. While Jamie washed the cage and cleaned the midden, he would watch from the swing and whimper. He whimpered like a child, with his tiny fists in his eyes. She told me she thought this must mean: "Look what you're doing! Throwing out all we've got for winter! We'll starve, that's what we'll do, starve!" She always saved the best of his stores, though. And she added new ones, so he was soon busy building another midden and making new rooms.

He never tried to quarrel with Jamie or bite her when she cleaned his cage. The tie between them was too strong. When she went to Indiana University in the summer, he sat and whimpered and refused to eat. Now and then he would look hopefully around, calling a sad "Whist!"

One day while she was gone and I was trying to give him some fresh water, he got out of his cage. At the same moment Sugar, the groundhog, came out on the sun porch. Little Bit had never seen a groundhog. And Sugar had never seen a chickaree. They stopped and stared at each other as if to ask, "What on earth is that?" I hurried up, afraid one might hurt the other. But this didn't happen. Instead Little Bit pranced forward and then away, as if inviting Sugar to romp. In another moment they were going around and around the room in a sort of catch-me-if-you-can game. Both were grinning broadly. It was a surprising and appealing sight. The companionship helped Little Bit to feel better about Jamie's absence.

Sometimes Susie Possum went into

the room where he lived. He would stretch up in his cage, almost on tiptoe, watching her. He was very curious about her but didn't want her to come near. He would scold her with a noisy *brrrrrrrr!* as she ambled past. All chickarees are good at scolding other animals, especially any that come near the midden. They grind their teeth and jerk their tails. They stamp their tiny feet, chirp and scream and jeer.

People who have observed chickarees closely know that as a family they seem to have a gentle affection

for one another. In a litter of young (sometimes as many as seven or eight), there seems to be a close "family feeling." Though they are quarrelsome by nature, they never seem to quarrel with one another. They nestle together fondly. If one leaves the nest to look at the world, the others seem worried and restless until he is safely back again.

Little Bit seemed to consider Jamie his "family." When she tried to release him, he would not go. We thought he would make a home in one of our trees. But instead he kept coming back and clinging to the screen, whimpering

to be let in. At last Jamie decided to let him stay. She feared he would die if she did not.

Little Bit lived almost seven years. As he grew older, his little face grayed around the muzzle, like the face of an old dog. He became very grouchy and seemed to grow stiff in his joints, as if he had rheumatism.

In his old age he still whistled for Jamie. But his *whist!* was less strong and shrill now. Sometimes when a raccoon climbed the tree outside his door at night or a possum paced across the patio in the dark, he did not give even a small alarm. But he still wanted Jamie to reach in and pet him. He sniffed happily when she put cologne on her fingers, for all squirrels like flower scents.

He was a "little old man" now. His strength was failing. One morning when she heard no sound from him, she found him lying quiet in his bed. He had died in his sleep.

The other day she told me, "I buried him in the garden nearly three years ago. But sometimes I find I'm still listening for his alarm call and his little whistle."

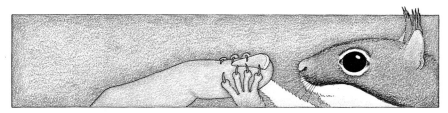

CHECK FOR UNDERSTANDING

1. How did Little Bit come to live at the Kellners' house?
2. Why do you think Jamie named the squirrel "Little Bit"?
3. How do chickarees in the wild feel about the other members of their family?
4. Why did Little Bit refuse to go when the Kellners tried to release him?
5. Why does Esther Kellner believe that the animals she cares for should be returned to the wild?
6. Do you think the Kellners enjoyed having wild animal visitors in their home? Explain your answer.

WRITE ABOUT *"Little Bit, the Chickaree Squirrel"*

Imagine that Jamie's class at school was studying animals that store food. Jamie was asked to give an oral report on Little Bit and his midden. Write a report for Jamie. In the report you should describe the midden and explain how Little Bit uses the midden.

STUDY SKILLS

PARTS OF A BOOK

Amelia was visiting her cousin Victor in Phelpsburg. It was the first time Amelia had ever been to Phelpsburg, and she was eager to see the sights.

"I have to work this morning," said Victor, "but don't wait around for me. Why don't you go to the zoo instead? You can walk there from here, and afterward you might want to stop at the Science Museum. It's only a block from the zoo."

Amelia started briskly down the street. Then all of a sudden she stopped. Where was she going? Victor had forgotten to give her directions. She didn't even have a map of the city. She had no idea how to find the zoo or the museum. In fact, she was lost.

There are many ways of getting lost. Like Amelia, you might someday find yourself in a strange city without a map. Or you might start building a motor and then discover that you don't know what to do next. You need additional instructions. You might even lose your way in a book, uncertain where to look for the information you need.

Fortunately, books usually have directions built into them. Both the **table of contents,** at the front of a book, and the **index,** at the back of a book, tell you where to find things in the book.

354

The table of contents names all the parts, units, and chapters in the book and shows what page each one starts on. For example, part of the table of contents of a language arts book might look like this:

Sometimes the table of contents tells you a little bit about the content of each chapter:

If you wanted to see whether there is a reading selection in every chapter, or if you wanted to find out where Chapter 4 begins, you would turn to the table of contents. You might also look quickly through the table of contents to get a general idea of what the book is about.

The index contains some of the same information as the table of contents, but it is arranged differently. Instead of listing the chapter titles in order of appearance, the index lists all the topics and subtopics in alphabetical order. As a result, you might find a topic that is discussed in Chapter 1 directly after a topic that is discussed in Chapter 4. Here is a section of the index for the language arts book whose table of contents you just saw.

Vague words, 78-79, 91

Verbs, 30-32, 34-36, 38-40, 52, 59, 67
   action, 34-36
   in predicate, 30, 31, 55
   of being, 38-40

Vestry, William, 24

Voices, 17

In the index, every page that has something about verbs on it is listed under the topic *Verbs*. In addition, three subtopics of *Verbs* are shown. If you are looking for information just about action verbs or just about verbs of being, you can locate it easily. The index also lists the titles of reading selections and the names of the authors of those selections.

Looking at the index will not give you a very clear idea of what the book is about or how many chapters it contains or how long the chapters are. The index will, however, show you exactly what topics and subtopics are covered and on what pages each one is discussed. When you are trying to find a specific piece of information, it is usually better to consult the index rather than the table of contents.

The table of contents and index will help you find your way around a book. Sometimes, though, maps of this sort are not enough. A map, for example, might help Amelia get to the zoo and even locate the gorilla house once she were there, but it would not give her information about the gorillas. If Amelia wanted to know where gorillas come from, what they eat, or what their scientific name is, she might look at the sign next to the exhibit. There might even be a booklet provided by the zoo that would give her this extra information.

Many books—especially textbooks—also provide additional information for their readers. Two places to look or material that will add to your understanding of a book are the **glossary** and the **appendix**. Both are located at the end of the book.

The glossary contains a list, in alphabetical order, of new or unusual vocabulary words that are used in the book. Here is a sample from a language arts textbook:

---

synonym   A word that means the same or nearly the same as another word.

tense   The time—past, present, or future— shown by a verb. (See also Future tense, Past tense, Present tense.)

verb   A word that shows mental or physical action. It is the main word in the predicate of a sentence.

verb phrase   A main verb together with all its helping verbs.

Notice that each word or term listed in the glossary is followed by its definition. Sometimes, too, there is an instruction to "see also" other words or terms that are related. For instance, for more information about tense, you could look up *future tense*, *past tense*, and *present tense*. Some glossaries also include a pronunciation respelling to tell you how to pronounce each word.

In the appendix, you will find information that is not absolutely necessary in order for you to understand the book but that adds to your understanding. This information can take many forms— charts, tables, graphs, maps, or even additional text.

In a social studies book, for example, you might read about each of the presidents of the United States. The material about them would probably not be all in one place. Other events would be discussed in between the election of Thomas Jefferson and the election of James Madison.

In the appendix, however, you might find a list of all the presidents of the United States, with the dates that each one was born and died, the political party each one belonged to, and the dates served as president:

George Washington (1732-1799)	No Party	1789-1797
John Adams (1735-1826)	Federalist	1797-1801
Thomas Jefferson (1743-1826)	Republican	1801-1805 1805-1809
James Madison (1751-1836)	Republican	1809-1813 1813-1817

You could understand the text without looking at the appendix. This material in the appendix would increase your understanding and appreciation of the text, though. It summarizes information and puts it into a form that makes certain facts stand out visually.

Using What You Have Learned

A. Which part of a book would you turn to—the table of contents, the index, the glossary, or the appendix—to find the answer to each of the following questions?

    1. Is there a reading selection by Paule Marshall in this book?

2. How many chapters contain information about America before the American Revolution?
3. What is the complete text of the Declaration of Independence like?
4. What does the term *predicate noun* mean?
5. What is Unit Three of this book about?
6. What information about imperative sentences does this book contain?
7. What does the word *judicial* mean?
8. What is the capital of each state in the United States of America, and when did each one become a state?
9. Does this book teach students much about writing?
10. On what page does the poem "Bridges" appear?

B. Find a book in the library or in your classroom that has an appendix. Report to the class on what the appendix contains. Describe how the material in it is related to the rest of the book. Suggest one more item that could be added to this appendix.

Expanding Your Skills

Find a book in the library or in your classroom that does not have one of these parts:

index   table of contents
glossary   appendix

Make up a sample of the missing part. Your sample should be long enough to show what the whole book part would look like. You might want to use an index, table of contents, glossary, or appendix from another book as a model.

Horse Sense

by LYNN HALL

If you have ever tried to train an animal, you know it is not an easy task. It takes patience and hard work, especially if the animal is determined not to cooperate. In this story, Megan finds that training the new horse, Berry, is more challenging than she expected.

What is the first thing Megan must teach Berry? How does Megan go about training Berry?

I waited for the baggage handler to lead her down the ramp. The mare put one foot on the wooden ramp. Then she backed away from it, terrified. He urged, she balked. The more he urged, the more grimly the little red mare refused.

I was about to come up the ramp myself, to see if I could lead her down, when the mare made her own decision. She lowered her head and backed swiftly into the shadows of the car. Then she burst out toward me, clattering, leaping out into the air and landing wide-eyed and wide-legged on the ground. Her feet hadn't touched the ramp.

Instinctively I grabbed the rope before she had time to collect her wits and bolt away. "There now," I soothed her with my voice. "Don't you feel like a fool, behaving that way? Never mind, we'll teach you. Come along then. We'll go home."

I signed the delivery receipt and led the little horse out onto the road toward home. When we were out of sight of the station, and anyone who might tell Dad, I jumped onto the mare's back and settled in for the ride home. I remembered Dad's instructions to lead her home. But it went against every fiber of my being, every instinct in my nature, to lead a horse for two miles when there was that lovely glossy back just waiting for me.

She went along quietly for me. She seemed worn out by the tension of the train journey, and walked along calmly, nodding her head in rhythm with her step and letting her ears relax.

I relaxed, too, and stroked the sunset-pink neck and thought about the mare. Berry, her name was. Dad had

said last night that she was a five-year-old, half-thoroughbred, half-New Forest pony. As I studied her, I could almost read her pedigree in the lines of her body. Her head and neck showed a thoroughbred elegance. But her body was short-coupled and her legs a bit more sturdy than a thoroughbred's. And her size, not much more than thirteen hands, was pure New Forest.

Her size was a bit of good luck for me. She was too small to carry Dad. She was even too small for Mum to ride comfortably. Mum stood close to six feet tall and felt out of place on any horse less than a sixteen-hand hunter.

And so, I figured, Berry would be mine to work with. I loved her already. I loved her beauty, her silveryrose color, her miniature-thoroughbred elegance. But then I found something to love about almost all of the horses that passed through my life.

About a mile from home, we came to a bridge across a narrow stream. It was an old arching stone bridge, earth-floored, with grass growing along the edges. As we approached, I debated whether to try to ride her across the bridge and risk having her balk, or to ride off the road and wade her across the stream. Attempting the bridge would be dangerous, not because I might be thrown but because I was not prepared to force her across if she should refuse. I had no whip or stick or spurs. There was no bit in her mouth, nothing but the halter and lead rope. Very poor controls with which to go into battle with a stubborn horse.

One of Dad's firmest rules in training horses was that we must never allow the horse to get the better of us. Never give a command unless we were in a position to enforce it. Never allow a horse to feel that he was boss. I knew that if I rode Berry at the bridge and she refused

🐎 363

to cross it, I would be unable to force her across. She would have won the battle. This would prove to her that she was dominant over me. I should never be able to train her properly after that, because she would not respect me.

So, reluctantly, because I was curious to know if I could have ridden her over the bridge, I turned off the road, and we splashed through the stream.

Just before home came into view I slipped down from Berry's back. I brushed her hairs from my trouser legs and led her sedately into the farmyard.

Dad was schooling a young hunter over the jumps in the low meadow. Mum and the veterinarian had their heads together over old Terrance, who had chronic foot problems. He was past thirty and had belonged to Mum ever since she was my age.

I put Berry in an empty stall and brought her food and water. Then I stood outside the stall door with the sun on my back, watching her.

Our stable was a long, L-shaped building with each stall opening directly onto the cobblestone yard. Our house formed the third side of the square. It was quite old, four or five hundred years in parts. It was a dear old place, made of dressed flint and dark timbers and creamy plaster, with vines that grew all the way to the roof tiles in places. Now and then Mum tried to grow flowers in the side gardens. But she was more interested in the horses than in weeding flower beds, and it seldom came to anything. Once when I was ill, Mum turned Tiger loose in the side garden so that I could pet him through my window. The flower beds were never quite the same after that. Tiger could eat the blossoms off a rose so neatly that no thorn ever touched his lips.

Eventually the veterinarian drove away. Dad brought his hunter in from the jumps, and he and Mum came to see Berry.

"Bit small, isn't she?" Dad said, frowning.

"Not for some people," I chirped. He gave me a wry look.

Mum said, "Did she lead home all right, Megan?"

"She didn't give me a bit of trouble." I saw Mum twisting her head back to look at the seat of my pants.

Then she raised her eyebrow at me. I turned slightly away from her too-knowing eyes and went on.

"She didn't want to come down the ramp from the baggage car, though. Seemed to be afraid of it. Finally she took a run at it and jumped all the way to the ground. Missed the ramp completely."

Dad said, "Hmm," and nodded. "She's a smart little thing, I've no doubt. These thoroughbred-pony crossbreds are like that sometimes. They've got the sensitivity of the thoroughbred and the wiliness of a pony. They can be tough as nails to train, these smart ones. They challenge you every step of the way. They watch for any sign of weakness on your part, and then they take advantage. But if you can master them, ah, then you have something. Spirit and brains and heart and sensitivity."

"Will you let me work with her?" I asked.

Dad snorted. "I expect I'll have to. Your mum and I, either one, would be too heavy for that fine-boned little frame. But you're not to ride her until I can be there to give you a hand. I won't have you taking chances with her, understand?"

Meekly I nodded and turned my horse-marked trousers to the stable wall.

That evening we turned Berry out in the small meadow behind the house. There she could stretch her legs and relax and graze.

Next morning at breakfast Dad said, "I'm going to work Grahame over the jumps for a bit, Megan. Then we'll have a go at the little roan mare. You can be getting her caught up and groomed. See if there's a bridle to fit her. Let's try a mullen-mouth pelham bit first."

"Spot on, chief," I said, and scraped up the last of my porridge on my way to the sink. I ran out the back way and across the wild-grown back garden to the low stone wall of the meadow. Berry was grazing a little distance away.

I called and she ignored me. Understandable enough.

I climbed the wall and approached her. She watched, calmly, until I was close. Then she turned and trotted away.

All right, still understandable. I pulled up a handful of grass and followed her, offering the grass.

Again she watched until I drew near, then moved away.

She was playing games with me. I knew it and she knew it. She had the run of a lush meadow, and she had no desire to be caught and ridden. I knew that if I ran after her, she would gallop away faster than I could run. I also knew that if I gave up and let her win, I would never be her master. I ran to the stable for a pan of oats and came back, determined to get her.

She looked at the oats, and she looked at me. Suddenly I had the feeling that she was laughing at me, at my transparent attempt to bribe her into captivity with oats.

She turned and strolled away.

I followed.

Around and across the meadow we walked. When I stopped, Berry stopped, too, and put down her head to graze. But when I came closer than two or three yards, we were off again, walking, she with calm amusement, I with grim patience.

Dad appeared at the wall and watched for a while.

"That's it," he called. "You can outlast her. I'll go lunge the yearlings for a bit. Give me a call when you're ready to ride."

I nodded at him and muttered, "If we haven't both died of old age before then."

The morning passed. The sun grew hot. My shirt stuck to my back. My legs grew wobbly weak. I hoped the mare was as uncomfortable as I was, but she appeared to be enjoying our four-hour stroll back and forth, 'round and 'round the small meadow.

Some time around midday Mum brought me a sandwich and a jug of cold water. I ate and drank, and trudged on.

"Keep it up," Mum cheered from her cool seat on the shady wall. "She's bound to give in sooner or later."

It was past two o'clock when Berry finally stopped and stood and allowed me to come up to her. I gripped her halter. We looked long and hard at one another. The challenge was still there in her eyes. Faking affection I was far from feeling at this point, I crooned to her and rubbed her neck and praised her. I led her to the pan of oats and gave her a few bites.

Then I turned her loose.

Mum and Dad were both watching from the wall by this time. Mum called, "What did you let her loose for, you goose? You just spent six hours catching her."

But Dad understood. "Good show, Meg," he called.

As soon as I was old enough to listen, but still too young to understand much of what he said, Dad talked to me about training horses. I think he liked to hear his theories voiced, and I was his only audience. Mum had her own theories and would get impatient at having to listen to his.

I didn't always understand what he told me. But one thing he said, early on in our talks, did stay with me. Think like the horse thinks, he told me. You've got to put yourself inside that animal's brain. See things the way he sees them and *then* outfox him.

So today I thought as Berry would think. If being caught always led to being ridden, then being caught was to be avoided. But if being caught meant praise and petting and a snack of oats, and then freedom again, all good things and no bad things, then being caught was not something to be avoided after all.

Berry walked away from me. I forced my aching legs to follow her. This time it took less than an hour to catch her. Again she was praised and given oats. Again she was released.

I rolled into the long cool grass under a tree. I dozed and rested while Berry grazed nearby. When I felt ready, I got up, walked to her, and caught hold of her halter. It might have been my imagination, but this time her eyes seemed to glow more softly, with perhaps even a glimmer of respect.

CHECK FOR UNDERSTANDING

1. On the way home from the station, why did Megan decide not to ride Berry over the bridge?
2. Why was Megan quite certain that she would get to train Berry?
3. What was the first thing Megan had to teach Berry?
4. How did Megan go about training Berry? How did she try to think?
5. Why did Megan's father approve of the way she was training Berry?
6. Do you think "Horse Sense" is a good title for this story? Explain your answer.

WRITE ABOUT *"Horse Sense"*

Imagine that Berry, not Megan, were telling this story. What thoughts might Berry have had during the training session? Write about Berry's first day with Megan as Berry might have told the story. Describe the day from the horse's point of view.

Riding Lesson

by HENRY TAYLOR

I learned two things
from an early riding teacher.
He held a nervous filly
in one hand and gestured
with the other, saying, "Listen.
Keep one leg on one side,
the other leg on the other side,
and your mind in the middle."

He turned and mounted.
She took two steps, then left
the ground, I thought for good.
But she came down hard, humped
her back, swallowed her neck,
and threw her rider as you'd
throw a rock. He rose, brushed
his pants and caught his breath,
and said, "See, that's the way
to do it. When you see
they're gonna throw you, get off."

371

COMPREHENSION

Important Details

When you read for pleasure, your purpose for reading is different from your purpose when you read for information. Your method of reading and your reading rate are different. What are important details for you to understand and remember are also different.

When you read "Horse Sense," you probably did not know what a *mullen-mouth pelham bit* was. Not knowing what kind of bit Megan's dad suggested she try did not prevent you from understanding what was happening at that point in the story. The important thing to understand about her dad's instructions was simply that they *were* instructions. He was telling her how to begin training Berry.

Later Dad comes by the meadow to see how Megan and Berry are doing. He calls out encouragement to Megan and then tells her he is going to "lunge the yearlings for a bit." In this case, too, not knowing what it meant to lunge horses did not keep you from understanding what was going on. Dad had other tasks to do, but he would be back later.

The story "Horse Sense" took place in England. The family in the story were "horse people." They raised horses; they trained horses; they had a great deal of knowledge about horses. The author of "Horse Sense" used terms that have to do with raising horses and expressions used in England to make the characters in the story more convincing and realistic. If you were not sure exactly what every term and expression meant when you were reading, it did not prevent you from understanding and enjoying the story.

When you are reading for information the details you must understand and remember are different. If you were reading a book on training horses, and the book said you should use a mullen-mouth pelham bit for a certain purpose, it would be important for you to find out exactly what kind of bit that was. Even when you are reading for information, the details that are important to you may vary because the kind of information you need may be different.

Read these paragraphs about Joan Embery, the Goodwill Ambassador for the San Diego Zoo. What different kinds of information can you get from these paragraphs?

Joan Embery began working part-time at the Children's Zoo while she was still in college. For Joan, the Children's Zoo was a great place to start. It gave her a chance to work with wild animals. Because the animals were young, they were easier to handle.

According to Joan the best way to learn to handle wild animals is to spend time with them. Time and experience teaches you how animals behave and what to expect from them. Wild animals are easily frightened and are sensitive to stress. They move quickly and can be difficult to control. Young animals are easier to handle because their instinct for survival is not totally developed. Working with young animals in the Children's Zoo was an excellent way to learn and gain experience.

Which details would be most important to you if you were reading to get information about careers that involved working with animals? Which details would be important if you wanted information about handling wild animals?

In "The Comeback Dog," Lady ran away and came back after she had tangled with a porcupine. In this story, Joe's cat, Lily Black, wanders off and gets lost.

How does Joe find his cat? What problem bothers Joe when he has Lily Black back again?

Whose Cat?

by ELIZABETH PARSONS

Every summer Joe and his family went to Maine. Their cat, Lily Black, went with them. In Maine, Lily Black was free to roam. But late one summer, Lily Black wandered too far. When it was time to leave, Joe and his parents could not find her.

That winter, Lily Black had to survive on her own, until an old lobsterman found her and took her in. He fed her and talked to her and grew very fond of her. He even took her out with him on his boat.

When summer returned, so did Joe and his family. They hoped that Lily Black was still alive and that they would find her.

374

Joe and his family had come back the week before. It was a real homecoming for them, seeing everything again. They looked up their old friends and opened the house, sweeping up the thousands of dead flies and letting the warm wind blow through the rooms. They bought paint and new flashlight batteries and seeds. They planted the vegetable garden and the little flowerbed.

One thing they often mentioned as they went about these familiar chores: they still had the idea that perhaps Lily Black was alive and that she'd know they were there now, and when she got good and ready, she'd come back.

"If she's anywhere around, I *know* she'll know we're back," Joe told himself every day, very determined.

He painted his punt—a good bright orange outside and blue-green inside—and launched her. The first day he took her out he rowed so far he got terrible blisters on the insides of his thumbs. He went for a row every day, happy to be out on the water again. The wonderful thing was to come back year after year and find things just as he remembered them. The colors and the smells and the big landscape were always the same. His old clothes and books and treasures were right where he'd left them. The smells were the best, after the city—the woods and the sea and the clam flats, and the creosote on the shingles of your house on a hot sunny day. Then there was the rain-spout splashing into the rain barrel outside your window when you were going to sleep on a stormy night. It had been best when Lily Black had been curled up beside him, dry and warm and safe, just as he was.

Only this year there was no little cat. But Joe refused to give up hoping.

Generally, in the morning, if the tide was right and The Basin was brimming with the water that rushed in from the sea through the narrow entrance, he would make the round of his favorite places. He would maneuver through tiny passages where he had to pole his way along with an oar. Sometimes he would go ashore on some bare little island and lie for a while in the prickly grass. There was one with a beach of real sand, about as big as his bedroom on the hill, between two high rocks. He would have a swim there. He had made his parents a promise about swimming. "You can go in alone," Pa told him. "Just as long as you can put one toe on the bottom—no deeper." He was very good about sticking to that rule.

One morning, when he was rowing along, he noticed a small lobster boat he hadn't seen in The Basin before. It was going from buoy to buoy in a leisurely way. Pretty soon their paths began to cross. When they were quite close the bigger boat stopped while its owner bent over and caught hold of the trap he had just hauled up. Joe was admiring the boat's pretty lines and fresh gray paint when he saw something so peculiar, so ridiculous, that he stopped rowing to have a good look. What he was seeing was a little black and white cat, sitting bolt upright on the stern deck.

"Lily!" he shouted, without even thinking. "Lily! Lily Black!"

The little cat stood up at that and stared right at him. Joe rowed up alongside, hardly able to believe his eyes, and yet—and yet! *Could* it be Lily? Could it possibly be, sitting there on a strange boat, of all places? The old fisherman, whose back had been turned, but who had

heard Joe call out, now heard him say, "That *is* you, Lily! I know that's you! I knew you'd turn up—I knew it!" He looked around at the boy whose red head was not much above the deck of the *Lettie V.*

Joe was so excited that he forgot everything. All he wanted to do was grab up his cat and row away as fast as he could.

"That's my cat!" he said rudely, in his excitement, to the old man. "We lost her last summer, just when we were leaving. I mean, she disappeared when we were leaving. I know that's her!"

The old man took his time about all this. "Good mornin'," he said, as though nothing peculiar was going on. "I've seen you before. Live up on the hill, summers, don't you?"

"Yes, we do," said Joe. The old man's calmness made him remember his own manners. He set his oars down along the thwarts, very businesslike, and stood up. Holding on with one hand to the *Lettie V.*'s rail, he reached out the other one to Lily Black. *Then* Lily came up to him, purring. She licked his hand and nudged it hard with her head, waving her tail to and fro.

"Well, I guess she knows you, all right," said the old man, looking at the two of them wonderingly. "She came way over to my place, on the Point." He jerked his head in the direction of his fish house. "She turned up there early last winter, and I took her in. She's a real nice little cat. I'm glad you got her back."

But he wasn't a hundred percent glad. He had never really expected to lose her, certainly not this way. He was caught by surprise, and it was a hard thing to bear—but he *was* going to lose her, right there and then, without any warning at all.

Joe was petting Lily Black, and she was remembering—what? Who knows, but *something,* something from a long time back.

Then the old man said, and his voice sounded not at all right to himself, "There, you take her now. Take her home. Go along with you, Miss Kitty. Be a good girl and don't you go strayin' off again." And in one second he had caught her up, handed her to Joe, and pushed the punt away out of reach with a great shove. In fact, Joe nearly fell overboard with Lily in his arms, and he sat down quickly.

Lily Black hopped up where she could see everything. Suddenly she realized that she was being parted from her good old friend. She looked from one human face to the other in some puzzled cat distress, while the distance between the boats slowly grew wider and wider. She seemed so troubled that for a minute Joe thought she would jump overboard and swim back to the *Lettie V.* Luckily she didn't.

"So long," the old man said, and Joe answered, "So long." Later he remembered he hadn't even said thank you.

The old man started up his engine and went off to his next trap. "Better so," he told himself. "She ought to be where she belongs, where she'll be taken care of properly. One of these days I may not be around to look after her at all. But I'll miss her, yes I will."

He decided not to bother to haul any more that day, but to go on home. He didn't even stop at the fish house. He didn't feel like seeing the empty dishes on the floor by the stove or the hollow place worn in the gravel near the door where his little cat had loved to scratch and roll.

Joe rowed home fast, talking all the time to Lily Black, who sat facing him. She never took her eyes off his face. When they got ashore, she scampered up the path ahead of him to the house with her tail in the air. She knew perfectly well where she was.

Of course, there was a great reunion. Never had Lily had so much loving in her life, or so much food all at once. Her family was so excited they kept interrupting each other. They hardly gave Joe a chance to tell about the old man and his boat, and how Lily had stayed with him all winter and how much he loved her. But they finally got the story straight. Meantime Lily was stuffing herself

with all kinds of good things that Joe had put down for her. After that she went padding all around the house looking at everything. They could hear her in the next room, her paws pattering lightly in a single-foot beat. After she had satisfied herself that things were as they should be, she spread herself out on Joe's bed, washed her face and paws, and went to sleep, as though she hadn't been away at all.

"You see?" said Pa, as he walked by the door and saw her in there. "Just what I always said. We run a first-class hotel for Miss Lily Black." He laughed as he said it.

Joe, during the next few days, was bothered about something. The old fisherman had taken care of Lily Black all winter—wonderful care. Perhaps she really belonged to *him*. He had hated to part with her. Joe could tell from the abrupt way he'd done it. Wasn't the old man feeling now the way he himself had felt last fall when Lily dis-appeared? He brooded about it a lot. He didn't tell any-body, but he made a plan.

This is what he did. He kept track of the days when the *Lettie V.* came into The Basin. Then he began going out himself in the punt on those days. He and the old man would wave to one another, very formally, from a distance. After a while they brought their boats together and got to talking, mostly about Lily, but about other things, too. They became good friends. Oddly enough, the old man didn't have a single grandson. He had five granddaughters. He doted on them, but in his heart he always wished he had had a grandson, a small boy in the family hanging around. He began to take a shine to Joe. He was always glad to see the bright-colored punt and its red-haired oarsman coming out to waylay him. Sometimes he gave him a few lobsters to take home. You can imagine who got her share.

Then one morning Joe took Lily Black out with him. The old man was as pleased as Punch to see her and invited them both on board. They sat peacefully together while the *Lettie V.* drifted at a snail's pace up The Basin on the flood tide, with Joe's punt trailing astern and Lily sitting in her regular place on the afterdeck.

From then on, they went out quite often.

For a while Joe was too shy, and also too scared, to speak to his friend about his worry. At last he did, the week before he was going to leave. Mother was already throwing out sneakers and bathing suits that wouldn't last another summer. Everybody was feeling disrupted and cranky.

On this particular day, one of the last ones, Joe and Lily Black were sitting on the deck of the *Lettie V.* They were all a little subdued. You could tell it was the end of summer by the difference in the light along the shore—now it was pale and hazy.

Joe said quickly, before he really knew he was going to speak, although he had rehearsed the words to himself a hundred times, "I don't feel right about taking Lily away from you." There! He had said it.

"Why not?" said the old man, astonished. "She's your cat, isn't she?"

"Well, she's your cat, too, sort of," Joe said. "Maybe *you* should keep her, not me. You saved her life. Why shouldn't she be yours?" But he felt so miserable he barely finished that last sentence. His hand went out to Lily Black's head.

"Now you listen to me," the old man said. "She's not my cat at all. No question about it. I may have made her winter a little easier. By good luck you and I met up, and so she got home safe and sound. Don't you think another thing about it. You take her back to the city where she'll be safe and comfortable, just the way she used to be. When you come back next summer, you can bring her out to say hello to me."

"All right, if you say so," Joe answered. "But you take her home with you for a visit *now*, before we leave. And every summer you ought to have her for a while. Then she'll belong to both of us."

The old man shook his head, smiling. "Oh, no," he said. "No, I wouldn't want to do that, Joe. I'd like to see her out here with you once in a while, that's all."

384

They stopped talking then. Lily turned her back on them and watched the gulls that floated around them. Joe stared at the worn cloth cap the old man was holding loosely in his big hand. The old man looked at Lily and appeared to be about to say something, but he kept still. This was the first time in Joe's life that it had occurred to him that grown-up people—*old* people—can be as miserable as children can be. This discovery was something he never forgot. He saw, then, that it was time to leave. He pulled the punt up alongside and jumped in and called to Lily Black. Undecided for a minute, she only turned her head to him. To go or to stay, she seemed to be asking. Joe had to reach over, pick her up, and set her down in the small boat. She was stiff in his arms, not resisting, but not happy either. She got up on the stern thwart and sat there with her tail curled around her front feet.

"So long," Joe said to the old man, taking up his oars. "And I sure want to thank you." The old man didn't answer, but he raised his right hand in a little gesture that might have been "Good-by," or "Farewell." He started his engine and then remarked, kind of absent-mindedly, "You could paint that punt before you leave—then she'd be all ready for you next summer. Haul her out tomorrow, so she'll dry out good first." So it was really good-by. He didn't want to see them again that year.

He turned away, and the *Lettie V.* moved off. All the gulls rose, crying and very white in the sunlight, to follow her.

Joe set out for home, slowly, watching over his shoulder as the big boat's wake spread out wider and wider on

the calm water. He started to say something to Lily about the old man, but she was looking fixedly ahead at the great granite ledges and the familiar woods, for she was getting hungry. Anyway, he didn't feel like talking, even to her. He just rowed home.

CHECK FOR UNDERSTANDING

1. How did Joe find his cat?
2. How did the old man feel about giving the cat back to Joe? Explain how you know this.
3. What problem bothered Joe when he had Lily Black back again?
4. Why was Joe afraid to tell the old man that he didn't feel right about keeping Lily Black?
5. What discovery did Joe make about grown-ups?
6. Who do you think should have Lily Black—Joe or the old man? Explain your reasons.

WRITE ABOUT *"Whose Cat?"*

Many people keep journals in which they write about things that happen to them and things they think about. Imagine that you are Mr. Henry, the old man in the story. Pretend that you are writing in your journal about the day you gave Lily Black back to Joe. Explain what happened and how you felt about giving up the cat.

The Returning Cats

Lily Black wandered away when Joe and his family were in Maine. They didn't find her again until the next summer, when they returned to Maine. This article tells about cats that found their way back to their owners after being lost far away from home. One of these cats is named Jingles.

How far did Jingles travel to reach home? What do some animal experts compare the "homing instincts" of cats to?

In the autumn of 1968, a woman in the suburbs of a large Midwestern city heard scratching sounds at her front door. Puzzled, she went to the door. She opened it slowly, and after a few seconds exclaimed, "Jingles!"

Jingles was the family's black-and-white cat. The woman could scarcely believe her eyes. Jingles had been lost for more than four weeks—ever since the family had missed the cat while on vacation at a lake resort nearly 300 miles away. When, at the end of the vacation, the cat had not shown up, they had had to leave without him.

At first the woman thought she must be mistaken. The cat *looked* like Jingles, but its fur was so matted and dirty that it was hard to tell. Also, one of its ears was torn and there were patches of dried blood on its back. But when the woman saw the grimy white star on the cat's black chest, she knew it must be Jingles.

The woman took Jingles into

387

the bathroom and cleaned him up as best she could. Then she fed him. Except for his torn ear and a slight limp from a cut on one of his legs, Jingles seemed to be in reasonably good shape after his ordeal.

Around the dinner table that night, the family talked about what poor Jingles must have gone through. How had the cat managed to stay alive for all those days and miles? How had it found food? How had the animal known in which direction the city lay? Once he had reached it, how had he made his way through the busy streets to the correct suburb and his home? The lake resort was so isolated. Twisting, confusing roads led to it. Jingles must have had to travel long miles through fields and woods on his way back. There were also several small rivers that the cat must have had to swim across.

As the family shook their heads over these mysteries, Jingles purred happily on the sofa. Already he seemed to have forgotten his terrible experience. He was content simply to be back with the people he loved.

This story is not an unusual one. Cat owners all over the world have reported similar cases of their pets traveling long distances, overcoming tremendous obstacles, to find their way back to their homes. One cat returned from New Jersey to Brooklyn. It must have had to cross the Hudson and East rivers. Whether it used bridges or swam, no one will ever know. Yet it reached home safely. Another cat was lost in the Arizona desert.

Somehow it made its way across the sandy wasteland to its home in Phoenix—more than 100 miles away.

Some animal experts have compared this amazing ability of cats to that of homing pigeons. But there is one big difference. Pigeons must be trained by their owners to return. Each training period, they are taken farther and farther from their homes, until they have learned to fly back over great distances. But cats are given no such training. They just seem to *know* the way back.

Does this "homing instinct" have something to do with cats' keen sense of smell? It doesn't seem likely. Even for cats, the smells of home would be too far off for them to sniff their way back. One scientist has suggested that homing pigeons—and perhaps cats as well—somehow use the earth's magnetic field to guide them. But the scientist does not explain how this actually happens. There is also a theory that the cats' strong sense of belonging to certain people and to a certain place somehow furnishes them with a special gift for knowing just how to return to those people and that place. It is still a mystery.

CHECK FOR UNDERSTANDING

1. How far did Jingles travel to reach home?
2. What obstacles did Jingles have to overcome during his journey?
3. How might Jingles have solved those problems?
4. What do some animal experts compare the "homing instincts" of cats to? Why is this comparison not entirely accurate?

Elements of Plot

A story is like a vehicle that takes you on a journey. The journey begins with the first word of the story and ends with the last word. On this journey, the "scenery" consists of all the people and events along the way.

The theme of the story is a bit like the engine of this vehicle. It is out of sight and not part of the scenery, but you couldn't make the trip without it. The plot is like the road your vehicle is traveling on. It is the path taken from one character and event to another.

For your trip through a story to be interesting, the plot has to have certain features. First a story must have characters. The characters do not have to be people. They could be a dog and a cow. Characters do not even have to be animals. A story can be about robots or a table and a chair or even two blades of grass. But whether the characters in a story are human or not, they must have the kind of *responses* human beings have. Down deep, a story is good to read because we can relate the things that happen in the story to our own lives.

In life, there are long periods of time in which things go smoothly and as usual. A story that deals with life as usual is not only boring, it is not really a story. The vehicle sits in one place with the engine idling. The plot of every story must have a conflict that causes a change. *Conflict* as part of a story plot does not mean a battle or an argument. It means something that makes it difficult to carry on life as usual. In "The Comeback Dog," for example, Lady causes a conflict in Daniel. He wants a dog to

replace the one he has lost, but the dog he gets is not his idea of a "good dog." A change has to take place for the conflict to end. Life as usual for Daniel was loving dogs. Lady caused a conflict in Daniel's life because she was hard for him to love.

Every conflict that is part of the plot has to have a resolution. A resolution is not just a happy ending. It is anything that makes the conflict go away so that things can return to life as usual. The resolution of "The Comeback Dog" is a happy ending. The conflict ends when Daniel changes. He stops expecting Lady to be like his first dog. After this change, the resolution comes when he takes care of Lady and begins to love her.

As you read "The Last Crow in Piney Woods," try to identify these elements of the plot. Decide who the main characters are and how they reveal feelings all human beings have. Decide what the conflict in the story is. Think about how the conflict might be resolved later in the book.

The
Cry of
the Crow

by Jean Craighead George

Just·A·Taste

The Last Crow in Piney Woods

Mandy lives in the Florida Everglades, at the edge of a forest called Piney Woods. In this story, Mandy adopts an unusual pet—a helpless baby crow that she names Nina Terrance.

Why is Nina Terrance the last crow in Piney Woods? How would the other members of Mandy's family react if they knew that Mandy had a pet crow?

The young crow huddled against her brother in their stick nest in Piney Woods. Her tail feathers were short and stubby; white plumes of down trimmed her head. Her milky-blue eyes were those of an eyas, a nestling bird yet unable to stand on her toes or fly. The pair sat rock still, for their parents were away.

The March dawn was hot and muggy. Insects buzzed around the nest, their glassy wings reflecting the red sunlight. The little female looked past them to a spider spinning her web almost a quarter of a mile away. Her eyes were like telescopes, and she practiced using them while she sat in the nest. Her brother slept, a black lump blending with the black sticks.

Footsteps sounded on the pine needles below and the eyas listened to their beat. *Crunch da dum.* She tensed, for she recognized the footfall of the crow hunter. Her parents had taught her a deep fear of this sound, "Ca! Ca! Ca! Ca!" they would cry at the sound, then pull their feathers against their bodies and crouch silently.

The footfall softened and died away.

Wide-awake now, the eyas heard her parents announce from the Glades that they were on their way home with food. Her ears were as keen as her eyesight. She could distinguish the sounds of her parents' voices from all the other crows of Piney Woods as well as from the clan of crows in Trumpet Hammock, a tree island in the saw grass of the Everglades, a swamp-like river that creeps slowly down the tip of Florida under warm sub-tropical skies.

As her parents flew home, the eyas listened for the voice of the Piney Woods guard crow. He had not warned of the *crunch da dum*, nor did he announce her parents. The forest was ominously quiet and had been ever since the crow hunters began shooting a few days ago.

With a rustle of feathers, her mother alighted on the edge of the nest.

"Ah ah ah, cowkle, cowkle," the eyas begged as she lay on her breast, trembling her wings and opening her beak. Her bill was rimmed with yellow edges. She could not yet eat by herself, for she was only ten days old, and since food had to be thrust in her mouth, the red-and-yellow coloring made it possible for her parents to find the gullet instantly. Her mother stuffed her with delicacies from the Everglades.

Her father arrived, his feathers glistening blue-black in the soft morning light. Her brother begged for food.

From below came a gun blast. Lead balls ripped through the stick nest. Another blast lifted the nest out of the tree. The young eyas gripped a stick as the nest splintered, cracked, then floated apart. She looked down through the pieces and saw the eye and brow of the hunter.

"I got youv," he shouted. The voice and eye were stamped forever on the young crow's mind.

Then she fell.

Mandy Tressel heard the gun blasts and rolled over in her bed, dragging the pillow down on her ears. She wondered who was shooting at the crows in Piney Woods this morning, her father or one of her big brothers, Jack and Carver. Drummer, her younger brother, was too young to be allowed to handle a gun.

The strawberry crop was coming on, and Mandy's father wanted every crow dead before they ate or damaged the valuable fruits.

The odor of gunsmoke trickled through her open window, and she got out of bed and looked out. The sun was beginning to light up the strawberry field that stretched from the backyard to the far end of Piney Woods. To the south of their small cinder-block house and the greenhouse, the banana patch grew. The big drooping leaves were motionless in the still air. Even the woman's-tongue tree in the yard, whose seed pods clattered in the slightest breeze, was quiet. The orange and fig trees were still. The buds of the red hibiscus were waiting for the sun before they bloomed. Mandy breathed deeply. The scent of the night-blooming jasmine bush was still on the air, although the flowers had closed with the dawn.

Mandy understood why her father wanted the crows killed, but nevertheless she felt sick each time she heard the deafening blasts.

Once, on a family picnic, she had played with a crow in the nearby Everglades National Park of Florida. She was exploring a trail when suddenly the bird alighted beside her and walked with her along the dark mangrove path. She stopped and held out a leaf. The crow jumped nimbly over it, then pecked it. It sat down when she sat down, backed up when she backed up. She realized the bird had come to her for a reason, and leaned down to hear its message. Then Jack called her. The crow listened to his voice.

"Ca! Ca! Ca! Ca!" it cried and stole off between the warped and twisted branches of the mangrove trees. For the entire afternoon she did not see or hear a crow.

The next morning Mandy asked her mother if crows could recognize hunters by their voices. Barbara suspected they did. "They are keen to danger," she said.

As Mandy dressed for school this day, she thought about that mysterious crow and wondered why he had walked with her. Fairy tales of animals who were princes came to mind, but nothing reasonable. She tramped thoughtfully downstairs. Her brothers were already gone; her mother, she could hear, was showering before going to work.

Mandy skipped out the door and ran through the yard to the

path beside the strawberry patch that led to Piney Woods. The sun was glittering on the pine needles, and she hummed as she swung through a half mile of forest to the golf course in Waterway Village, a cluster of one-story apartments where retired people lived. Barney, the surly dog, barked as she passed Mr. Hathaway's apartment. She stuck out her tongue at him, ran past the swimming pool, and came out on the road where the school bus stopped. The crows and wild things on her mind, she arrived at school in a daydream.

During study hall Mandy wrote a story in her red notebook. She labored hard, erasing and changing the words. Still she was not pleased with what she had written, and coming home through the woods, she stopped, reread her work, and changed two more words. A dragonfly spun around her head like a tiny bomber, and a zebra butterfly alighted on her shirt.

"Good omens," she said and hurried on.

As she came to the fork in the path that led to Trumpet Hammock, black feathers from some gunned-down crow swirled up from the ground. She paused and glanced around. Just off the path a sable palm tree grew. It had never been pruned, and its old dead leaves hung down like a skirt on a green-headed lollipop. She often came to the palm and crawled between the great drooped leaves. Within this natural tent she read and dreamed in privacy.

Mandy felt as if someone were staring at her. She pushed back a dry palm leaf and peered into the circular room. Almost at her feet, huddled against a leaf, sat the

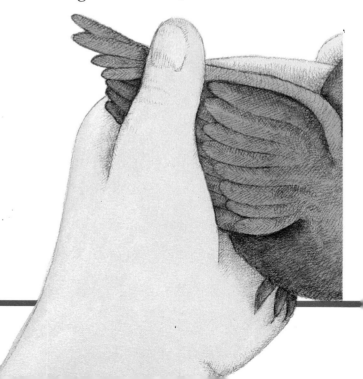

eyas, gazing up at her. The bird was frightened; her eyes were wide and her feathers were clamped tightly to her body.

"The last nest in Piney Woods," Mandy gasped. "Someone found it, and you're all that's left." She bit her lips together.

The eyas had been studying Mandy in the brief seconds while she peered into the shelter. She had read Mandy's personality through the soft curve of her spine, her curled fingers, and her gray eyes veiled with long lashes. These were readings to be trusted, and she relaxed as Mandy dipped to her knees.

"Oh, poor little bird," Mandy said.

"Ah ah ah, cowkle, cowkle," begged the eyas and fluttered her wings. Opening her mouth, lifting the feathers on her head to make herself round and appealing, she told Mandy very clearly that she was helpless and needed food. Mandy opened her lunch box and took out the crusts of her sandwich.

She held out the food. Once more the eyas fluttered and begged with open mouth. Mandy fed her the remainder of the bread, and when the eyas begged again, she wished she had not eaten all of her lunch. Recalling that crows like grubs and worms as well as fruits and grains, she walked into the forest, kicked open a rotted log, and found several beetle grubs. Creeping back under the great skirt of leaves, she fed the bird until she begged no more. Gently Mandy picked her up. The bird had already made her judgment of Mandy. She did not struggle, simply felt the warmth and softness and nestled down in her hands.

"I know you're a girl, so I'll name you Nina Terrance," she said, using the name she would have given herself if she had had a choice. Peering out into the woods to see if anyone was coming, she crawled behind the trunk into her "reading room." The air was cool in the shade of the huge shingles of leaves. Once her father had suggested to her brothers that they rip the old leaves off this sable palm as people do in gardens and along city streets, to make the palms neat and keep them fireproof, but no one had gotten around to it.

"This is your new home," she said to Nina Terrance, standing up in the cool, dark room. Several months ago she had pulled off a few of the inner dead leaves to enlarge the shelter so that she could stretch out and read. Now she had another construction job to do. Placing Nina Terrance on the ground, Mandy skillfully wove the fingers of a drooping leaf into a strong cup, then placed the eyas in it. The bird was about three feet off the ground and secure.

The eyas roused—lifted her feathers and shook them—to say that she was at ease in Mandy's presence and that she liked her. Having been taught by her parents to eat and remain still, she wiggled her stubby tail and sat down in her new nest.

Across the quiet forest came a call: "Ca! Ca! Ca! Ca!"—four sharp reports. The guard crow of Trumpet Hammock was speaking. Nina Terrance pulled in her neck and nestled low in the nest. She had recognized the alarm signal. This was one of about fifty "words" used by the well-organized and highly social crows. This call meant death and danger lurked somewhere nearby.

"What did he say?" Mandy asked the eyas. "Daddy says crows have a language. He says they can tell each other where the food is or where the enemy is. He says they can warn where death comes from. What did that crow say to make you crouch?"

Mandy dropped to her knees and stuck her head out of the palm tent. No one was coming that she could see, and yet the eyas crow had reacted as if hiding from an enemy.

"Ca! Ca! Ca! Ca!" Mandy hollered, trying to imitate the guard crow. Nina Terrance blinked her eyes as if she had not heard.

"Well, you sure don't know what *I'm* saying." She tried the call again, got no response, and gave up. She stroked the downy head.

"I need practice to pronounce whatever I'm saying in crow talk," she said. "Now don't you move 'til I come." Mandy crawled to the exit and, looking both ways, hurried to find her books on the trail. At the edge of Piney Woods, she glanced out across the miles of saw grass that grew in the low water of the Everglades. They plunged and leaped, then Drummer appeared.

"Hey," Mandy exclaimed, happy to see her youngest brother. "Where've you been?"

"Explorin'," he said and Mandy chuckled. Drummer loved the Glades. In this swampy wilderness, he pretended he was the great Seminole Indian Chief Osceola out hunting for his tribe. He threw reed spears at alligators and pounced on frogs.

She glanced back toward the sable palm tree to make certain that Nina Terrance was not following, then walked down the path to the house with Drummer. Mandy swung the gate open and Drummer pushed ahead. Jack and Carver were in the driveway hunched over the engine of their foreign car.

"Hi!" Mandy called to her older brothers. They did not answer, so she walked closer.

"I have something for you," she said.

"I think it's the distributor," Jack said to Carver. "We need a new one. Time to put out another issue of *The Waterway Times*."

"Guess so," answered Carver. "The hardware store is having a sale, and Pete wants to advertise by printing coupons to clip. Got any news?"

"No, I don't," said Jack.

"I do," said Mandy.

Jack unkinked his back, stretched, and looked down at his sister. "Another story about a mouse in a closet?" He laughed. "No thanks. We only print news about the *people* in Waterway Village, old people."

"That's just what I've got," said Mandy.

Jack reached into the engine. "Unscrew this bolt and the one un-

der here, Carv," he said. "That'll let the whole thing off. I'll take it to Ray's junkyard. He must have a secondhand distributor. We'll replace the whole thing."

Mandy watched them work for a minute, then turned and walked to the back door. She kicked it open and stepped into the family room, the new addition her father had built last year with the money from the strawberry crop. Three sides of the room were windows. The sun shone in on bookcases, dining table, TV, and chairs. Soft trade winds blew through the room, for the windows were kept open except during storms.

She paused by the bookcase, picked up a copy of *The Waterway Times*, and opened it. The newspaper had been written and typed by Jack, illustrated by Drummer, financed by Carver's selling ads, and duplicated at the Ink Spot, a printing shop in the shopping center on the far side of Waterway Village. She longed to be part of the exciting newspaper that made such a stir in the village whenever it appeared, which was more and more often, for it came out whenever her brothers needed parts for their car. Mandy smiled to herself. Perhaps this time they would accept one of her stories. They needed a distributor, and they had no news. She reread the last issue. Stories told of the firing of a nurse at the village, of a great-grandchild visiting; and headlines announced the scores of the golf and shuffleboard contests. Thoughtfully she opened her notebook and reread her own story.

Drummer came in the back door, threw his books on the table, and flipped on the TV.

"Want something to eat?" asked Mandy, closing her notebook. Her voice was so airy that Drummer turned around to see what made her happy this afternoon. He could not guess.

"I'd like a grilled cheese," he answered.

Mandy made two, put one on a plate, and wrapped the other in waxed paper and stuffed it in her lunch box as she called Drummer to eat. Jack came in the door. He was almost six feet tall and seemingly all knuckles and bones. His black hair looked like a motorcyclist's helmet bulging above his wide-spaced blue eyes. Mandy instinctively moved back to make room for this brother whose personality matched his body.

"Well, let's hear your story," he commanded.

Surprised, she knocked over a cane chair as she reached for her notebook.

"Well?" said the editor. "I'm listening."

Mandy cleared her throat. Drummer stopped chewing.

"Bright ripples circled out from the fishing line," she began. "The day was hot and Betty Howard, 73, was hungry. Suddenly her bobber went under. She pulled. A large fish flopped on the end of her line. She reeled in. The fish fought and the water rose in silver fountains.

"After a tiring battle, Mrs. Howard landed the fish and pulled it to her feet. For a long time she stared at it. The big sunfish would make such a good meal. The fish gasped in the air and began to die.

" 'You want to live, too, don't

you, fish?" she asked. Then she stopped, unhooked it, and let it go."

"Aw, come on," said Jack. "Are you kidding? That's no news story."

Carver had come in as she had begun reading and was looking over her shoulder.

"It's not news when a person catches a fish," he said. "Only when a fish catches a person." He laughed at his own cleverness.

"But she let it go instead of eating it," Mandy said. "That's news. Not many people would do that if they were poor and hungry."

"She's nuts," said Jack and picked up the telephone to call the Waterway Village office for news of upcoming trips, games, and visiting relatives.

Mandy closed her notebook, walked through the kitchen, and opened the door to the dark stairs that led to the attic where she and Drummer each had a dormer room. She walked up slowly, head down. Presently the staircase door opened, and Drummer climbed to her side.

"I liked your story, Mandy," he said. "I think it *is* news that Mrs. Howard let the fish go. It really is." His brow wrinkled, and he ran his fingers through his hair.

"You and Mom don't like wild things to be killed, do you?" he added.

"No."

"What about crows? They eat the crops."

"No."

"But Daddy shoots them."

"Doesn't mean we have to like it."

"Suppose the crows ate *all* the strawberries, then would you shoot them?"

"No."

"Suppose the crows ate all the strawberries and all the bananas? Then would you?"

"No."

"Suppose they ate all the strawberries and all the bananas and then attacked Daddy? Then would you?"

"No."

Drummer's forehead puckered.

"That's dumb. I would. I want to be just like Daddy."

Mandy looked down at her little

brother. His uncombed hair twisted in all directions like cypress twigs, and his brown eyes stared thoughtfully. She loved this brother so much. They had raised a baby marsh rabbit together, mended a mockingbird's wing, and watched the otter family dive in and out of the limestone holes on Trumpet Hammock. Now he was growing up and practicing to be a man by talking big about hunting.

They went in silence to the top of the steps.

"Are you going to write something else for the paper, Mandy?" he asked. "You do write good stories."

"I don't think so," she said. "I'm very busy now."

"Really?"

"I have a new friend."

"What's her name?"

"Nina Terrance."

"Is she pretty?"

"Cute, I'd say."

"I've never heard of her. Does she go to our school?"

"No. Her mother is very protective of her. She goes to a private school. I only see her at the dentist's office. She has braces, too."

"If you only see her at the dentist's office, how come you're so busy?"

"Well . . . I help with her favorite charity. She's rich."

"Guess you don't want to come catchin' frogs, then."

"No, I guess not." Mandy opened the door to her room, recalling Jack's criticism of her story. "Nuts," she said and flung herself on the bed to bury her face and cry as she had done after every other rejection. But no tears came. She was thinking of Nina Terrance.

Mandy keeps herself very busy with her new friend, Nina Terrance. She learns to talk to Nina Terrance by imitating the calls of other crows. Mandy also learns that Nina Terrance can speak English: she can imitate the voice of the hunter who shot her nest.

Read more about Mandy and her unusual pet in **The Cry of the Crow,** *by Jean Craighead George.*

CHECK FOR UNDERSTANDING

1. Why is Nina Terrance the last crow in Piney Woods?
2. How does Mandy find Nina Terrance?
3. Why did Mandy make up the story about her new friend named Nina Terrance?
4. How would the other members of Mandy's family have reacted if they knew that Mandy had a pet crow?
5. The members of Mandy's family have different opinions about hunting crows. Do you think Mandy is right? Or do you agree with Mandy's father and brothers? Explain your answer.

WRITE ABOUT *"The Last Crow in Piney Woods"*

"The Last Crow in Piney Woods" is the beginning of a novel by Jean Craighead George called *The Cry of the Crow.* Think about the characters you met in the story. Think about the conflict that is introduced in the story. Then imagine that Nina Terrance got into the strawberry field and started to eat the prize berries. What would Mandy do? Look for clues in the story that help you predict how Mandy would deal with the problem. Then write a short story telling what happened.

THINK ABOUT IT

Think about how the animals and the people in these selections affected each other's lives.

- Scrub set an example for David and helped him endure pain and not give up.
- Lady helped Daniel learn to love her by showing Daniel that she had learned to trust him.
- Little Bit "adopted" a human child as its mother and refused to return to life in the wild.
- Megan reached an understanding with Berry by thinking the way a horse thinks.
- Through Lily Black, Joe learns that two people may have an equally strong claim on something and that deciding what is right and fair is not always easy.
- Mandy finds that her secret friendship with a baby crow forces her into conflict with members of her family.

Think about the lessons the characters learn from their relationships with animals. How does each of these lessons apply to life and human relationships?

WRITE ABOUT IT

Select one of the characters from a selection in this unit. Think about the lesson the character learned. Then imagine the character in another life situation in which what was learned from the experience with an animal would help him or her in some way. Describe the problem and explain how the character deals with the problem by drawing on his or her earlier experience with a pet.

READ ABOUT IT

Summer of the Falcon by Jean Craighead George. Thomas Y. Crowell Co., 1962. When June trains a sparrow hawk named Zander, she learns a great deal about hawks, nature, and freedom.

Danza! by Lynn Hall. Charles Scribner's Sons, 1981. Paulo, a young Puerto Rican boy, goes to Louisiana to be with his grandfather's magnificent stallion, who is recovering from a serious illness.

A Boy Called Fish by Alison Morgan. Harper & Row, Publishers, 1973. Fish is the new boy in school. He is very lonely until he finds a stray dog which he names Floss. The two become inseparable companions until Floss is suspected of killing sheep.

Rascal: A Memoir of a Better Era by Sterling North. E. P. Dutton, 1963. In this autobiographical book set in 1918, Sterling finds a baby raccoon and brings it home. Rascal, the clever raccoon, leads Sterling into many adventures.

The Trouble with Tuck by Theodore Taylor. Doubleday & Co., 1981. Helen is determined not to let her dog's blindness limit his life. She thinks of a unique approach to the situation. The story is based on true events.

5
YESTERDAY IN AMERICA

How were people in the past different from people today? Did they have the same kinds of feelings as we do today? Did they want the same things out of life as we do today? Were they concerned with simpler, more basic things than we are today?

Most likely you have dreamed at one time or another about traveling into the past to see what it was really like when America was a new and untamed country. Of course, no one has ever succeeded in actually traveling backward in time. In this unit, however, you will do the next best thing: you will read about what life was like yesterday in America.

Paul Revere's Ride

by HENRY WADSWORTH LONGFELLOW

Listen, my children, and you shall hear
Of the midnight ride of Paul Revere,
On the eighteenth of April, in seventy-five;
Hardly a man is now alive,
Who remembers that famous day and year.

He said to his friend, "If the British march
By land or sea from the town tonight,
Hang a lantern aloft in the belfry arch
Of the North Church tower as a signal light,—
One, if by land, and two if by sea;
And I on the opposite shore will be,
Ready to ride and spread the alarm
Through every Middlesex village and farm,
For the country folk to be up and to arm."

Then he said, "Good night!" and with muffled oar
Silently rowed to the Charlestown shore,
Just as the moon rose over the bay,
Where swinging wide at her moorings lay
The *Somerset*, British man-of-war;
A phantom ship, with each mast and spar
Across the moon like a prison bar,
And a huge black hulk, that was magnified
By its own reflection in the tide.

Meanwhile, his friend, through alley and street,
Wanders and watches with eager ears,
Till in the silence around him he hears
The muster of men at the barrack door,
The sound of arms, and the tramp of feet,
And the measured tread of the grenadiers,
Marching down to their boats on the shore.

Then he climbed the tower of the Old North Church,
By the wooden stairs, with stealthy tread,
To the belfry-chamber overhead,
And startled the pigeons from their perch
On the somber rafters, that round him made
Masses and moving shapes of shade,—
By the trembling ladder, steep and tall,
To the highest window in the wall,
Where he paused to listen and look down
A moment on the roofs of the town,
And the moonlight flowing over all.

Beneath, in the churchyard, lay the dead,
In their night-encampment on the hill,
Wrapped in silence so deep and still
That he could hear, like a sentinel's tread,
The watchful night-wind, as it went
Creeping along from tent to tent,
And seeming to whisper, "All is well!"
A moment only he feels the spell
Of the place and the hour, and the secret dread
Of the lonely belfry and the dead;
For suddenly all his thoughts are bent
On a shadowy something far away,
Where the river widens to meet the bay,—
A line of black that bends and floats
On the rising tide, like a bridge of boats.

Meanwhile, impatient to mount and ride,
Booted and spurred, with a heavy stride
On the opposite shore walked Paul Revere.
Now he patted his horse's side,
Now gazed at the landscape far and near,
Then, impetuous, stamped the earth,
And turned and tightened his saddle-girth;
But mostly he watched with eager search
The belfry-tower of the Old North Church,
As it rose above the graves on the hill,
Lonely and spectral and somber and still.

And lo! as he looks on the belfry's height
A glimmer, and then a gleam of light!
He springs to the saddle, the bridle he turns,
but lingers and gazes, till full on his sight
A second lamp in the belfry burns!

A hurry of hoofs in a village street,
A shape in the moonlight, a bulk in the dark,
And beneath, from the pebbles, in passing, a spark
Struck out by a steed flying fearless and fleet:
That was all! And yet, through the gloom and the light,
The fate of a nation was riding that night;
And the spark struck out by that steed, in his flight,
Kindled the land into flame with its heat.

He has left the village and mounted the steep,
And beneath him, tranquil and broad and deep,
Is the Mystic, meeting the ocean tides;
And under the alders that skirt its edge,
Now soft on the sand, now loud on the ledge,
Is heard the tramp of his steed as he rides.

It was twelve by the village clock,
When he crossed the bridge into Medford town.
He heard the crowing of the cock,
And the barking of the farmer's dog,
And felt the damp of the river's fog,
That rises after the sun goes down.
It was one by the village clock,
When he galloped into Lexington.
He saw the gilded weathercock
Swim in the moonlight as he passed,
And the meeting-house windows, blank and bare,
Gaze at him with a spectral glare,
As if they already stood aghast
At the bloody work they would look upon.

It was two by the village clock,
When he came to the bridge in Concord town.
He heard the bleating of the flock,
And the twitter of birds among the trees,
And felt the breath of the morning breeze

Blowing over the meadows brown.
And one was safe and asleep in his bed
Who at the bridge would be first to fall,
Who that day would be lying dead,
Pierced by a British musket-ball.
You know the rest. In the books you have read,
How the British Regulars fired and fled,—
How the farmers gave them ball for ball,
From behind each fence and farmyard wall,
Chasing the red-coats down the lane,
Then crossing the fields to emerge again
Under the trees at the turn of the road,
And only pausing to fire and load.

So through the night rode Paul Revere;
And so through the night went his cry of alarm
To every Middlesex village and farm,—
A cry of defiance and not of fear,
A voice in the darkness, a knock at the door,
And a word that shall echo forevermore!
For, borne on the night-wind of the Past,
Through all our history, to the last,
In the hour of darkness and peril and need,
The people will waken and listen to hear
The hurrying hoof-beats of that steed,
And the midnight message of Paul Revere.

The most famous ride in American history could not have been made without a horse. Have you ever wondered how the horse felt as it galloped to Lexington carrying Paul Revere and his urgent message? In this story, the horse tells just what happened.

What happens that makes the ride a personal triumph for the horse? In what way is the horse like Paul Revere and the other Sons of Liberty?

Galloping to Lexington

by ROBERT LAWSON

Scheherazade (shə her'ə zäd') came to the Colonies with His Royal Majesty's Fourteenth Regiment of Foot. She was the horse of Leftenant Sir Cedric Noel Vivian Barnstable, a British officer and gentleman.

In America Scheherazade's fortunes changed. Her master lost her in a card game, and Sherry became a cart horse for a local glue factory. Eventually Sherry was rescued from this humiliation by Sam Adams. He claimed her for the Sons of Liberty and presented her to Paul Revere, who needed a horse to carry out his duties in the cause of freedom.

This story is an account of Paul Revere's famous ride told from the point of view of Sherry, his horse.

Tuesday evening finally came. And before it was scarcely dark, there also came Colonel Conant, Richard Devens, and several other members of the Committee of Correspondence. The general nervousness had begun to affect even me. I was restless and rather unpleasant when Colonel Conant insisted on saddling and bridling me hours before it was necessary.

"Father said they wouldn't move before the moon rose," Miss Deborah said, somewhat impatiently. "And Father always knows." She loosened my girth and stroked me quietly.

"It's surely Cambridge," someone said. "Ed Whipple was over there this afternoon. There was a scad of officers, down around the landing place mostly."

Now in the deepening dusk we could see all the longboats being cast off and slowly rowed in to the Boston shore, along where the Common ran down to the water. Mrs. Revere, having put the children to bed, came out and joined the group.

After what seemed hours, the sky in the east began to glow. The buildings of Boston became silhouettes. Slowly the moon rose, fat and orange. The spire of Old North was a sharp paper cutout.

"There they go," someone cried. Beyond the *Somerset* we could now see the lines of barges and longboats crawling across the

417

river. They moved like a procession of huge black beetles. Now and then the moonlight winked on a bayonet or a buckle. The procession seemed endless.

Old North boomed out eleven, and still no signal. Colonel Conant and Richard Devens began to argue as to which should ride—in case Mr. Revere did not make it back from Boston.

Their voices stopped abruptly. High up in the dark spire a light flickered a moment, then settled down to a steady clear pinpoint. Seconds later another appeared, far enough away from the first to show clearly two distinct dots of light.

"By Cambridge," everyone breathed.

If the strain of the last two days had been hard, the next half hour was well-nigh unbearable. Now every eye was on the *Somerset*, black and menacing. The procession of barges still continued. The men paced back and forth and cleared their throats. Miss Deborah braided and unbraided my forelock twenty times.

Still there came no sign of life from the warship. There was no shouted challenge, no flash or roar of guns.

So intent were we that everyone gave a great start when the bell of Old North clanged out one stroke. Eleven-thirty!

Colonel Conant sighed, settled his hat, and started toward me. "The half hour is up," he said. "I will ride, Devens."

But before he had reached my side, there came a bumping and scraping on the shore, a splash and the scramble of footsteps. Miss Deborah yanked my girth tight as Mr. Revere came hurrying up the slope from the water.

With hardly a word—with only a hurried embrace for his wife and a pat on the cheek for Deborah—he grasped the reins, leaped into the saddle, and we were off.

After the strain of the last two days, it was a glorious relief to be in action again. For the first few miles, the road to Lexington led over open moorlands. The moon was bright, the footing good, and

I fairly flew. Later, when we came to shadowy woodlands, we would have to proceed with more care for fear of ambush. Now was our chance to make real speed.

Mr. Revere suddenly slapped the pommel, looking for his pistols. "That Conant," he laughed. "No doubt he was fussing around all evening, being a pest to everyone. Then forgets my pistols. Oh well, never mind, I couldn't hit a barn with them anyway." He, too, seemed in a high good humor, now that the strain of waiting was past.

As we galloped, I was haunted by the recollection of all the British officers we had seen on the road last Sunday. Surely such an important expedition as this one would have many scouts out watching the roads. I must be unusually wary.

Now we were in more wooded country almost halfway to Lexington and had met no one. As we passed patch after patch of ominous black shadow without a challenge, I must have become overconfident or careless. For

419

what happened next, I consider myself wholly to blame.

We were approaching a great spreading oak tree that bathed the road in deep shadow when the first thing we knew there was a shout, a rush. Two British officers burst out of the blackness, blocking our way. I slid to a stop before Mr. Revere had even realized our danger. One officer wheeled and galloped up the road a space, lest we should escape the first, who was now charging down on us with drawn pistol.

In a split second I recognized him as my old master, Leftenant Barnstable. He was mounted on Ajax, my companion in the Fourteenth Regiment!

Ajax, I am sure, meant to run me down. At the last instant I skipped aside just enough to escape his heavy charge and the Leftenant's snatch at my bridle. We were now fairly trapped. One officer was ahead of us, one behind.

Furious at my carelessness, I whirled, sprang, and cleared the stone wall beside the road. It was only a low wall, and I made my landing as gentle as possible. But

420

I was terrified lest Mr. Revere be unseated. He was—almost. He fell forward heavily on my neck, lost one stirrup, scrambled frantically for a moment. Then he somehow managed to right himself.

We were in a huge open field, dotted here and there with boulders and clumps of bayberry, but excellent footing. Now I could show this pompous, overstuffed barracks brute what running really was! I let myself out and skimmed the ground like a racing cloud shadow. Far behind I could hear Ajax crashing through the brush, thundering over the wall, pounding across the rolling field. I could easily have outdistanced him, dived into the woods and lost him completely. That would have wasted time. I had a better plan.

Now I was thankful for my thorough knowledge of the countryside. I remembered that that dark mass of trees and brush near the far side of the field overhung a deep stagnant pond. I also remembered that on this side the ground dropped in a steep gravelly bank to the water. I made for it, slowing my pace to allow Ajax to catch up. Mr. Revere knew of the pond, also. Wisely he left everything in my hands. He made no attempt to hasten my now slow pace or to guide me in any way.

Ajax was almost on my heels. I could hear his laboring breath. I could smell the stale stable odor of his saddle blanket. With a roar the Leftenant's pistol went off. The bullet whined harmlessly past my left ear.

Not until we reached the very brink did I wheel in a sharp right-angled turn. Mr. Revere must have sensed it coming, for, to my great relief, he managed somehow to hang on.

As we sped off across the field, there came to our ears a most gratifying sound. There was a heavy crashing of bushes, the ring of ironshod shoes on sliding cobbles, a screamed volley of oaths, then a tremendous splash.

There flashed through my mind Ajax's bitter words: *I never speak to civilians. . . . Deserter! Traitor! Spy!* I burst out in a long derisive whinny. Slapping me on the shoulder, Mr. Revere shouted:

"Good girl, Sherry. Well done. One down and Concord to go."

We found an open gate and were out on a small backcountry road. I recognized it at once as being close to Medford. In a few moments, we rattled across the wooden bridge spanning the Mystic River and bore down on the sleeping town.

We paused only a moment at the door of Mr. Doolittle, the sheep raiser. Mr. Revere set up a great pounding, shouting, "The Redcoats are out! Turn out, Minutemen!" Before the echoes of his first knock had died away, Enoch Sawtell, the shepherd, came briskly forth. He was fully dressed and carrying his musket. He fired it once into the air and, with only a wave to us, ran for the meeting house.

As we galloped down the short village street, lights were springing up in all the houses. The steady thudding of an alarm drum began. The meeting house bell burst into a wild clangor. Medford was well awake.

The encounter with the British

officers had forced us considerably out of our way. We lost much precious time. However, the road from Medford to Lexington was so small and little used that we doubted it was being watched. Watched or not, ambush or no ambush, we must now press on with all possible speed, regardless of danger. I settled down to a steady gallop and ran as though I were competing for the King's Cup.

Farmhouses were few. When we passed one, Mr. Revere would shout at the top of his lungs, "Turn out, Minutemen! The British are out!" This and my pounding hoofs were usually enough to set all the dogs to barking and rouse the household.

Only once did we pause. At the top of a high open rise, Mr. Revere drew rein and for a brief moment we looked and listened. Behind us we could almost see every hilltop crowned with a blazing beacon fire. Far and near the meeting house bells kept up an unceasing clamor that spread ever westward. Here and there could be heard the rattle of a drum, occasionally a musket shot.

I found my heart beating harder than the exercise warranted. All our other trips, while necessary and important to the cause, had really been mere messenger service. There were no ambushes, no blazing pistols. But this was war, bloody war, or perilously close to it.

Mr. Revere slapped my neck and I resumed my gallop. The soft dirt road was a delight underfoot. The moon was bright. Great trees here and there cast black shadows, any of which might conceal a lurking scout. But I had now cast aside all thought of scouts or ambushes. My one thought was speed—and Lexington.

CHECK FOR UNDERSTANDING

1. At the beginning of the story, what signal was everyone waiting for? What would the signal tell them?
2. Why did Scheherazade blame herself for running into the British?
3. What happened that made the ride a personal triumph for Sherry?
4. What made Ajax both friend and foe to Scheherazade?
5. In what way was Sherry like Paul Revere and the other Sons of Liberty?
6. What details about Paul Revere's ride are included in this story but are not mentioned in the poem? Do you think these details are facts?

WRITE ABOUT *"Galloping to Lexington"*

Write two paragraphs describing what happened when Paul Revere and Sherry ran into Leftenant Barnstable and Ajax on the road to Lexington. The story gave Sherry's account of what happened. Her old stable mate Ajax would probably tell a different version of the story. Your paragraphs should tell the story the way Ajax might have told it.

VOCABULARY · LANGUAGE

Base Words and Affixes

What's stranger than a talking horse?
A horse that speaks *quite well*, of course.

Scheherazade was truly a remarkable animal. Not only could she talk, she could express herself very well. One might even say that she had a way with words. You can easily imagine Scheherazade snorting and stamping impatiently as she complained, "I was restless and rather unpleasant when Colonel Conant insisted on saddling and bridling me hours before it was necessary."

Restless and *unpleasant* are both adjectives. They both describe how Scheherazade felt. But they are also similar in another way. Each word is made up of a base word and a prefix or suffix.

A base word is a word that can be used to build other words. You might say that a base word is the basis for new words. The base word in *restless* is *rest*. When the suffix *-less* is added to *rest*, an adjective meaning "without rest" is formed.

What is the base word in *unpleasant*? In this case, you must look very closely, because *unpleasant* has a prefix and a suffix. The base word is *please*. The word *unpleasant* was built by adding the prefix *un-* and the suffix *-ant.*

Prefixes are added to the *beginning* of base words. Each prefix has its own meaning. Here are some prefixes and their meanings.

un-	not	*pre-*	before	*over-*	too much
im-	not	*re-*	again	*out-*	more than better than

Suffixes are added to the *end* of base words. Suffixes change the way words are used in sentences.

-less	fear/fearless	a *fearless* adventurer
-ful	care/careful	a *careful* worker
-able	love/lovable	a *lovable* puppy
-ant	please/pleasant	a *pleasant* surprise
-ness	soft/softness	a pillow's *softness*
-ly	happy/happily	to chuckle *happily*

Since Scheherazade had a large vocabulary, many of the words she used contained prefixes and suffixes. According to Sherry, Miss Deborah spoke *impatiently,* the procession of boats was *endless,* and the strain of waiting was *unbearable.* On the road, Sherry confesses, she became *overconfident,* and her *carelessness* put Mr. Revere in danger. She was *thankful,* however, that she was able to *outdistance* the enemy.

Look back at the words in italic type. Identify the base word and the prefix or suffix that make up each word.

You will frequently come upon new words when you are reading. Identifying the parts that make up new words—the base words and the prefixes and suffixes—often can help you to figure out their meaning. The next selection, "Digging into the Past," for example, explains that archaeology is the study of ancient or very old things. The suffix *-ist* adds the meaning "one who does or studies" to a word. What do you think an archaeologist is?

While reading "Digging into the Past," you will also learn about prehistoric times. You may not be familiar with the word *prehistoric.* What prefix, base word, and suffix make up the word *prehistoric?* What does the word *prehistoric* mean?

Digging into the Past

by VELMA FORD MORRISON

Archaeology is a science that helps us know about people who left no books to tell us about themselves. In "Digging into the Past," you will learn how archaeologists find out things about people who lived long ago by studying artifacts.

What is an artifact? How do archaeologists know where to dig for artifacts?

Pieces of a Puzzle

Did you ever dig a hole in the ground to see what you could find? If so, what did you uncover? Was it a bone? An oddly shaped stone? A piece of colored glass? An arrowhead?

Did you wonder about what you found? Could you tell if the bone was that of an animal, bird, or human being? Did you wonder: Could the sharp edge of that stone have been used by someone long ago for cutting and scraping? Was that piece of colored glass a part of a vase? Or a window? How long had that arrowhead been buried there?

Trying to answer these questions is like trying to put together a jigsaw puzzle. It may be difficult, but it can sometimes be done. There is a science that teaches people how to solve the mysteries of things buried in the earth. It is called archaeology, from the Greek *archaeo,* meaning ancient or old, and *logy,* which means a study or a science. So we might say that archaeology is the study of ancient or very old things.

Men and women who study this science are called archaeologists. Like detectives, archaeologists are always looking for clues that might help solve the puzzle of how people lived thousands of years ago.

In ancient or prehistoric times, people did not read or write as they do now. They left no letters, no diaries, no history books. Yet they did leave a record of their way of life. Now buried in the earth, the record of this life is told in the remains of the things they left behind—skeletons, bones, teeth, food, plants, and artifacts, such as tools, trinkets, utensils, carvings, and paintings.

Knowing Where to Dig

Are you wondering how archaeologists know *where* to dig? Or *where* to look? Do they simply take a spade and begin digging any place at all? No indeed. Unless they have some idea of where to start, they could spend a lifetime and never uncover a single

artifact. Most often they have some sort of clue to guide them. Usually the site is a place where someone has already found bones, arrowheads, trinkets, shells, or bits of pottery.

To the trained eyes of the archaeologists, the type of land and the lay of the land are often clues. Many prehistoric peoples chose the great river valleys of the midwestern United States as the best place to live. Mounds constructed by these early humans may be found scattered throughout Middle America. Archaeologists are usually able to spot these mounds and the outlines of bygone villages. Such places hold many secrets of the past.

River banks, dry rivers, lake beds, sea beds, and creek beds are also good places to dig or look for artifacts, especially after a storm.

Other places worth checking are peat bogs, rock shelters, caves, and pit caves. For thousands of years, prehistoric humans inhabited rock shelters and caves. They left behind fire pits, tools, shells, utensils, and the bones of the animals they ate. Pit caves are very deep holes or cracks in the earth. Many, many years ago animals and people sometimes fell to their deaths in these openings. Through the study of the remains preserved in such sheltered places, scientists are learning about the people and animals that once lived in the surrounding areas.

Often near historic sites such as battlefields, military and colonial relics can be found. A metal detector may be useful in locating items such as old coins, cannonballs, gun parts, and eating utensils. Of course, metal detectors can only locate metal. Sometimes, however, when metal objects are uncovered, other objects are also found.

Surprising Discoveries

Archaeology can be a fun science, full of surprises and excitement. Further, it is one science in which amateurs, or persons with little or no special training, can take part and be a real help.

Some of the most important treasures in the world were not discovered by archaeologists but by amateurs—just ordinary people. Workers laying a pipeline in Arizona discovered a buried Indian village. A farmer in Illinois uncovered shells, bones, and arrowpoints which led to the discovery of an ancient site containing thirteen different cultures. An alert rancher in Colorado plowed up some large bones which led to the discovery of the remains of an Ice Age bison kill. Discovery of the Folsom site—a very important one—in New Mexico was made by a cowboy in 1925.

Not all discoveries have been made by adults. Many have been made by children. Not long ago a young boy found bones which proved to be those of a mammoth, an animal now extinct. Many ancient hunting weapons and bones of extinct animals have been found by children in Alaska and Siberia. Other items unearthed by children which led to important discoveries are ancient tools of stone and bone, copper artifacts, pieces of pottery, arrowheads, beads, and coins.

The joy of archaeology is not in discovery alone. Working on a real dig or visiting one can be very exciting. Most people think of archaeological sites as being located only in foreign lands, and many travel to faraway places like Egypt, the Yucatan, and Stonehenge to see them. But some of the most exciting digs are right here in the United States in our own backyards.

The Mound Builders

Scattered throughout the central and eastern United States are thousands of prehistoric, human-made mounds. More than ten thousand have been found in Ohio alone! They are all sizes and shapes. Some are square, some are round, and some are oval. Some are formed in the shape of humans, animals, and birds.

One mound, called Serpent Mound, is 1300 feet long and covers 60 acres of ground. It is made of stone and clay in the shape of a coiling snake with its jaws wide open. It's the largest effigy mound in the world. (An effigy is an image—for instance, a statue—of some living thing.)

Another example is Rock Eagle Effigy Mound in Georgia, an eagle with wings spanning 120 feet. In southern Wisconsin there are five thousand human and animal effigy mounds in the shapes of eagles, buffalo, elk, moose, deer, wolves, and panthers. Some of the panthers have tails 350 feet long. Some of the wing spans of the eagles measure 1000 feet.

In west central Illinois lies America's first prehistoric city north of Mexico. It is called Cahokia for the Cahokia Indians of the Illinois Nation. It covered six square miles and had a population of more than forty thousand people, which was very great for such ancient times.

In this ancient city of Cahokia is the largest prehistoric earthen construction in the world. Its base is even larger than Egypt's great pyramid! It covers sixteen acres of ground. It is so big that many people thought it must have been built upon a natural hill. But scientific tests have proved that it is all human made and that it was built in fourteen different stages. Called Monks Mound, it was named for some monks who lived in that area from 1808 until 1813.

Monks Mound once stood in the midst of more than one hundred smaller mounds. Of these, forty have been preserved. The main Cahokian mounds were flat on top and made entirely of earth. The soil was broken up with digging tools made of wood, shell, or stone and carried in handwoven baskets to the construction site. On the top of Monks Mound once stood a massive building at least 105 feet long and 50 feet high.

Imagine the labor and the engineering ability it must have taken to construct these great mounds by hand—without the help of the modern machinery and tools we have today.

The Cliff Dwellers

Some of the most magnificent prehistoric ruins in the United States are in the Southwest—in Colorado, New Mexico, and Arizona.

Hundreds of years ago, long before white people came to America, Indians living in southwestern Colorado built their homes along overhanging walls of canyons for protection against other tribes. Some of the homes were built in the open. But many were in caves, where they were well protected from the weather. By studying the remains found in and around these dwellings, archaeologists have been able to piece together the story of the life and customs of the people who once lived there.

The cliff dwellers, as they are now called, were short and black-haired. The backs of their heads were flat because, as babies, they were carried on hard cradleboards. This caused their soft young bones to become permanently flattened. Their homes were often four, five, and even more stories high. The rooms were small and oblong in shape and built in a stair-step design. They were stacked one upon another. Each room was set back a few feet from the room beneath it so that the roof of one would be the front yard of the one above it. There were no doors or windows on the ground floor. The roofs were reached by ladders. In case enemies attacked, the ladders could be drawn up, and the people would fight from their house tops. The structure was like a big apartment house with many people living there. It was a village in itself.

These cliff dwellers were good

farmers. They grew corn, squash, beans, cotton, and tobacco. Their bowls and dishes were beautifully decorated. Their tools were made of bone and flint, and their weapons of polished stone.

For eight hundred years, these peace-loving people built their cliff dwellings and farmed their lands. Then a strange thing happened. They all began moving away, leaving most of their possessions behind. Why did they leave? Where did they go? No one knows for certain. Some archaeologists believe that a long drought drove them away. Without water, the people could not survive. They were forced to leave their homes and many of their possessions and seek new places in which to live.

Other archaeologists believe that the people were forced away because of frequent enemy attacks. Whatever the reason, everyone left. Many centuries went by. Then, one wintry day in 1888, two cowboys exploring southwestern Colorado came upon an unbelievable sight. Up high in a cave along the overhanging walls of a can-

yon, they saw what appeared to be a huge white palace. Imagine their surprise at seeing such a sight in the middle of nowhere! Before long they knew they had discovered an ancient cliff dwelling. They named it Cliff Palace.

Cliff Palace is the largest and best-preserved prehistoric cliff dwelling in the world today. It rises eight stories high and con-

tains more than two hundred rooms. The flat roofs are gone, but the walls are still standing. Among the ruins were hundreds of artifacts—bows and arrows, clothing, food, jewelry, and even some mummies of the people themselves. Many of the artifacts have been placed in the state museum in Denver.

The area around Cliff Palace is known as Mesa Verde (mā'sə vərd'ē), which is Spanish for "green table." It was given this name because it is covered with many green juniper and piñon trees. Besides Cliff Palace, there are many other interesting archaeological sites at Mesa Verde. Mesa Verde is actually an enormous outdoor archaeological museum full of wonderful, exciting things to see.

The Search for America's Past

More and more archaeological sites are being discovered in the United States. In Alaska near Kotzebue (kat' si byoo'), archaeologists recently unearthed ruins of ten prehistoric cultures. They found hearths, tools, and many other artifacts. Another site of interest in Alaska is in Kobuk Valley. There, in peat bogs 33,000 years old, archaeologists found fossils of woolly mammoths and evidence of hunters having killed caribou.

Not long ago in a rock shelter near Pittsburgh, Pennsylvania, archaeologists discovered fire pits and charcoal pieces showing that humans were living there fourteen to sixteen thousand years ago! This is the earliest evidence of people living in the eastern part of the United States south of Alaska.

In 1976, an early colonial settlement was discovered in Virginia. In the debris were parts of armor, a British helmet, coins, gun barrels, knives, ax heads, graves, and skeletons, and the earliest dated piece of British-American pottery ever found. From these, archaeologists are piecing together the story of life in an early colonial village.

In Missouri, some 1800 promising archaeological sites have been identified on the Salt River. Along the Osage River, excavations have uncovered remains of mammoths and mastodons thousands of years old.

Six hundred archaeological sites are under study in the state of California. These include old Indian settlements, rock paintings, burial sites, mining camps, and Gold Rush towns. The sites span more than three thousand years of local history. There are thousands of archaeological sites in the United States—from Alaska to Florida, from the shores of the Atlantic to the shores of the Pacific, and on to Hawaii.

Most of the archaeological sites in the United States are open to the public. But some are not. Archaeologists feel that some places need to be protected. Among those not open to all are Paleo (Stone Age) Indian sites. Once they have been excavated, there really is nothing to see. People of the Paleo culture left few tools or weapons in any one place because they were hunters and always on the move. Artifacts found at Paleo sites have been placed in museums.

There are many hundreds of fine archaeological museums throughout the United States. Some are located at dig sites, but most are not. Large collections of artifacts have been gathered and placed in museums far from the sites at which they were found.

Museums are wonderful places! They tell us about our past. They preserve prehistoric remains for many to see and enjoy. Everyone cannot travel to a real archaeological site, but most people can visit a museum. There, with a little imagination, a person can picture many interesting things as they happened in the past—bison and mammoth kills, fights with the enemy on the rooftops at Mesa Verde, and the villagers of Cahokia patiently filling baskets with earth for the construction of the great Monks Mound.

Each of us is a maker of history. As makers of history, we need to know the past—the things that have happened to make the world what it is today. Many secrets of the past are still hidden in the soil and sea. Many questions remain unanswered. In spite of all that has been learned, there is much more waiting to be discovered.

CHECK FOR UNDERSTANDING

1. How are archaeologists like detectives?
2. What is an artifact? What are some examples of artifacts?
3. How do archaeologists know where to dig for artifacts?
4. Why are river valleys good places to look for artifacts?
5. Why do you think children have been responsible for some important discoveries in archaeology?

WRITE ABOUT *"Digging into the Past"*

Select an object within your reach right now that you think would help an archaeologist in the future understand something about how we live today. Pretend you are the archaeologist in the future. Write one paragraph in which you explain how the object reveals something that is actually true about life today. Then write a paragraph in which you, again as the archaeologist, draw incorrect conclusions about present-day life based on the artifact.

The things we use every day could be the artifacts studied by future archaeologists.

What kinds of things would make good artifacts for archaeologists in the future? What kinds of things might puzzle future archaeologists?

Artifact Games

by BRUCE PORELL

Archaeologists study the material remains of our past. Material remains, called artifacts, are simply the objects used by people in their everyday lives. Artifacts are the pots we cook in and the dishes we eat from. Artifacts are the chairs and tables in your living room, the rubber ball in your bedroom, and the toothbrush in the rack over your bathroom sink. Artifacts are everywhere. They are our tools, toys, furniture, decorations, gadgets, and weapons. Even the buildings we live and work in are artifacts. Look around you. You are wearing artifacts and you are surrounded by them.

Is the tree outside your window an artifact? No, not unless you cut it down and hollow it out to make yourself a canoe, remove a branch and whittle a whistle, boil the roots for tea, or burn the wood for heat. Wood is an obvious source of artifacts. Hundreds of artifacts have been made from trees.

Here is a game to play with a group of friends. Let each of your group bring in one artifact from home. Then get together and make up an imaginary person who might use all of these artifacts. Take notes and write as complete a description as possible using only the information you can discover from the artifacts. Use cautious words like *probably, sometimes, might, could,* and so on, to describe your mystery person. If one of your artifacts is a coffee cup, you might write: "This person probably drank coffee or tea." You should not write: "This person definitely drank coffee or tea." You don't know that for sure. It's just possible that the coffee cup was used for hot chocolate and nothing else. How do you think you could find out what the cup was used for? (If a coffee can were among the artifacts, it might lend strength to the coffee theory. But still the proof would not be definite.)

Archaeologists often don't know for sure what an artifact was used for because different cultures do things very differently. For example, what would someone who had never seen a can of soda-pop imagine a flip-top from the can to be?

Here's an exercise for your imagination and creativity. See how many uses you can think of for a junked car. You can use the car as a whole or take it apart piece by piece. Make a tire swing with the tires. (Tires have lots of uses. What else could you do with them?) Cut off the roof and plant a garden in the body of the car. Make a sculpture for your bedroom by gluing together parts from the engine.

How creative are you? Can you think of twenty-five uses? Fifty? One hundred?

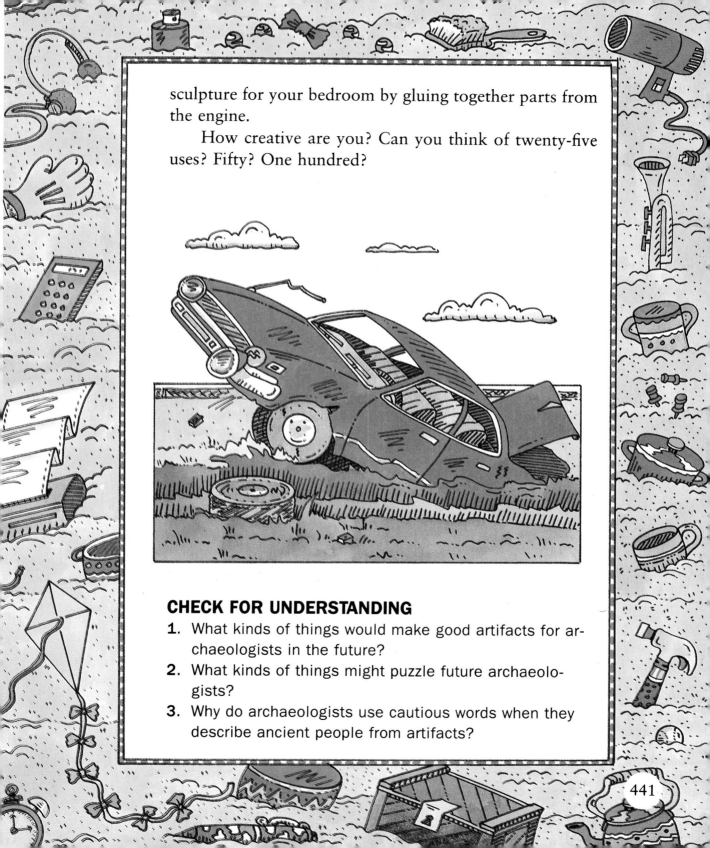

CHECK FOR UNDERSTANDING

1. What kinds of things would make good artifacts for archaeologists in the future?
2. What kinds of things might puzzle future archaeologists?
3. Why do archaeologists use cautious words when they describe ancient people from artifacts?

Planning the Nation's Capital

by CLAUDE LEWIS

The story of the planning of Washington, D.C., is a fascinating one. A man named Benjamin Banneker played a very important part in the story. In fact, without Banneker, Washington, D.C., would not be the city it is today.

What happened to the original plans for Washington, D.C.? How did Benjamin Banneker save the city of Washington?

Benjamin Banneker was born in 1731, the son of freed slaves. Banneker had little formal education, but he was gifted and curious and taught himself mathematics and astronomy.

Around 1772 Banneker became acquainted with the Ellicotts, a well-educated family who owned mills near Banneker's farm. George Ellicott helped Banneker in his study of astronomy by lending him books and instruments. In 1783 Banneker began work on an almanac, measuring the movement of the planets to predict weather and chart tides. The Benjamin Banneker Almanack, the first of a series of annual almanacs, was published in 1791.

While he was finishing work on his almanac, Banneker had another opportunity to demonstrate his abilities. In 1790, Congress had passed a bill to create a capital city on the Potomac River. President George Washington appointed Major Andrew Ellicott, George Ellicott's cousin, to the survey commission. Major Ellicott, who knew of Banneker's talents, chose him to assist the commission.

George Town, to be annexed as Georgetown, a part of Washington, D.C., a century later, was a bustling little city in 1791. Major Pierre Charles L'Enfant, the Frenchman whom President Washington had named Chief Architect and Engineer, and Ellicott were to work out of George Town, surveying the District of Columbia. Washington had chosen the 85-foot hill on which the Capitol was to be built (now known as Capitol Hill or simply The Hill).

L'Enfant's difficulties began the day he arrived in George Town, as he said in a note to Washington. "On arriving I made it my first care to wait on the Mayor. He appeared much surprised. He assured me he had received no previous notice of my coming nor any orders concerning the business I was sent upon."

Washington's commissioners knew L'Enfant was coming but apparently felt no duty to alert other officials.

Undaunted, L'Enfant dispatched his surveyors to the federal district and set feverishly if somewhat secretly to work. Land speculators already were interested in the project, and Congress hoped to keep the plans private until all the needed land could be acquired.

"We want to build most of the government buildings to the east of Capitol Hill on that high plateau with which you men are all familiar," L'Enfant told a meeting of the District Commission one spring afternoon. "The site drains well, and we could save the government a good deal of grief in coming years by planning for there instead of that lower land to the west near the Potomac River. We should keep this information to ourselves, though."

"I'm afraid, sir, it's too late. Your plan has leaked out, and land speculators already have bought most of the land to the east of Capitol Hill. The prices they are asking are indeed dear," said Major Ellicott.

L'Enfant went into a towering rage. "Which one of you did this?" he shouted at the commissioners. "Who is cutting the land out from under us for a few pieces of silver? Must every noble effort be spoiled by greed?"

No one answered. L'Enfant stormed from the room.

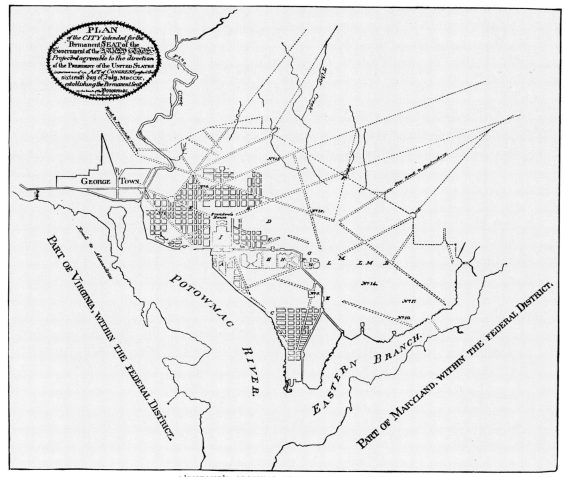

L'ENFANT'S ORIGINAL PLAN OF WASHINGTON.

Congress, in disgust, eventually changed plans and purchased the soggy marshland west of Capitol Hill, where many government buildings now stand.

L'Enfant had quickly recognized the talent and quiet manner of Benjamin Banneker. They worked well together, and Banneker was seen often by his side studying maps and plans, offering suggestions, and reporting discoveries revealed in the surveys.

Spring had been rainy, making the work difficult. Mud clogged the equipment, clung to the boots, made the terrain slippery. But summer was worse, as a summer can be only in Washington even today.

L'Enfant's relations with the commissioners grew worse as the summer wore on, and the heat didn't help tempers already frayed. L'Enfant became more secretive, finally reaching a point where he practically refused to tell the commissioners what he was doing.

Ellicott and Banneker were among those L'Enfant continued to trust and keep informed. Alphabetically lettered streets were to run east and west and numbered streets north and south, the surveyors were told. Intersecting these would be twenty-one diagonal avenues.

There would be one grand avenue extending from the eastern branch of the Potomac (Anacostia River) past Capitol Hill into the northwestern quarter of the city. It would be 160 feet wide. Millions now know that avenue as Pennsylvania Avenue, down which march all the Presidential inaugural parades.

The commissioners issued a brief but official report on September 9, 1791:

"We have agreed that the federal district shall be called

'the Territory of Columbia' and the federal city 'the City of Washington.' "

There would be a map if L'Enfant would ever release it. His plan was to make the map public and widely distributed only when every detail had been worked out.

Banneker and Ellicott brought L'Enfant the report that finally destroyed any hope the engineer and the commissioners would settle their differences.

"Something has come up which you should know about, Major," Banneker said to L'Enfant.

"Yes. What mischief is afoot now?" he replied.

"A house has been built up in violation of your lines, Major," Ellicott said.

"What's that?"

"Our calculations show that this house lies partly across one of your proposed avenues," Banneker said.

"Impossible," L'Enfant said. "I must see for myself."

Ellicott produced a map and marked it with an X. "That's where the building is, Major." The X was on what is today New Jersey Avenue.

The color drained from L'Enfant's face. "What fool would do such a thing?" he said.

"I'm afraid it's one of the commissioners, sir. Commissioner Carroll, I think," Ellicott said.

L'Enfant was furious. He paced the room, angry with those who would change the pure lines of what would be the most important city in the nation.

He could control himself no longer. He shouted at his surveyors, "We will tear it down." L'Enfant issued the order and the following day workers began tearing down the mansion.

The President was angered. He had personally appointed the commissioners. Now this high-handed engineer, friend though he was, had insulted one of them. He probably had broken the law as well. Washington ordered the house rebuilt on a different location, but it appeared that the damage was done. This time L'Enfant had gone too far. Tearing down a man's house was very serious business.

In March, a year after the project had begun, Thomas Jefferson, the Secretary of State, told the commission that it had been found impractical to continue with L'Enfant. The major had just now been notified that "his services were at an end."

Knowing the temper of the young architect, it should have been possible to anticipate what happened. L'Enfant stormed out of his office, all his plans, notes, and records wrapped up in a carrying case, and left for New York. Where

now would Congress turn for a map of the City of Washington in the District of Columbia?

Jefferson called a meeting of the commissioners, the surveyors, and everyone else who had been working on the project.

Could anyone suggest what they should consider doing next?

No one in the room stirred. Ellicott looked at Benjamin Banneker, an unspoken question in his eyes. Banneker stared back. He knew what the question was, and he thought he knew the answer. Slowly, he stood up.

"Mr. Secretary," he began, "I might have an idea."

He waited. Here he was, suggesting that he might be able to accomplish what nobody else had any notion how to handle. Would Jefferson let him speak?

"Yes," Jefferson replied, "what is it?"

"Sir," Banneker began, "were the original plans satisfactory?"

Jefferson nodded.

"As you know," Banneker proceeded, "Major Ellicott and I worked closely with Major L'Enfant, especially in the last few months. I have his plans for the City of Washington—here in my head."

Before anyone could express astonishment at the statement, Ellicott stood up, nodding vigorously. "He probably does, Mr. Secretary. Benjamin Banneker has an incredible memory. I've known him for years. If he says that he remembers the plans, I believe he does."

"That's a rather remarkable claim," Jefferson said.

"I realize that, Mr. Secretary," Banneker said quickly. "But if you would give me a month, I believe I could draw plans to duplicate the original."

Again the room was quiet. If anyone thought he had a better idea, he was being careful to keep it to himself.

"Well, gentlemen?" Jefferson paused and looked at each man there, one by one. "It seems we have had one suggestion made as to how we might save the City of Washington. I see nothing to be lost by trying. Mr. Banneker, please proceed."

Benjamin Banneker left for home that afternoon. He had spoken bravely to the commissioners. Did he really have the plan in his head?

It was indeed a remarkable memory, as Ellicott had stated. Poring over available maps, the few papers L'Enfant had left behind, his own notebooks and calculations, Benjamin Banneker, in just over a month's time, drew up a new map for the City of Washington in the District of Columbia.

With a new set of plans, the commissioners were able to order the work to begin again. Ellicott was appointed to succeed L'Enfant. Banneker continued to work at the side of Ellicott. Slowly the city began to take shape, true to the concept of the brilliant young Frenchman whose vision, preserved in the memory of Benjamin Banneker, would create one of the world's most beautiful and historic sites.

CHECK FOR UNDERSTANDING

1. Where did L'Enfant want to build most of the government buildings? Why weren't they built there?
2. Why do you think L'Enfant trusted Benjamin Banneker and wanted Banneker to work closely with him?
3. What did L'Enfant do when he found out that someone had built a house in the middle of what was to become New Jersey Avenue?
4. What happened to the original plans for Washington, D.C.?
5. How did Benjamin Banneker save the city of Washington?

WRITE ABOUT *"Planning the Nation's Capital"*

Imagine that you are George Washington. Write a letter to Commissioner Carroll, the person whose new house was torn down on Major L'Enfant's orders. Your letter should apologize for what happened and tell the Commissioner that his house will be rebuilt in another place.

ADJUSTING READING RATE

How fast do you walk? How slowly do you eat? The best answer for both of these questions is probably, "It depends."

If you are already five minutes late for school, the most beautiful day of the most beautiful season of the year can't make you slow down. On the other hand, walking through a meadow bursting with spring flowers can take all day if you have the time. Where you walk can also make a difference in your walking speed. Climbing a rough mountain trail, where you sometimes need to search for the path, takes much longer than covering the same distance on a city street. The speed at which you walk varies depending on what you are trying to do.

When you finish mowing the lawn on a hot summer day, you can drink a pitcher of water in no time at all. A Thanksgiving dinner, on the other hand, is something most people like to linger over—to enjoy both the food and the company. You eat or drink slowly or quickly depending on what your body needs and on what kind of occasion it is.

Do you know how fast you read? Reading these selections will help you find out.

Selection 1: Find Flora Bailey's telephone number.

Baggert, Ralph	783-5943
Baghdas, Eli	746-9815
Bagimen, Sylvester	798-4322
Bahtur, Ulan	743-6789
Baid, Wendy	787-3487
Bailey, Flora	746-8973
Baily, Frances	787-6869

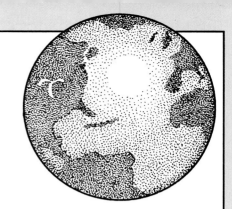

Selection 2: Define continental drift.

Imagine that each piece of land on Planet Earth is like an island, floating in a giant sea. Each island moves very, very slowly. Eventually, one island collides with another and sticks together. Now imagine that each island is really a huge body of land called a continent, which drifts around the globe.

Selection 3: What do you think will happen next?

Sam didn't want to listen. He put his hands over his ears, trying very hard not to hear. It was no use, No matter how he tried he couldn't help hearing the footsteps. Now they had crossed the living room, and now they were climbing the stairs toward his room—his safe, safe room here in the only house on the island.

One way to answer the question is to say, "I read as fast as I walk or eat." Or you could say, "It depends on what I am reading and why I am reading it."

There are some things that cannot be read word for word. When you needed Flora Bailey's telephone number, you ran your eye down the page until you found it. When you are doing a report on American life in 1800, you might look at the table of contents of three or four different books to get an idea of how many pages each one has on this period. You might also skim through the index to see if it has any entries for particular people or places you want to write about.

STUDY SKILLS

Getting an overall view of something or finding a name or date is the fastest kind of reading for information. When you read other books for information—your textbook for example—or when you read a set of directions that describe how to build or use something, you must read more slowly. You will not be able to understand or to use the information unless you pay close attention to all the details.

One way you have learned to read a textbook is the PQRST method. These five letters stand for the five steps that will help you understand and remember information better.

P = **Preview**   Look over what you are going to read to get a general idea of what it is all about. Headings, pictures, captions, and words in boldface are all clues to the content of the selection. Look at the sample on the next page. What clue words do you find?

Q = **Question**   Make up questions about the material you have previewed. What questions do you want answered about the sample? (Remember to divide your paper into three columns. Label the columns HEADING or KEY WORD, QUESTION, and ANSWER. Write the headings and the key words in the first column. Then turn each heading and key word into a question.)

R = **Read**   Read to find the answer to the questions you have made up. After you have read the sample selection, decide if you want to add more questions to your list.

S = **Study**   Write the answers to the questions on your list. Check the text to be sure your answers are correct and complete.

T = **Test**   To complete your studying, give yourself a test. Fold back the ANSWER column of your paper and ask yourself each question. Make sure that you remember each answer correctly.

The XYZ Affair

John Adams was elected President in 1796. He faced a major problem with France, which was acting as if America were an enemy. The whole matter blew up in what was called the "XYZ Affair."

The Background of the Affair In 1796, England and France were at war. The United States had a **treaty** with England that allowed the British to seize any French goods found on American ships. The French started to capture and hold American ships in return. When Adams took office, the French had seized 200 American ships.

Adams sent three Americans as **envoys** to Paris to meet with the French **Foreign Minister**, Talleyrand. Talleyrand sent three of his own assistants to meet with the three Americans. The assistants suggested that nothing could be done unless the United States made a loan to France and gave nearly a quarter of a million dollars to Talleyrand himself. Furious, the Americans reported to Adams what had happened. In their letter, they described Talleyrand's assistants as X, Y, and Z.

The American Reaction A furious America turned against the French. Adams' party adopted the slogan, "Millions for defense, but not one cent for **tribute**." American ships started fighting back, capturing 80 French

ships. Although Congress did indeed vote millions for defense, the United States did not actually go to war with France.

The End of the Affair All this time, one of the American envoys had stayed behind in Paris. In 1799 he reported that the French might be ready to sign a treaty with the United States. The next year, the French and the Americans did sign a treaty of friendship. It marked the start of a peace with France that has never been broken.

This special kind of reading takes time, but it works. You will use this method of reading all your life—whenever you have to remember what you have read.

What about things you don't have to read for school? How quickly do you read the sports page of a newspaper, or a movie review, or an adventure story? Read these two passages to see if you read each one differently.

Before the season even began, Mel was worrying about his fastball. Last year, after a string of losses, he thought that he would never get another ball past another batter. Was it the August heat that did it? This year, he wasn't going to take any chances. He was going to get used to heat before it got to him. So there he was, on his farm in Minnesota, sitting in a sauna that he had built, and making the temperature go to over a hundred and thirty degrees.

With a soft THUPP, the ship settled in the dust of the red planet. Karleel waited for the instruments to register zero before she touched the sonal button. The sensor device attached to the underside of the ship unfolded itself from the storage pod and curled a metal tentacle through the dust, pushing it aside the way a human finger would push aside a bit of fluff. Then, locking its plates together, it became a rigid probe that drilled through the hard surfaces.

You probably liked one type of story better than the other, and you might have read it faster. You probably skipped over any words you didn't know, and you didn't bother to look them up. When you read for pleasure, the whole book or story is what counts, not the individual parts.

Your reading rate will be different, depending on what you read and why you read it. Knowing ahead of time what kind of reading you are doing will help you adjust your reading rate to the right speed for the job.

Using What You Have Learned

Quick reading (skimming), PQRST (reading for information), and reading for pleasure are three reading rates you use every day. Which reading rate would you use for each reading task?

1. You have just brought home the latest novel by your favorite author.

2. You are using a bus schedule to find the next bus to your friend's house.

3. You must read two chapters in your science book tonight.

4. Your scout troop is giving a first-aid course and your first assignment is to read about helping choking victims.

5. You turn to the weather map to find the temperature in South Dakota.

Expanding Your Skills

Offer to read aloud to a younger child. First read something, like a book on science or animals, that is filled with facts. Then read a story. Did you read one faster than the other? Did you stop to explain things in the fact-filled piece? Report your findings to the class.

Many of the people who took part in important events in American history were not famous people. Sacajawea was such a person.

How did Sacajawea become part of the Lewis and Clark expedition? How did joining the expedition help Sacajawea fulfill her own personal dream?

SACAJAWEA

by MARION GRIDLEY

In 1803, an expedition was organized to explore the West. Meriwether Lewis and William Clark would lead the expedition. The purpose of the Lewis and Clark expedition was to explore the territory of the Louisiana Purchase and the country west of the Rocky Mountains.

The expedition set out from St. Louis in May 1804. Lewis and Clark spent their next winter in Mandan Indian villages, near what is now Bismarck, North Dakota. During that winter, a young Shoshone woman named Sacajawea joined the expedition as a guide.

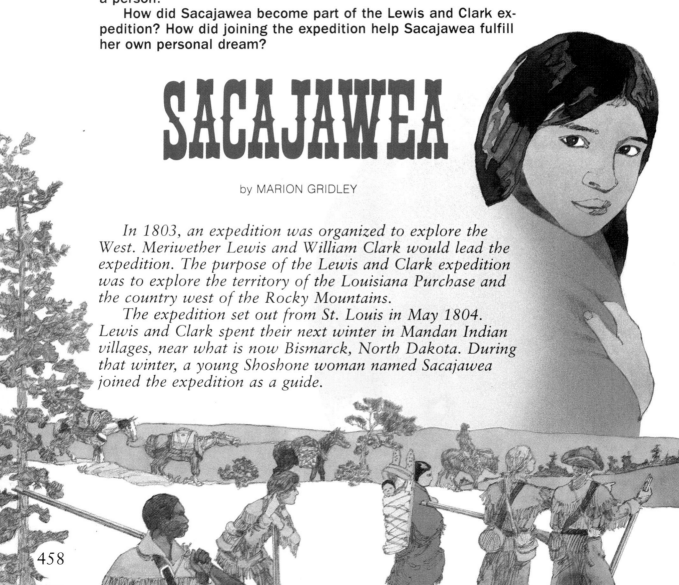

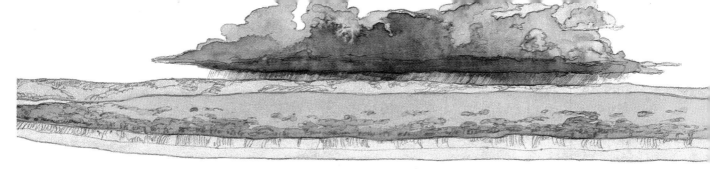

Though her name may not be familiar to everyone today, Sacajawea, the Shoshone girl who guided the Lewis and Clark Expedition to the Pacific coast, is one of the most honored women in American history. There are several statues of her. A number of monuments have been placed along the trail that she traveled as well as on the site of her birthplace in Idaho. It is said that there are more statues and monuments to Sacajawea than any other woman in this country.

When Sacajawea was nearly fourteen years old, the Shoshones were attacked by the Hidatsas while they were preparing buffalo meat after a hunt. The Shoshones lived in the mountains, but they hunted on the plains, moving about after the buffalo herds.

Sacajawea was seized and lifted to the back of a warrior's horse. As she was carried away, she saw her brother in the midst of the fighting. That was the last time she was to see her people for several years.

The Hidatsas kept Sacajawea as a slave. But she was not treated unkindly. The women showed her how to plant corn—how to dig the soil with a pointed stick, how to push in the seeds, how to hoe the ground with a buffalo shoulder blade. When the crops were ripe, Sacajawea helped with the harvest. The fields of corn were a

constant wonder to her. Her own people were nomads and did no planting. The round, earth lodges of the Hidatsas were a wonder, too. Sacajawea had always lived in a skin tepee and never in one place.

When Sacajawea was about sixteen, the Hidatsas traded her to Touissant Charbonneau, a French trader. She became Charbonneau's wife.

In the winter of 1804, Lewis and Clark, with their men, arrived on the first lap of their long journey. They would rest through the rugged months until spring, getting supplies together and boats in order for the task ahead.

Charbonneau was hired as an interpreter for the expedition and he decided that Sacajawea would go with him. She could still speak her own language, she knew trails through the mountains, and a woman with the party would indicate to the tribes that this was a peaceful mission.

Sacajawea was eager to go. Perhaps she would see her people again. And she would see what

lay on the other side of the mountains. A great ocean, the white men said. What was an ocean like?

Sacajawea's son, Baptiste, was born in February. In April, the expedition started out. With her baby on her back, Sacajawea rode in the lead boat. Baptiste was carried close and tight by his mother's blanket-shawl for the whole journey of more than four thousand miles.

Sacajawea knew just where to find wild plants that would supplement the constant meat diet.

Her sense of direction was unerring. She remembered many places from her childhood. Because her knowledge of the Hidatsa and Shoshone languages, she made it possible to communicate with tribes met along the way. At night, when they camped she sat by Captain Clark and in a combination of sign language, halting French, and English told of Indian trails and villages, warned of bad water or poisonous plants.

Strong winds and rough water fought the heavily laden boats, forcing the expedition to move slowly. Once a boat filled with valuable instruments and papers capsized. It was Sacajawea, Baptiste still on her back, who plunged into the icy water and swam about until she had saved everything. She was carried to a roaring fire on the shore. There the men gave her a hearty cheer. Sacajawea did not know why the things were so valuable, but Captain Clark was delighted that they had been saved. She did not consider that she had done anything unusual.

As the expedition neared Sacajawea's homeland, the two leaders were worried. No white men had ever passed to the west of her people. Would the Shoshones recognize her? Would they listen to her?

When Sacajawea saw the Shoshone camp, she gave a cry of joy. The braves, with their chief, awaited the approach of the white men. Sacajawea rushed forward and threw her blanket around the shoulders of the chief.

"We are of one blanket," she cried, for the chief was her brother, Cameahwait.

There was great rejoicing over

Sacajawea's return. A council was held. Sacajawea spoke in behalf of Lewis and Clark while the Indians listened with close attention. She told of their great need for horses. Without them the party could not cross the Great Divide. She asked for guides to help them along the way.

The Shoshones gladly gave the expedition horses. They provided a guide to help them get through the mountains to the navigable waters of the Columbia. The expedition did not leave the Shoshones until the end of August and the hardest part of the journey lay ahead of them. Winter storms were already swirling through the mountains. They clogged the trails with snow and bombarded the expedition with sleet. Both horses and men were exhausted from the steep trails. It often seemed that they could not endure the hardships another day.

Then, one November day, the flag was raised to the top of a tall tree. In sight of the ocean, Captain Clark claimed the land for the United States. The men stood in awed silence. Sacajawea held Baptiste up to see the waves breaking on the shore. She was the first woman to cross the Great Rocky Mountains. Because of her, the whole Northwest Territory would be opened up.

CHECK FOR UNDERSTANDING

1. How did Sacajawea become a slave of the Hidatsas? How did they treat her?
2. How did Sacajawea become part of the Lewis and Clark expedition?
3. For what two reasons did Charbonneau think Sacajawea would be helpful on the expedition?
4. How did joining the expedition help Sacajawea fulfill her own personal dream?

Over the Rockies with Lewis and Clark

by CHARLES BOHNER

When the Lewis and Clark expedition left the Shoshone camp, the worst part of the journey was still ahead. They still had to cross the rugged Rocky Mountains. But the most thrilling part of the journey was also still to come: reaching the Pacific Ocean.

This is a fictionalized account of the final lap of the journey. Hugh McNeal, the youngest member of the Lewis and Clark expedition, tells the story.

In what ways was the journey over the Rockies different from the rest of the trip? What signs indicated that the expedition was nearing the Pacific Ocean?

From where we were camping we could see the mountains wrapped in late summer haze. They looked scary to me. Even Sergeant Ordway, who had grown up among the White Mountains of New Hampshire, said there was nothing back there to match these. Having lived through what we had, I reckoned we could cross those mountains. We were in high spirits and well fed. We had found the Shoshone, and we were on the right track.

We did cross those mountains. But nothing we had seen, not grizzlies or rapids or mosquitoes, had prepared us for what was to come. It was as if that great continent, lying silently in wait and watching us swell with pride, had purposely saved the greatest battle for last. Only the Rocky Mountains stood between us and our victory.

Among the Shoshone we found a grizzled old warrior to guide us. We could not wrap our American tongues around his name, so we just called him Old Toby. Sacajawea could understand him. But to the rest of us his voice sounded like pebbles rattling in a cedar bucket.

By early September we were ready to start. We had to cross a saucer-shaped valley crowded with spruce and pine and fir. Those trees were the highest I ever saw. When we made camp that first night, the trail was folded in behind us by the hills and we were landlocked in that valley.

I felt odd. And as I lay in my blankets, it suddenly came to me why I felt so strange. Up until then I had always lived on the river. Our expedition had been on the kinds of rivers I understood. Whatever shoals and rapids and falls had been ahead, they were dangers that I knew and respected. I had grown up on the Ohio. I knew the rowdy rivermen. I knew the floods and the droughts, the possibility around every bend of excitement and change. The current lapping at the shore was a language I understood.

For the first time in my life I was hemmed in by mountains. I didn't like them. They were too high and too cold and too quiet for me.

Our party moved forward in single file. I was given a little sorrel mare to lead. I named her Dolly.

She was heavily loaded with trinkets for the Indians.

"These are the last, Hugh," Captain Clark said. He helped me load the bundle onto the mare's back. "We'll need them for the Indians beyond the mountains."

Dolly picked her way gingerly among the stones. Her hooves were raw and broken from the rocks and pebbles. She gasped and wheezed in my ear and rolled her eyes as if pleading for relief.

"Easy, easy," I whispered to her.

Reuben Field was ahead of me. He started back down the file and gave her a slap on the rump.

"Move it!" he shouted at her.

"I'll look after her," I said to him sharply.

Reuben glared at me, shrugged, and walked on.

Old Toby somehow stayed on the trail that landslides and fallen timber and mountain streams had done their best to hide from him. A tree blown across the path meant hours of clearing a way through twisted limbs and dead leaves. Streams thundered over

465

ledges down into gorges. We had no choice but to ford icy currents that snatched at our ankles.

I'd venture slowly out into the stream, holding Dolly's tether. I'd slip on a rock, lose my footing, and plunge waist-deep into the stream. But the little mare braced herself against the current until I was on my feet. Several times we both fell. We rolled over in the water, gasping and sputtering, until we washed ashore fifty yards downstream. After one dunking, Dolly came up with a raw and bruised foreleg. She began to limp.

At last we were up above the timber, picking our way along a knife edge that dropped off steeply on both sides. We were high enough so that clouds hid the canyon below.

"It's going to rain," Pat Gass said. "My old wounds are throbbing."

Pat was right. The sky was darkening. The wind came off the peaks, bringing rain behind it. In fifteen minutes it had turned to snow. Wet, driving snow stung our faces and froze on our eyebrows.

Captain Lewis came down the line.

"We'll stop," he shouted. "Old Toby can't see a thing in this snowstorm. Make ready for a cold night."

That night gave us the first taste of what was to come. We had no shelter, but slept exposed on that high, bare mountainside. There was just enough wood for a single fire, and only a handful of jerky to eat.

I think I would have frozen that night, and many others, if Dolly hadn't been there. I curled up behind her in my blankets, her back protecting me from the heavy snow that whirled off those peaks.

In the morning the baggage was stiff and frozen. Although several of the horses had wandered off, it was easy to round them up. Their tracks showed clearly in the fresh snow.

I searched for a few leaves for Dolly to eat, since we were up above pasture land. She munched them when I held them out and nuzzled my pockets for more.

There was no more. For that matter, there wasn't much food for the humans. We couldn't pack enough on the horses for all, and we planned to live off the territory. Nobody was to blame. The captains hadn't known what to expect. The snow had driven the elk and deer down the mountain in search of food. Our hunters returned with nothing but tantalizing tales of a few faint deer tracks. George Drewyer never failed, and he came in with three pheasants. But they couldn't feed thirty hungry people. For water up there we melted snow—in such weather there wasn't much demand for ice water.

Old Toby cared nothing about the weather. And he never seemed to eat. I asked John Shields, who said he, too, had never seen him eat. The old Indian could live anywhere. When the trail disappeared under his feet, his shrewd eye would scan the land in front of us. He would step along as if he were on a corduroy road.* When all was buried in snow, he would study the branches of trees where the packs of Indian horses had rubbed the leaves. He would stop, point ahead, and say something

* A road built of logs laid side by side.

in his gravelly voice. Sacajawea would tell Charbonneau in Shoshone, Charbonneau would tell George Drewyer in French, and George would report to the captains in English.

For terror those mountain passes beat even the Missouri in flood. We'd struggle up the slopes in wet snow. I would pull Dolly's tether, and somebody, John Shields or Pat Gass, would heave from behind. The little mare would stagger, fall to her knees, heave back up, and turn her eyes toward me for rescue.

"Leave her alone," I always said to Pat. "She'll get up."

Finally, I was the only one who could get her on her feet.

"Easy! Easy!" I'd whisper, and she'd roll her eyes at me and heave once more. Coughing and panting, she'd slowly struggle to her feet.

At night Dolly would limp over and stand near my bedroll. Somehow I'd manage to save her something to eat. I would crawl into my blankets and fall dead asleep. In the morning I would find her at

my head, blocking the wind and snow that howled now without mercy.

We were very high, and we had run out of food. All I could think of was those summer nights on the Missouri when I had gnawed a few choice morsels off a rib and then thrown the rest to Captain Lewis's dog, Scannon.

Dolly was staggering. I was carrying part of her load. Pat Gass

was carrying even more. In those mountains you struggle up a long ridge, come to the top, and there, stretching out before you, is a dry, stony valley and still one more ridge. Our spirits rose as we climbed up each ridge, only to sink again as we saw, looming ahead, a higher peak.

The morning snow had changed to drenching rain. I was trudging along, sore and bruised, my mind a blank. Suddenly, the tether jerked my arm as if to pull it from my shoulder. I had wrapped it around my palm.

Dolly let out a high, shrieking whinny. She lost her footing, stumbled, and began to slide.

I was pulled over onto my side into the stones and for twenty feet slid on my elbows and belly.

Pat Gass yelled, "Let go! Let go!"

I lay sprawled out on my stomach with my face in my arms. Up from the valley echoed a distant, terrible thud. Then everything was silent.

Pat Gass came running up.

"Are you all right?" he shouted at me, as if I were on another peak.

Tears were rolling down my face. I tried to stop, but it was no use. I lay with my head in my arms and sobbed.

I heard Captain Lewis softly give the order to stop. We would go no farther that day. Somebody gripped me on the shoulder, and I could hear camp being made around me.

That night the scouts came in and said that the ridge to the south was the last. Beyond it lay a long green valley and the Columbia River. The river would carry us to the Pacific Ocean.

We knew now that we would make it. Nothing could stop us. The men sang and shouted.

But somehow I couldn't enter into the joy of it. All I could think of was the high, shrieking whinny of Dolly, plunging and rolling down that barren slope.

For the third time the Corps of Discovery was building the craft to carry them along a river. Captain Lewis called us together the first morning to divide up the

work. Only half the party, however, could be mustered. The men were too sick or too weak from hunger to rise off their blankets. Captain Lewis himself could barely sit in the saddle. Some of the men had fallen by the trail and had to be packed down the last mountain on Indian ponies. We were lucky to come among peaceful Indians, the tribe of the Nez Percé. If they had been hostile, we'd have been easy prey.

George Drewyer, as tough as hickory, had gone off at daylight before even the captains were up. By midmorning he was back with a fat deer. I stuffed myself and, unused to such rich food, got mighty sick. The Nez Percé supplied us with dried salmon and roots. Slowly we recovered our health.

In a week we were gliding down water so clear that I could see fish swimming twenty feet below the surface. The country out there was always changing. Plains stretched away to highlands or cliffs of rugged black rock towered out over the river. Everywhere the Indians came down to the shore to watch us go by.

How that shore rolled by! Some days we made thirty or forty miles. There were fierce rapids that we would never have risked earlier. We shot them now, gambling our equipment and our lives. The canoes twisted and bucked like wild horses. We hung on, yipping and whooping for sheer joy. Our passage through that land was headlong. We had seen the wonders of the West. All we wanted now was to come to the end.

One river flowed into the next, each broader and deeper than the last, until we were in the Colum-

bia. We paddled still faster and harder, peering around every bend, our eyes searching for that last blue opening to the ocean.

One afternoon, paddling past a crowd of Indians standing on the bank, Pat Gass let out a yip.

"Look!" he shouted. "That coat!"

Sure enough, an Indian was wearing a blue sailor's jacket. He could have gotten it only by trading with a white man near the ocean.

After that, we saw signs every day. I saw a British musket. The others caught sight of brass tea-kettles, blue and scarlet cloth, pistols, and tin powder flasks. The Indian jewelry, we noticed, was now made of seashells.

The river opened up until it was a mile or two across. We began to pass Indians canoeing downstream to trade. The water turned salt, and along the shore you could see the tide line.

The final morning was thick with fog. Ordinarily we would have waited, but we were up early and shoving the canoes off a sand beach soon after daybreak. The tide was with us and we were making good time. We were out in the middle, running with the current.

The sun was slanting down through the haze. Slowly the fog began to lift. The light dissolved in ribbons and wisps. Here and there a clear patch gleamed. At first there was only a blue blur ahead. And then, so gradually that you could not at any moment say *There! There it is!* we saw emerge out of the mist the faint line of the horizon. Another moment and the vast, blue, glittering Pacific Ocean was spread out before us in the morning sunshine.

Everybody was shouting and cheering. Paddles waved in the air.

Captain Lewis shot off his pistol.

Captain Clark raised his hand. "Listen!" he called across the water.

Far off we could hear the thunder of the breakers dashing up on the rocky shore.

472

CHECK FOR UNDERSTANDING

1. In what ways was the journey over the Rockies different from the rest of the trip?
2. What was unusual about Old Toby's skills? What was unusual about him personally?
3. What were two of the most difficult problems the expedition had crossing the Rockies?
4. Why were the people in the expedition particularly grateful that the Nez Percé Indians were friendly?
5. What signs indicated that the expedition was nearing the Pacific Ocean?
6. Why were the people on the expedition so happy to have reached their goal?

WRITE ABOUT

"Over the Rockies with Lewis and Clark"

Imagine that Old Toby, the Shoshone who led the expedition over the Rockies, kept a journal. What might his thoughts have been about the people he was leading and the purpose of their journey? Pretend that you are Old Toby. Write a paragraph or two about your experience with the Lewis and Clark expedition.

COMPREHENSION

Sequence of Events

When you tell someone about something that happened to you, you probably begin at the beginning and continue straight through to the end. You start with the first thing that happened and describe the events in the order in which they occurred. Sometimes, however, when you are telling a story, you may find it necessary to tell about something that happened *before* the series of events you are describing. You usually do this to give background information that will help your listeners understand why something that happened is particularly important. At other times you may find it necessary to mention something that happened afterward. You might do this to give your listeners an idea of what occurred as a result of the events you are describing.

Read these two paragraphs. Do the highlighted sentences describe things that happen before or after the other events?

I was reading about the Oregon Trail in the encyclopedia. The article explained that mountain men were responsible for making the trail known to settlers. It said that a mountain man named James Bridger was known as a guide. I had read tall tales about Jim Bridger, but I never knew before that he was a real person. So I looked up BRIDGER, JAMES in the encyclopedia. I found out that he was a mountain man who became famous for spinning tall tales.

Last summer our family visited Plymouth, Massachusetts. The first thing we did was tour the replica of the *Mayflower.* I was surprised to see how small the ship

was. Now whenever I think of the Pilgrims, I imagine a hundred and two people crowded onto that little ship for a two-month voyage. After we toured the *Mayflower,* we visited Plymouth Rock. Then we went to Plymouth Plantation, which is a re-creation of the original colony.

In the first paragraph, does the highlighted sentence describe something that happened before or after the other events? What clues helped you decide?

In the first paragraph, word clues help you to recognize that the event took place earlier. The verb tense changes from *was reading* and *said* to *had read.* The word *before* is also a signal that what is described happened earlier. Words and phrases that indicate time and time relationships can help you identify sequence of events.

In the second paragraph, does the highlighted sentence describe something that happened before or after the other events? How did you decide?

In the second paragraph, the highlighted sentence describes something that occurred after the other events. The word *Now* gives you a clue about the time relationship. But even if the word *Now* did not appear you could probably figure out the sequence. Seeing the *Mayflower* is the cause. Imagining the hardship of the voyage is the effect. An effect must always occur after its cause. Identifying cause and effect is often the most useful way to understand the sequence of events.

When you read "Jim Bridger's Alarm Clock," think about how cause and effect determines the sequence of events in the story.

Sweet Betsy from Pike

Oh, don't you re-mem-ber Sweet Bet-sy from Pike,

Who crossed the big moun-tains with her hus-band Ike,

With two yoke of cat-tle, a large yel-low dog,

A— tall Shang-hai roost-er, and one spot-ted hog.

REFRAIN

Say-ing,"Good-by, Pike Coun-ty, Fare-well for a while.
We'll— come back a-gain When we've panned out our pile."

One evening quite early they camped on the Platte.
'Twas nearby the road on a green shady flat,
Where Betsy, quite tired, lay down to repose,
While Ike gazed with wonder on his Pike County rose.

They soon reached the desert, where Betsy gave out,
And down in the sand she lay rolling about,
While Ike in great tears looked on in surprise,
Saying, "Betsy, get up, you'll get sand in your eyes."

Sweet Betsy got up in a great deal of pain
And declared she'd go back to Pike County again.
Then Ike heaved a sigh, and they fondly embraced,
And she traveled along with his arm 'round her waist.

The Shanghai ran off and the cattle all died.
The last piece of bacon that morning was fried.
Poor Ike got discouraged, and Betsy got mad.
The dog wagged his tail and looked wonderfully sad.

They passed the Sierras through mountains of snow
Till old California was sighted below.
Sweet Betsy she hollered, and Ike gave a cheer,
Saying, "Betsy, my darling, I'm a new millionaire."

One morning they climbed up a very high hill
And looked down with wonder at old Placeville;
Ike shouted and said when he cast his eyes down,
"Sweet Betsy, my darling, there's gold in this town!"

Jim Bridger's Alarm Clck

by SID FLEISCHMAN

To live in the wilderness, people had to be strong and able to deal with any situation. In this tall tale, you will meet Jim Bridger, a character who has all the qualities needed to survive in the wilderness, and then some.

In what ways does the author make Jim Bridger larger than life? What three things is Jim Bridger *not* famous for?

Jim Bridger was a mighty tall man. When he stubbed his big toe, it took six minutes before he felt it and yelled "Ouch." But he's not famous for being tall.

Jim Bridger was a long-haired mountain man. In fringed buckskins and Indian moccasins, he wandered through the wilderness of the Old West before almost anyone else. It was Jim who brushed the hair out of his eyes and discovered the Great Salt Lake. They might have named it after him, but no one believed he'd found water you couldn't sink in. Jim shrugged his big, bony shoulders and headed back to the mountains.

One day his horse broke three front teeth grazing on a patch of green grass. That's how Jim discovered a petrified forest. The grass and trees had turned to stone for miles around. "Petrified, all petrified," he reported when he got back to civilization. "The bees and the wild flowers, and yes sir, some of those trees had petrified birds on their limbs singing petrified songs."

But he's not famous for all those things.

Jim Bridger was a ramshackle, sharp-eyed army scout. In time they named a fort and a forest after him, and a pass and a creek and a mountain or two.

He once pointed to a mountain in the distance, flat-topped and red as a Navajo blanket. "Stranger," he said.

Jim liked to talk to strangers; they were so few and far between in the wilderness. "Stranger, look how that mountain has grown! When I first came out here, it was nothing but a red anthill."

And that's what Jim Bridger's famous for. That mountain. He made an alarm clock out of it.

The way it happened, Jim was out in the wilderness, as usual, when a blizzard whipped down out of Canada. His beard froze. The fringe in his buckskins froze. And his long hair hung like icicles. Then a spark from his campfire lit inside his moccasin. That spark was so cold it frostbit him, and Jim decided it was time to seek himself a warmer climate. He headed south.

He traveled through the snow for days and nights. He didn't dare to stop and rest. He knew a man could sleep himself to death in the blizzard and bitter cold.

Jim was all tuckered out and knew he couldn't go much further. Then, through the chill daylight, he caught sight of that red, flat-topped mountain in the distance. It was slab-sided, too, and he had bounced echoes off it many a time. He reckoned from where he now stood, it would take about eight hours for an echo to return.

Jim Bridger gave a yip of joy and made camp. He laid out his bedroll on the snow. Then he gave an ear-quivering yell.

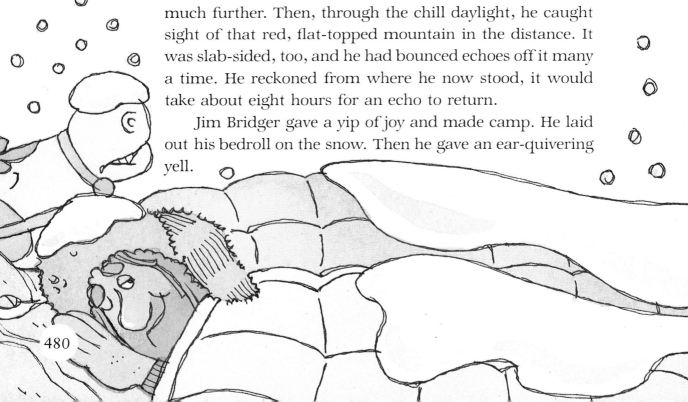

"WAKE UP! WAKE UP, JIM BRIDGER, YOU FROSTBIT, NO-ACCOUNT RASCAL!"

Then he climbed into his bedroll, clamped his eyes shut, and fell away to snoring. Oh, he snored thunderbolts, and dreamed of hot biscuits and gravy.

Exactly seven hours and fifty-six minutes later, Jim Bridger's Alarm Clock went off.

"WAKE UP!" roared the echo. "WAKE UP, JIM BRIDGER, YOU FROSTBIT, NO-ACCOUNT RASCAL!"

Jim roused from his bedroll, all refreshed and feeling strong as a new rope. It was a week before he reached Fort Bridger, where the sun was shining and no one believed his story.

481

But a trapper came straggling in and said, "It's true, every word. I found the coals of Jim's campfire and bundled up in furs to catch some shuteye. Next thing I knew, that mountain commenced booming. I didn't get a wink of sleep. Doggonit, Jim, you snore loud enough to drive pigs to market!"

CHECK FOR UNDERSTANDING

1. In what ways does the author make Jim Bridger larger than life?
2. What three things is Jim Bridger *not* famous for?
3. Why wasn't the Great Salt Lake named for Jim Bridger?
4. Why didn't the trapper get a wink of sleep?

Miss Louisa and the Outlaws

by FRANCES B. WATTS

What is courage? In this play, the students in Miss Louisa's class learn a lesson in courage.

How does Miss Louisa define courage? How does Miss Louisa show courage?

CHARACTERS

MISS LOUISA, *the schoolteacher*

THEODORE
WILLIAM
ANNABELLE } *pupils*
CLARA
REGINA

OTHER PUPILS

BENNY } *outlaws*
DEAD-EYE DAN

SHERIFF

SHERIFF'S ASSISTANT

TIME: *A day in October, at the turn of the century.*

SETTING: *A one-room schoolhouse.*

483

AT RISE: *Miss Louisa is standing at her desk. The pupils sit at attention, with their hands folded.*

MISS LOUISA: For our history lesson this afternoon you all were to learn the first three stanzas of "Paul Revere's Ride." Theodore, would you come to the front of the room and recite, please?

THEODORE (*Rises uneasily from his desk and walks slowly to front. Recites haltingly*): Uh—uh—"Listen, my—children, and you—shall hear." Uh—uh—

INK

MISS LOUISA (*Sternly*): I see that you haven't studied your lesson, Theodore. You will stay after school and learn the lines before you leave this afternoon. Do you understand?

THEODORE (*Mumbles as he slinks back to his seat*): Yes.

MISS LOUISA: Remember your manners! Yes *what*, Theodore?

THEODORE (*Straightens up and speaks with respect*): Yes, *Miss Louisa.*

MISS LOUISA: William, let's see how well you have learned the stanzas.

WILLIAM (*Stumbles to front, stares up at ceiling and recites slowly*): Uh—uh. "Listen, my children, and you shall hear." Uh—uh. "Of the midnight ride of Paul Revere." Uh—uh— (*fidgets*)

MISS LOUISA: William, you will join Theodore after school. Do you understand?

WILLIAM (*Mumbles as he returns to his seat*): Yes.

MISS LOUISA: Yes *what*, William?

WILLIAM (*With respect*): Yes, *Miss Louisa.*

MISS LOUISA (*Sighs*): Boys and girls, I asked you to memorize it in hopes that you will recog-

nize the courage and strength some of our forefathers possessed when they founded our great country. Do you know what courage is?

CLASS (*After a moment's hesitation*): No, Miss Louisa.

MISS LOUISA: Well, courage is behaving bravely when you are most afraid. All of us, at some time, have been afraid. Those who discipline themselves and control fear in times of stress are exhibiting courage. Is that clear?

CLASS: Yes, Miss Louisa.

WILLIAM (*In a whispered aside to Theodore*): I'll bet Miss Louisa has never been afraid in her life!

THEODORE (*aside*): You said it.

MISS LOUISA: Annabelle, do you think you can recite the lines for us?

ANNABELLE: Yes, Miss Louisa. (*She goes confidently to front and recites*):
"Listen, my children, and you shall hear
Of the midnight ride of Paul Revere."

(*She recites first two verses. Then outlaws enter down right.*)

BENNY: Stay where you are!

THEODORE (*Fearfully*): Outlaws! It's Benny the Kid and Dead-Eye Dan! The ones that robbed Dodge City Bank last week!

WILLIAM: It is! It is! Their pictures are up in the Post Office. Wanted, dead or alive! A hundred dollars reward! (*The children scream with terror. Some of them run to the back of the room.*)

MISS LOUISA (*Rapping on desk with a ruler. Speaks sternly*): Back to your seats, everyone! How often have I told you never to leave your seats without permission! (*Timidly, but obediently, children return to seats.*)

DAN: Nobody's going to get hurt, kiddies, as long as you set there quiet.

MISS LOUISA (*With great dignity*): Watch your grammar in front of my pupils, sir. The proper expression is—*sit there quietly*—not—*set there quiet.*

DAN (*Baffled*): Huh? Oh. As long as you *sit there quietly*.

BENNY: Just in case somebody tipped off the Sheriff that we're in town, my pal Dan and me are going to hide out here till the two-thirty freight train comes through. Then we'll make our getaway. So don't anybody get any bright ideas like yelling out the window or running for help, see?

DAN (*Nodding at two vacant desks in row nearest to audience*): Let's take a load off our feet, Benny. May as well be comfortable till train time.

MISS LOUISA (*Firmly*): Just a moment, Daniel! I believe that is your name. You and Benjamin will kindly wipe your feet on this mat before you sit down. (*Points to mat in doorway*)

BENNY (*In confusion*): Say, what is this? Dan and me is outlaws. We don't have to take orders from you.

MISS LOUISA: It's Dan and *I are* outlaws, sir. And as long as

487

you and Benjamin take refuge here, I shall insist that you obey the laws and rules of our schoolhouse. Kindly wipe your feet, gentlemen! *(She stares at the men.)*

DAN *(Grudgingly)*: All right. All right. We'll wipe our feet.

MISS LOUISA: Mind your manners, sir. When I speak to you, you are to answer, "Yes, Miss Louisa." Do you understand?

BENNY *and* DAN *(Meekly)*: Yes, Miss Louisa. *(They wipe their feet, then tiptoe to the vacant desks.)*

BENNY *(Aside to* Dan, *seems puzzled)*: I don't know why we let this schoolteacher lead us around by the nose. By all rights we ought to tie her up in the closet.

MISS LOUISA *(Brisk and efficient)*: Well, boys and girls, we shall continue our history lesson tomorrow. It is now time for music. Let's have a song. A jolly one. How about "Old MacDonald Had a Farm"?

REGINA: We can't sing, Miss Louisa. We—we're too scared!

(Lays head on desk and sobs)

MISS LOUISA*:* Afraid, Regina? Of what is there to be afraid? As far as we are concerned, we simply have two extra pupils in our room. We will follow our usual schedule. *(Coolly takes pitch pipe from her pocket and sounds the key. Class begins to sing "Old MacDonald." Miss Louisa interrupts song by rapping with ruler. Speaking to outlaws)* Benjamin and Daniel, why aren't you singing?

DAN *(Bewildered)*: Huh? Why should we sing?

CLARA *(Earnestly)*: Because, when we have music in this school, everybody sings.

ANNABELLE *(Nods)*: And that means *everybody*. It's a school rule.

MISS LOUISA *(To children)*: Clara and Annabelle, this is not your affair. *(To outlaws, firmly)* When we start to sing again, you will sing. Do you understand?

BENNY *(Mumbles)*: Yes.

MISS LOUISA: Yes, *what*, Benjamin?

BENNY: Yes, Miss Louisa. (Miss

Louisa *blows pipe again and waves her arms as she leads the song. The children's spirits rise noticeably as they progress through the various animal sounds of the song. The faces of the outlaws are comically serious as they sing along with the children. When song ends, Miss Louisa crosses over to window and gazes out with a worried frown.)*

BENNY: Stay away from that window, ma'am. We're not giving you the chance to signal for help.

DAN: You may be a schoolmarm, but you can't outsmart us. Nobody has ever outsmarted Benny the Kid and Dead-Eye Dan.

MISS LOUISA *(Stays at window. Speaks matter-of-factly)*: It looks a bit like rain. William, will you and Theodore please go out and bring in the flag? *(William and* Theodore *rise to obey.)*

BENNY *(To Miss Louisa)*: Do you think we're stupid? Why, the

minute those kids leave this room they'll run for the Sheriff.

WILLIAM *(Nervously)*: Don't insist that we go, Miss Louisa! It really doesn't look like rain.

MISS LOUISA: There are cumulus clouds forming in the west. It is May; showers begin suddenly in spring. *(To outlaws)* It is a rule in our school that we never allow the American flag to become wet. One of you may accompany the boys, if you wish. But our flag must not be rained upon! Do you hear? *(The outlaws exchange exasperated looks, then finally nod agreement.)*

BENNY: Oh, all right then.

MISS LOUISA *(Sternly)*: What did you say?

BENNY *(Meekly)*: Yes, Miss

Louisa. *(He heads toward the door and motions to* William *and* Theodore *to precede him. They exit.)*

MISS LOUISA: Now, boys and girls, we will have a spelling bee. Regina and Clara may be captains. You may start choosing teams, girls. (Clara *and* Regina *proceed to choose sides, calling out various children's names. The teams line up on opposite sides of the stage and face audience.* Benny, Theodore *and* William *enter. They wipe their feet carefully.* William *hands flag to* Miss Louisa, *who folds it and puts it on her desk.)*

REGINA *(Continuing with the choosing)*: I choose Theodore for my team. (Theodore *takes his place.)*

CLARA: I choose William. (William *takes his place.)*

REGINA: I choose Daniel.

CLARA: I choose Benjamin.

BENNY: Say, what is this? What's going on?

DAN *(With enthusiasm)*: A spelling bee, pal. Ain't you never been in a spelling bee before?

MISS LOUISA: *Haven't you ever,* Daniel. Watch that grammar!

DAN: Haven't you ever been in a spelling bee before?

BENNY: No, and I'm not going to now. Besides, it'll be train time soon. We have to stay on the alert.

MISS LOUISA *(Pauses, then nods sympathetically)*: Very well, Benjamin. I will excuse you from participating in the spelling bee. Naturally, it would be most embarrassing for you to be spelled down by a group of young children.

BENNY *(Blustering)*: Who's scared of being spelled down? Look, maybe I haven't had much schooling, but I'm not so dumb that a bunch of little kids can lick me at spelling.

MISS LOUISA: I admire your spirit, Benjamin. You won't mind joining Clara's team then. *(Waits patiently for* Benny *to line up)*

BENNY *(Sighs in resignation)*: Oh, all right.

MISS LOUISA *(Severely)*: What's that, Benjamin?

491

BENNY: Yes, Miss Louisa. *(He takes his place at the end of Clara's line. Miss Louisa stands with a spelling book at center stage and calls out words for the children to spell. Dan and Benny are caught up in the spirit of competition. They cheer and applaud the spellers along with the others. All spell correctly until Benny's turn.)*

MISS LOUISA: Now, Benjamin, I would like you to spell the word "thief."

BENNY *(Raises eyes to ceiling)*: Uh-uh. Lemme see. T—h. T-h-e-i-f.

MISS LOUISA: That is wrong, Benjamin. The correct spelling is t-h-i-e-f. You may take your seat.

WILLIAM *(Aside)*: Gee whiz! He *is* a thief, and he can't even spell it!

BENNY *(Stomps sulkily to his desk)*: Aw, so what if I'm not a good speller. I still make a good living. *(Sound of a train whistle is heard. It gradually increases in volume.)*

DAN *(Rushes to window)*: Yeow! There goes the two-thirty train!

BENNY *(Running over to window, stamping angrily)*: I told you it was time to get out of here! But you had to let that crazy schoolteacher talk us into a spelling bee!

DAN: All right. All right. So at least *I* didn't miss my spelling word. *(The children still stand in their lines, but they buzz* with excitement. Sheriff *and* Assistant *enter suddenly.*)

SHERIFF (*Draws gun, catching outlaws off guard*): Hands up! (*Outlaws raise hands. Sheriff and* Assistant *steer them toward the door, as children cheer.*)

THEODORE: Sheriff, how did you know the outlaws were here?

SHERIFF: I didn't know, son. But I gathered something was wrong when I happened to look out of my office window and saw that the school flagpole was bare. Why, you know as well as I do that, unless it's raining, Miss Louisa never lowers the flag until sundown. It's a rule of the school. Remember, Miss Louisa was my teacher, too.

MISS LOUISA (*To Sheriff*): I was hoping you'd notice that the flag was down, and would remember that rule, Rodney. Apparently my pupils remember *some* things that I teach them.

ANNABELLE (*Laughing*): Miss Louisa was just like Paul Revere's friend. She used a sig-

nal to tell about the enemy!

MISS LOUISA: That's right.

ANNABELLE (*To* outlaws): And if you gentlemen were the slightest bit educated about the ways of the weather, you would have known that cumulus clouds in the west rarely mean immediate rain.

BENNY (*To* Dan): I had a hunch that we should have tied that

493

teacher up in the closet the moment we came in!

DAN: Could *you* have tied her up?

BENNY (*Scratches his head in bewilderment*): No, I guess I couldn't have at that. There's something about Miss Louisa. Well, you just can't imagine tying her up in a closet. (*Pauses*) She doesn't scare easy, and before you know it, you're half-scared of *her*.

MISS LOUISA: The proper grammar, Benjamin, is—She doesn't scare easily.

BENNY: Yes, Miss Louisa.

SHERIFF: Well, we'll take these scoundrels down to jail where they belong. You'll receive the hundred dollars reward in a few days, Miss Louisa.

MISS LOUISA: Thank you, Rodney. I believe it will be just enough money to take the children on an outing to the Dodge City music festival. (*The children shout with delight.* Sheriff *and* Assistant *exit with outlaws.*)

MISS LOUISA: And now, children, I believe that I will dismiss you for the rest of the afternoon.

CLASS: Hooray! Hooray for Miss Louisa! (*They exit noisily.* William *and* Theodore *remain in their seats.*)

MISS LOUISA (*Sitting down limply at her desk. She holds her head in her hands. In a few minutes she looks up and sees the boys*): Well, boys, why are you still here?

THEODORE: You asked us to stay and learn the first three stanzas of "Paul Revere's Ride," Miss Louisa.

MISS LOUISA: Oh, so I did. Well, I will excuse you just this once. You see, I'm feeling a bit shaky. (*Rubs forehead*)

WILLIAM (*Thoughtfully*): Miss Louisa, you were afraid when the outlaws were here, weren't you?

MISS LOUISA: Oh, yes. Very much afraid. I did everything in my power to delay them, so that they might miss the train and be captured. Yet, I longed for them to leave before anyone was hurt.

THEODORE: Well, you didn't act scared. Not one bit!

494

WILLIAM *(Stoutly)*: Naturally, she didn't! She behaved bravely when she was most afraid. That's *courage*. Remember?

MISS LOUISA *(Smiling)*: Perhaps I taught you something today after all. *(She takes the flag from the desk and hands it to William.)* Before you leave, boys, please hoist the flag again. It's several hours yet until sundown. We must abide by the rules of the school, you know.

WILLIAM *(With admiration)*: Yes, Miss Louisa.

THEODORE *(With a quick bow of respect)*: Yes, indeed. Good-by, Miss Louisa. *(Boys exit, as curtain falls.)*

THE END

CHECK FOR UNDERSTANDING

1. What impression do you get of Miss Louisa at the beginning of the play?
2. How did Miss Louisa define courage?
3. How did Miss Louisa show courage?
4. How did Miss Louisa get the outlaws to obey her?
5. Why did the Sheriff think something was wrong at the schoolhouse?
6. What did William and Theodore learn about Miss Louisa's feelings after the outlaws had gone?
7. What impression do you get of Miss Louisa by the end of the play?

WRITE ABOUT *"Miss Louisa and the Outlaws"*

Imagine that a few months after the play takes place, Miss Louisa gets a letter from Benny, the outlaw. What do you think Benny would say to Miss Louisa? Write a letter just as you think Benny might write it.

Historical Fiction

Have you ever wondered how writers of history get information about the past? Usually, they study records and documents from the past. They read diaries, newspapers, and books written in the past. They also study small scraps of information from letters, receipts, lists, and even tombstones. Writers of history put all this information together to write the history of a period.

History books are good at explaining the events that happened in the past. But they do not give a very good idea of what real people felt and thought. They do not show how people lived day by day in the past. To fill this gap, there is a special kind of writing that combines history with the personal flavor of a story. This kind of writing is called *historical fiction.*

The writer of historical fiction uses the same kind of information the writer of history does. Historical fiction gives an accurate picture of the period in which the story takes place.

For one thing, the setting of historical fiction must show the world as it really was. If the setting of the story is Boston in 1776, the houses, streets, and shops described in the story have to be just as they were at that time. The story has to show how meals were cooked then and how people got from one place to another.

The characters and events in historical fiction can be of three different types. Sometimes historical fiction tells the stories of real people who played important roles in events that shaped history. This kind of historical fiction is different from history in this way. History reports what happened and explains the causes and the effects of what happened. Historical fiction tells about

the event as if it were a story, adding personal details that reveal how the people felt. "Galloping to Lexington" is an example of this kind of historical fiction.

Many times the characters in historical fiction are people who really lived but who never became famous or important. Sometimes a writer chooses to write about people because they left a lot of information about themselves in diaries or letters. At other times a writer may build a story around people who are just mentioned in historical records but are interesting in some way. The author of "Over the Rockies with Lewis and Clark" came across the name of Hugh McNeal while reading the journals of Lewis and Clark. He was interested in the youngest member of the expedition and decided to write a book about his adventures.

In some historical fiction the main characters are not real people and the central events of the story are not actual historical events. In such stories, the main characters often come into contact in some way with real historic figures. The events of the story, although they never actually happened, are usually brought about by real and important events in history. "The Big River" is an example of this kind of historical fiction. As you read "The Big River" think about how real events in history have affected the lives of the characters in the story. Also think about how real historic events might influence events that happen later in the book.

Gone to Texas

by RICHARD WORMSER

The Big River

Sometimes you have to look beneath the surface to find out what a person is really like. In "The Big River," Don and his father find that there is an unexpected side to a riverboat captain who has the manners of a bear.

How do Don and his father earn their passage across the Mississippi River? What unexpected things does Captain Brad do for the Lanceys?

When Mr. Lancey returned home after the Civil War, he found Kentucky a worn-out and weary land. Food was scarce, and money even scarcer. He and his wife decided that their son, Don, deserved a chance in a new land: Texas. Mr. Lancey had been to Texas at the end of the war. "Cattle running free, and horses, too." Texas was just the place for the Lanceys who had raised horses for generations. All they needed was a wagon and a team to make the journey.

When the mysterious Colonel Brevard makes the Lanceys an offer, they agree to it without question. If they will drive a wagonload of goods for him into Texas, he will give them two wagons and two teams.

So the Lanceys set off on the thousand-mile trek to Texas.

Every turn of the wagon wheels got Don more and more excited. At any minute they would see the Mississippi and the end of Kentucky. He had never been out of the state since the day he was born. Now he was about to see the Big River.

After another bend in the road, the river came into view. Amazingly it was above them instead of below. The strong horses pulled them up onto the levee, and there was the great, wide, muddy Mississippi, every bit as great and wide and muddy as Don had imagined it.

As he watched, a tree went downstream, headed for a wide island below them. The leaves were still on it, and it was covered with birds, which flew off as some unseen snag dragged their perch under the surface. When it rose again, they all landed, perhaps on the very branches they had been riding before.

The speed with which the tree had gone by, the yellow caps on the brown waves, all confirmed what Mr. Lancey had been told. No farmer-made raft would carry the wagons across. The horses, which they had planned to have swim behind the raft, would be borne away and drowned. The river roared on, the low grumbling Don had heard in Columbus was now a loud grumbling, warning people away from the waters.

Mr. Lancey cracked his whip to call Don's attention and pointed upstream. Don nodded, and his father clucked the horses up, heading north. Don followed.

The levee was smooth, grassed over, a nice place to drive. The bucket of axle grease under the tail of the lead wagon swung rhythmically. Most of the way from home it had been jerking and bouncing as the wheels labored through old ruts.

A mile up the river Mr. Lancey stopped at what Don now saw had been his goal: a riverboat, tied up

to the bank. It was a flatboat, but it had sidewalls about three feet high to turn waves. They were made, as was the whole boat, of well-milled lumber instead of just logs. In place of a rudder, the flatboat had a long, broad oar sticking out of its back. This sweep was tilted high into the air, like the tail of a rooster. There was a little cabin up on the front of the boat, with smoke coming out of its tin chimney.

Don sat on the wagon seat, dreamily wondering what it would be like to live on a flatboat, to sit

at night by a hot stove in that little house, warm and cozy, hearing the river go by and feeling its powerful force as the boat rose and fell, bumped the levee gently, and then cast off again.

His father knocked on the shanty door. After a moment it opened, and a lean, tall man came out. He was wearing a red knit shirt and a straw hat with at least two holes in it. Don couldn't see all the way around the battered headgear.

The two men talked for a few minutes. Then the tall man reached behind him to shut the shanty door and followed Mr. Lancey up to the front of the wagon. He touched his hat when Mrs. Lancey held out her hand to meet him, but he didn't take it off.

His father signaled Don to come up. "This is Captain Brad. He owns this boat. My son, Don, Cap'n."

The captain shook hands. His long fingers were all dry bone, but warm. "Husky lookin' youngster. He'll do, I reckon."

"I've made a deal with the captain," Don's father said. "If you and I'll cut four cords of wood, he'll ferry us over." Mr. Lancey stared at the sky. "There's maybe half a cord of daylight left."

Captain Brad said, "I got me two double-bit axes you are surely welcome to use."

Don sighed. The only axe the Lancey family had left barely was able to take a kindling wood edge. It had been used to hammer with so much the eye had spread. The head would barely stay on the home-whittled handle for three hard licks.

Don turned to the wagon he'd

been driving and untied the first knot in the heavy cord that kept the taut canvas down.

"No," his dad said. "Colonel Brevard said to drive his wagon to Texas. If he'd wanted us to know what was in it, he'd have said."

Don shrugged. The work would have gone a lot faster with two wagons, but at least one team of horses would be resting all the time. That might count for a lot in the long drives ahead. He went and helped his father unload the household gear. Then they took the bow frames out of their sockets and were ready to head into the woods.

They cut and loaded a cord, and Mr. Lancey said, "Want to rest here, or come down the river with me? It wouldn't hurt me forever to unload a single old cord of wood."

"I'll go along," Don said. Putting it that way was nice of his father. Of course, if he had stayed

at the wood-cutting site he, naturally, would have gone on cutting instead of resting.

Captain Brad came out of his shanty as the horses pulled the wagon easily up onto the levee. He came over and looked at the wood. He picked up a chunk, hefted it, and grunted. Then he turned and went back into the shanty without saying anything.

They cut another half cord of wood and loaded it into the wagon. Then they rode the horses, bareback, to the camp. Mrs. Lancey had supper cooking, smelling different from the supper at home. "Cap'n Brad came by with a catfish," she said. She laughed. "He said it jumped into his boat, and all the kicking he could do couldn't get it to jump out again."

Two mornings later, Don and his father were silent as they drove to the woods. They had worked harder in the past couple days than either of them was really used to. After sleeping on the ground, they were both stiff and aching some.

But work eased their muscles. The wood mounted in the wagon as the sun mounted in the sky. Finally Mr. Lancey said, "That's four cords we promised, but there's still some room in the wagon."

"Might as well fill it, so the horses won't get into bad habits."

Mr. Lancey laughed. "You'll do, Don. We might come back this way, and it'll be good to have a friend on the river."

The river had gone down some, and the boat was now almost ten feet below the levee. The drop made unloading the cordwood difficult.

Captain Brad came out of his shanty, as usual, and looked at them. "Leave room for your wagons and teams," he said. Then he walked up the steep gangplank to the levee. With no further word he stumped off upriver, toward the road to town.

He was not back when they finished the unloading and restacking. Mr. Lancey stood on the neat woodpile and said, "Well, that's that." Carefully he picked a splinter out of his calloused palm. "Like to know if the captain's taking us over today or in the morning."

"Either way, we better load the wagon," Don said.

"I reckon."

When they got back to the river with the loaded wagons, Captain Brad was back. So was something else, a small horse, really a pony, tied up on the flatboat, near the shanty. Dark brown horse, with a black stripe down its back and a stripe across its withers.

Captain Brad came out of the shanty without looking at the pony, came up the gangplank easily, and said, "Have to get some more planks up to get those big-footed horses of yours down." He flicked a thumb at a pile of three-by-tens stacked up in the front of the boat.

Don went off, hoping the planks weren't as splintery as they looked. They were heavy; he could pull only one at a time.

"Enough," Captain Brad said after Don had put down three planks. "Unhook the horses now, and fetch that little pony up to the bank."

Mr. Lancey unhooked the trace of the first team and led the off

horse up to the gangplank, where he let the stout animal put his nose down and blow at the boards. The horse hung back.

Don went to the pony and untied his halter rope. The little horse snuffled at his hand and came along very nicely, as though he had known Don all his life. He went down the gangplank daintily, using only one plank. His shoes rang on the board.

"The big fella'll follow him," Captain Brad said.

The off horse did indeed follow the pony down. The near horse, seeing his partner on the flatboat, went willingly down to join him. They didn't have any trouble with the team from Colonel Brevard's wagon either. A horse hates to be left alone.

Don tied the horses tight alongside the pony. Luckily, none of them had kicked a single kick all the way across Kentucky. They could be counted on to behave, unless a storm came up, which didn't seem likely. The river was pretty flat.

Captain Brad called, "Stay down there and help us spread them planks!"

Don nodded. By craning his neck, he could see that his father and Captain Brad were pulling the first wagon, the family one, up to the edge of the levee. Then they took hold of the outside plank and carefully spaced it so the wheels on that side would center on it.

Captain Brad took stout oak chunks and put them through the spokes of each of the four wheels. Then he uncoiled a long, heavy rope and snubbed it around a tree down in the bottom below the levee. The other end he tied to the rear axle of the wagon. He and Don's father fed rope carefully around the tree until Don shouted and the wagon wheel clattered on the flatboat's deck. Once a person knew how, it was no trick at all. The second wagon followed the first, nudging it into position.

Captain Brad deftly flipped the lines off, left them dangling from the levee. "Got another set on the other side."

At once the flatboat drifted away from the levee, as though anxious to do what a boat was supposed to do. The river had looked calm, the current not too fast. But as soon as they were free from the shore, Don could feel the terrible power of the Mississippi through his feet and all the way up his legs into his body. The flatboat pitched and rocked a little, and the current sucked them downriver at a speed that made the levee whiz by.

Captain Brad didn't seem worried. He strolled to the back of the boat and tilted the long steering sweep down until it went into the water. The boat came around and angled upstream.

Don trotted back and said, "Want help?"

Captain Brad shook his head. "Nope. It takes more knowing how than having a strong back. There's an eddy there, made by the river bouncing off Wolf Island. When we hit her, she'll shoot us upstream like a pea out of a shooter. Then we just coast down to the other bank. Nothing."

"I thought you'd just angle across and land downstream," Don said.

"If you did that, you'd be in New Orleans before you knew it," Captain Brad said.

They went into a strong current then. The very planks of the deck sang from it. The horses, getting the feeling through their iron shoes and up their bones, stamped and snorted. The pony just stood, as though water travel was an old story to him.

Captain Brad threw all his weight on the sweep, and the boat went around, in a long, flat U, then started downstream again.

Afterward it was easy. The regular current carried them downstream and into shore. Looking back, they seemed to be just opposite from Captain Brad's east-bank tie-up.

The west bank turned out to have a little sandy beach below the low bluffs, and the flatboat sailed in level with the ground. Captain Brad pointed at a tree and told Don he'd find a rope in its upper branches. "Boy's a good thing to have aboard," he added. "I purely hate climbing trees."

Don climbed, threw the loose end of the rope down, and the boat was tied to the shore.

Under the captain's order, Don led the pony out first. Then the teams happily went up the short rise and down to the sand and stood stamping. Then Don led the pony back on board.

Captain Brad yelled, "Get that horse off my boat. Riverboat's no place for a horse, unless he's a passenger. Who's going to pay that nag's fare back across? You, boy, look in my cabin there." He pointed at the shanty. "You'll find that pony's clothing cluttering up my place."

Don went into the shanty, fast. He had long wanted to see the inside of what Captain Brad called his cabin, and it was indeed worth a look. At least a quarter of the tiny room was occupied by a four-hole wood stove. Another half of the room was filled with a built-in bunk, now covered with a heavy crazy quilt. A saddle and bridle were on top of the quilt. Don

snatched them up before the captain could accuse him of snooping and took them out.

But the riverman didn't even look at him. So he went over and saddled and bridled the pony, leaving the halter on under the bridle. Then he led him ashore and to the tree with the mooring rope.

"Get that pony out of there," Captain Brad yelled. "Powerful horse like that might pull my tree down and set me adrift in dangerous waters!"

Mr. Lancey twisted the lines around the whipsocket of the family wagon and climbed down. "Cap'n, we kept our bargain. I don't appreciate your riding my boy this way."

"I'm not riding. He is. On that pony. Away from here. To Texas, if he's a mind to," Captain Brad said. "Had to take that horse for a passage across the river. Well, what kind of sailor carries a horse with him? I'd be laughed off the river."

Don's heart rose. The riverman was giving him the pony, the beautiful brown pony, complete with saddle, bridle—everything.

He said, "Captain Brad, thanks a lot, thanks a . . ."

"I'll thank you to get that horse out of here before it's seen. And good-by."

Mrs. Lancey, carefully not smiling, went and climbed to the seat of the colonel's wagon. Her husband got back up on the family rig. Don slung himself into the pony's saddle, and then bent to adjust the stirrups. A voice came up the rise toward them: "You cut a lot more wood than you ever contracted for, you Lanceys."

The Lanceys still have many miles to travel before they reach Texas. Their journey takes them through the heart of the Old West. Along the way they meet up with many different people—some helpful, like Captain Brad, some not so helpful.

Read more about the Lanceys' adventures in **Gone to Texas**, *by Richard Wormser.*

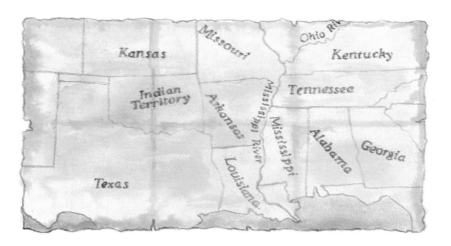

CHECK FOR UNDERSTANDING

1. Why was Don excited about crossing the Mississippi?
2. How did Don and his father earn their passage across the Mississippi River?
3. How much wood did Mr. Lancey agree to cut for Captain Brad? How much wood did Don and his father actually load on to the riverboat?
4. What unexpected things did Captain Brad do for the Lanceys?
5. How much truth do you think there was in the reason Captain Brad gave for wanting to get rid of the pony?
6. How is Captain Brad's reason for wanting to get rid of the pony similar to his explanation about the catfish?

WRITE ABOUT *"The Big River"*

Describe someone you know personally who is like Captain Brad in the story. The similarity between this person and Captain Brad should be the difference between the manner in which they act, and what they actually do.

THINK ABOUT IT

Think about some of the characters and events you read about in this unit.

- Even though he was not a good or experienced rider, Paul Revere made the most famous ride in American history.
- Without the talent and ability of Benjamin Banneker, who was only an assistant to the architect who designed the city of Washington, the plans for the most important city in the country would never have been carried out.
- Courage and endurance helped Sacajawea and the men of the Lewis and Clark expedition to survive the hardship of the journey and reach the Pacific Ocean.
- Miss Louisa taught her students a lesson in courage by setting for them an example of courage.
- A boy and his father find a way, through hard work, to get across the Mississippi River and earn for themselves an unexpected reward.

In what ways do the selections show that life in the past was different from life today? In what ways do the selections show that life in the past was really not very different from life today?

WRITE ABOUT IT

Think about the people from the past you have read about. What kind of modern event comes closest to each event you read about? Write a brief story in which the time is today but the events, as much as possible, are the same as the events in one of the selections.

READ ABOUT IT

Caddie Woodlawn: A Frontier Story by Carol Ryrie Brink. Macmillan Publishing Co., 1973. Caddie Woodlawn's experiences on a Wisconsin farm in the 1860s, her days in a one-room schoolhouse, and her amusing pranks make for enjoyable reading.

And Then What Happened, Paul Revere? by Jean Fritz. The Putnam Publishing Group, 1973. This fast-paced account of Paul Revere's famous ride to Lexington in 1775 includes humorous details about his narrow escapes along the way.

Wheels West: The Story of Tabitha Brown by Evelyn Sibley Lampman. Doubleday & Co., 1965. Set in the 1840s, Tabitha Brown is an adventurous and warm-hearted grandmother who persuades her family to pioneer a new trail to Oregon.

Ben and Me by Robert Lawson. Little Brown & Co., 1939. Here is a humorous account of Benjamin Franklin's life, as told by his good mouse Amos.

Runaway to Freedom: A Story of the Underground Railway by Barbara Smucker. Harper & Row, Publishers, 1979. Julilly and Liza, two twelve-year-old slaves, struggle to reach Canada and freedom, with the help of the Underground Railroad.

6

MEETING THE CHALLENGE

In everyone's life there comes a time when a person's courage and ability are put to the test. Sometimes people seek out challenge and take on a test just to see if they can get through it. For other people, challenge can be unexpected and frightening.

As you read the selections in this unit, put yourself in the place of the person facing each challenge. Think about the kind of courage or strength that is required to face each situation. Think about how you would feel if it were you who were meeting the challenge.

513

Blue Beach

by SCOTT O'DELL

Is it good luck or bravery that helps a person escape from unexpected danger? That question is raised in this selection from *Carlota,* by Scott O'Dell.

What is the secret purpose that brings Carlota and her father to Blue Beach? Is it good luck or bravery that helps Carlota escape danger?

There was no way to find the Blue Beach except by following the river, either down from the mountains or up from the sea. From the sea no one would ever find it because of a series of lagoons. From the direction of the mountains you would need to be very lucky, as lucky as my father and I had been in the beginning.

The river at this point, where it fanned out into the deep lagoons, ran narrow, between two sheer walls of granite, where even a mountain goat would be lost. At the bottom of these cliffs were two beaches, one facing the other across a distance of a hundred steps.

The beaches were strips of fine sand, finer than the sand you find on the sea beach itself. Both had a bluish cast, like pebbles you see through clear-running water. But they also had another color, a lighter blue that had a look of metal, as if there were copper deposits in the cliffs that had been washed down by the river and the rain and had mixed with the lighter color.

515

Someone might call the beaches green or the color of turquoise, but to us they were blue and this is what we called them— the Blue Beaches, more often, the Blue Beach.

On this day, as on the three other journeys I had made with my father to the Blue Beach, we tied our horses and climbed up from the stream to a towering rock. From this high place we could survey the trails, one coming along the river, and one from the sea.

"What do you see?" my father said. He liked to test my eyesight. "Are we followed?"

"I see nothing on the trail," I said, "either from the river or from the sea."

"What is the brown spot among the oaks?"

"Where?"

"Up the river about a hundred *varas*." [1]

"I see nothing."

"Look once more."

"Does it move?"

"Judge for yourself. But first you need to find it."

I looked hard and at last made out the brown spot among the oaks. "It is a cow grazing," I said.

"There are two, and one is not a cow but a yearling fawn. What do you hear?"

"The stream."

"What else?"

"A crow somewhere."

"Is that all?"

"Yes."

"Listen."

"A woodpecker behind us."

"Yes. And what else do you hear?"

"Nothing."

"Besides the stream and the surf at the mouth of the river and gulls fishing?"

"You have good ears."

"And you will have them someday."

"Never so good as yours."

"Better. *Mucho mas.*" [2]

[1] *vara* (vär′ə) A unit of measure equal to 31–34 inches.

[2] *Mucho mas* (mü′chō mäs) Much more.

Here we sat for an hour, to make sure that we had not been followed.

When the sun was overhead, we crawled down from the pinnacle. We reached the Blue Beach and took off our boots and stepped out into the middle of the stream. We made our way for a distance of some fifty paces, leaving no tracks behind us. A clump of willows grew amidst a pile of driftwood and boulders at this place. Here the river divided and ran in two smaller streams on both sides of the willows.

The boulders could not be seen at high tide. But the tide was low now and they stuck up in two crescents, facing each other and leaving a clear space between them. The water was cold, both the sea water that met the river at this point and likewise the river water itself.

I took off my leather pants and coat and splashed water on my legs and on my arms. I had found that the best way to approach cold water was by small shivers, suffered one at a time.

Throwing out my arms, I took

in a great gulp of air, held it for a minute, counting each second. Then I let out all the air in a quick whoosh. Then I raised my arms again and took in a greater gulp.

The air I held for two minutes, still counting the seconds in my mind—one second, two seconds, and so forth. I repeated this three times. The third time I counted up to four minutes.

It had taken me two years to build up to where I could hold my breath for this length of time. My father had heard of pearl divers in La Paz who could hold their breath for five minutes and even longer. I had tried this but had fainted.

Carefully we stepped into the wide pool between the two crescents of stone, beneath the canopy of willows. We inched our way to the center of the pool, cautious not to rile the sand.

As my foot touched a smooth slab of stone, I stooped down, lifted it with much care, and set it to one side. Beneath it was a rock-lined hole filled with water, the size of my body and twice its height.

At the bottom of this hole was something that, when we first saw it, seemed to be the trunk of a tree—a tree washed down from the mountains. Undoubtedly, it once had risen above the water, but over the years floods had worn it away to a worm-eaten stump.

It had been the mainmast of a ship, which my father said was some seventy feet in length. It had the wide beam, the high stern, of the galleons that two centuries before had sailed the seas between China and the coast of California and Mexico.

These ships, my father said, came on favorable winds and currents to northern California, then along the coast south to the ports of San Blas and Acapulco. They carried great treasures from the Indies, these galleons, so great that they became the prey of American and English pirates.

Some of these treasure ships had been captured. On some, their crews had died of scurvy. Others had run aground through careless navigation. Others were driven ashore by storms. Still others had sought refuge from their pursuers by hiding in lagoons such as the one at Blue Beach.

"This must have been a large lagoon at one time," my father said when we first discovered the galleon. "A good place to hide a ship. But when it was once inside, something happened to the ship and it never returned to the sea."

Hidden in the galleon's hold, near the stump of the mainmast, were two chests filled with coins. The coins were of pure gold. They showed three castles and the two flying doves that meant that they had been struck in the mint at Lima, Peru. The date marked upon each coin that we carried away on the trips we had made was the year 1612.

The two chests—each made of hardwood banded with iron straps and sealed with a hasp that had rusted and fallen off—were well beneath the surface of the water, whether at low tide or in the summer, when the stream ran low. This was fortunate, for had the chests been exposed, someone would have discovered them.

There were many things to do before the chests could be reached. Usually it took me a half a day to bring up a pouch of coins from the sunken ship.

The place where I dove, which was surrounded by jagged rocks and driftwood, was too narrow for my father. He had tried to squeeze through when we first discovered the galleon, but partway down he got stuck and I had to pull him back. It was my task, therefore, to go into the cavelike hole. My father stood beside it and helped me to go down and to come up.

I buckled a strong belt around my waist and to it tied a riata that was ten *varas* long and stout enough to hold a stallion. I fastened my knife to my wrist—a two-edged blade made especially for me by our blacksmith—to protect myself against spiny rays and the big eels that could sting you to death. In the many dives I had made, I had never seen a shark.

Taking three deep breaths, I prepared to let myself down into the hole. In one hand I held a sink-stone, heavy enough to weigh me down. I let out all the air in my chest, took a deep breath, and held it. Then I began the descent.

The sink-stone would have taken me down fast, but the edges of the rocky hole were sharp. I let myself down carefully, one hand-hold at a time. It took me about a minute to reach the rotted deck where the chests lay. I had now two minutes to pry the coins loose and carry them to the surface. We had tried putting the coins in a leather sack and hoisting them to the surface. But we had trouble with this because of the currents that swept around the wreck.

The coins lay in a mass, stuck together, lapping over each other and solid as rock. They looked, when I first saw them, like something left on the stove too long. I always expected to find them gone, but now as I walked toward the chests, with the stone holding me

520

down, I saw that they were still there. No one had come upon them during the seven months since our last visit.

The first time I had dived and brought up a handful of coins, I said to my father that we should empty both the chests and take the coins home.

"Then everyone would talk," my father said. "As soon as they saw the gold coins the news would spread the length of California."

"We don't need to tell anyone. I can hide them in my chest at home."

"The news would fly out before the sun set. At the ranch there are many eyes."

I still thought it was a better idea to empty the chests before someone else did, but I could see that my father enjoyed these days, when the two of us went to the Blue Beach, so I said no more.

The sun was overhead and its rays slanted down through the narrow crevice. There were many pieces of debris on the deck and I had to step carefully. With my knife I pried loose a handful of coins.

They were of a dark green color and speckled here and there with small barnacles. I set the coins aside.

My lungs were beginning to hurt, but I had not felt the tug of the riata yet, the signal from my father that I had been down three minutes. I pried loose a second handful and put my knife away. Before the tug came I dropped my sink-stone and took up the coins. Gold is very heavy, much heavier than stones of the same size.

Fish were swimming around me as I went up through the hole of the rocks and tree trunks, but I saw no sting rays or eels. I did see a shark lying back on a ledge, but he was small and gray, a sandshark, which is not dangerous.

On my third trip down, I hauled up about the same number of coins as the other times. The pouch we had brought was now full. I asked my father if we had enough.

"Are you tired?" he asked.

"Yes, a little."

"Can you go down again?"

"Yes."

"Then go."

I dived twice more. It was on the last dive that I had the trouble. The tug on the riata had not come, but I was tired, so I started away from the chest with one handful of coins. Close to the chests, between them and the hole, I had noticed what seemed to be pieces of timber covered with barnacles. They looked as if they might be part of a third and larger chest.

I still held my knife and I thrust it at a place where the two gray timbers seemed to join. It was possible that I had found another chest filled with coins.

As the knife touched them, the two timbers moved a little. Instantly, I felt pressure upon my wrist. I drew back the hand that held the knife. Rather, I tried to draw it back, but it would not move. The tide had shifted the timbers somehow and I was caught. So I thought.

I felt a tug upon the riata fastened to my waist. It was the signal from my father to come to the surface. I answered him with two quick tugs of the leather rope.

Now I felt a hot pain run up my arm. I tried to open my fingers, to drop the knife, but my hand was numb. Then as I stared down into the murky water I saw a slight movement where my hand was caught. At the same moment I saw a flash of pink, a long fleshy tongue sliding along my wrist.

I had never seen a burro clam, but I had heard the tales about them, for there were many on our coast. Attached to rocks or timbers, they grew to half the height of a man, these gray silent monsters. Many unwary fishers had lost their lives in the burro's jaws.

The pain in my arm was not so great now as the hot pains in my chest. I gave a long, hard tug on the riata to let my father know I was in trouble. Again I saw a flash of pink as the burro opened its lips a little, and the fat tongue slid back and forth.

I dropped the coins I held in my other hand. The burro had closed once more on my wrist. But

523

shortly it began to open again, and I felt a sucking pressure, as if the jaws were trying to draw me inside the giant maw.

Putting my knees against the rough bulge of the shell, as the jaw opened and then began to close, I jerked with all my strength. I fell slowly backward upon the ship's deck. My hand was free. With what breath I had I moved toward the hole. I saw the sun shining above and climbed toward it. The next thing I saw was my father's face and I was lying on the river's sandy bank. He took my knife in his hand.

After I told him what had happened, my father said, "The knife saved your life. The burro clamped down upon it. See the mark here. The steel blade kept its jaws open. Enough to let you wrench yourself free."

He pulled me to my feet, and I put on my clothes.

"Here," he said passing the reins of his horse to me, "ride Santana. He goes gentler than Tiburón."

"I'll ride my own horse," I said.

"Good, if you wish it."

"I wish it," I said, knowing that

he didn't want me to say that my hand was numb.

"Does the hand hurt?"

"No."

"Some?"

"No."

"You were very brave," he said.

My father wanted me to be braver than I was. I wanted to say I was scared, both when the burro had hold of me and now, at this moment, but I didn't because he expected me to be brave.

"It was good fortune," I said.

"Fortune and bravery often go together," my father said. "If you do not hurt, let us go."

I got on Tiburón and settled myself in the saddle. "Yes, let us go."

CHECK FOR UNDERSTANDING

1. How did Carlota and her father discover Blue Beach?
2. In what ways did Carlota think she would never be as good as her father expected her to be?
3. What was the secret purpose that brought Carlota and her father to Blue Beach?
4. Do you think Carlota's father felt responsible for her predicament on the last dive? Explain why you think as you do.
5. Was it good luck or bravery that helped Carlota escape danger?
6. In what ways did Carlota act bravely?

WRITE ABOUT *"Blue Beach"*

Imagine that Carlota and her father decide never to return to Blue Beach. Carlota, however, wants to leave written directions so that someone else can find the gold coins. Write directions that would help someone get from the mountaintop, where the story begins, to the place where the treasure can be found.

VOCABULARY · LANGUAGE

Compound Words

What do these words from "Blue Beach" have in common?

driftwood	sink-stone	mainmast
rock-lined	sea water	burro clam
mountain goat	eyesight	clear-running

All of these words are compound words. A compound word is made up of two shorter words. In many compound words, the two words are written together as one word. When the two words are written together they form a **one-word compound.** Two words do not, however, have to be written as one word in order to make a compound. Whether or not two words form a compound is determined more by pronunciation, meaning, and use than by the way the words are written.

Read these pairs of sentences slowly to yourself. Think about how you pronounce the words in italic type in each pair of sentences.

Many birds have remarkable *eyesight*. An eagle's keen *eye sights* the slightest movement on the ground.

You may *go ahead* of me in line. We must wait until we get the *go-ahead* from our team captain.

The hikers waded across the clear *mountain stream*. A *mountain goat* watched as they continued up the trail.

In the first pair of sentences, it is easy to recognize *eyesight* as a compound word. The two shorter words, *eye* and *sight*, are written together as one word to form *eyesight*. But compare the way you pronounce *eyesight* and the way you say "The eagle's *eye*

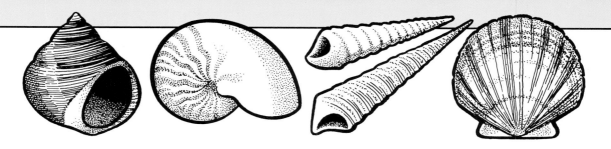

sights" in the second sentence. In the word *eyesight, eye* gets greater stress—(ī′sīt). In the second sentence, *eye* and *sights* get equal stress.

Now think about how you say the words *go* and *ahead* in the second pair of sentences. When you say "*go ahead* of me," *go* and the second syllable of *ahead* get equal stress. When you say "get the *go-ahead*," *go* gets the greatest stress. The word *go-ahead* is a **hyphenated compound.**

In the third pair of sentences, *mountain goat* is a **two-word compound.** Say the words *mountain stream* and *mountain goat.* What is different about the way you say these two pairs of words?

There are many compound words in the English language. Compounding—joining two words together to form a new word—is a favorite way to invent new words. Many of the words that name new things and new ideas are compound words. Think of the words we use to talk about space travel and exploration. *Spacecraft, launching pad, space probe, space capsule, blast-off, countdown* are all compound words.

Use these words to create ten compound words. Then check a dictionary to see if each word is a one-word compound, a hyphenated compound, or a two-word compound.

sky	hang	high
key	skate	diving
outer	ship	space
glider	rise	board

When you read "Night Dive," see how many different compound words you can find.

Have you ever been challenged to do something that you know you could do but were afraid to? In "Night Dive," a twelve-year-old girl is faced with just this kind of challenge.

Why is the girl, who is an experienced diver, afraid of diving at night? What happens when the divers turn off their lights underwater?

NIGHT DIVE

by ANN MCGOVERN

.I must be crazy. It's nighttime and here I am on this dive boat, in total darkness. I'm scared to death.

The sky above me is black except for a half-moon. The sea around me is black. I see lights twinkling on the distant shore. Land seems far away. Land is where most twelve-year-old girls should be. So what am I doing on the sea?

I'm going on a night dive, that's what I'm doing. In just a few minutes, I'll be in that black sea, and it's too late to do anything about it.

How did I get myself into this? By opening my big mouth, that's how.

Mom and I have been scuba diving on this beautiful Caribbean island for a week now. We've been diving every day. It's been great.

When Jim, who is in charge of diving, first met me, he asked to see my "C" card—my scuba certification card. It proves I've had the proper diving training. You have to be twelve before you can be certified. I went to the local "Y" for my course.

Yesterday Mom told Jim about her work as a marine biologist and about her interest in parrotfishes.

"There are lots of different parrotfishes on our reefs," he said. Then I blew it. Why don't I think before I speak, like Mom is always telling me to do?

"Really?" I said. "Do you have the kind of parrotfish that spins a cocoon around itself at night?"

Jim grinned. "Sure, kid," he said. "Since you're such a hotshot diver, how about a night dive to see for yourself?" So that's why I'm on Jim's boat tonight with Mom and the other divers. About to take the plunge into inky waters.

"Time to suit up," Jim calls. In dive language that means to get ready. On normal day dives, I'm ready before anyone else. But not tonight.

Jim switches on the boat lights. Mom pats my head. I think she knows how scared I am. She's getting into her special dive suit. Most of the other divers wear rubber wet suits, too.

It's a warm night and the water will be warm, too—about 82 degrees Fahrenheit. On these warm islands, you don't need to cover yourself up for the temperature. Wet suits or shirts and jeans protect you from stinging and scratching coral you might bump into—especially in the dark.

The only thing I don't like about diving is getting ready. There's so much stuff!

You need to wear fins on your feet, so you can move easily without using your arms.

You need a mask so that you can see clearly under-water. You need a snorkel only if you want to swim on top of the water.

You need to wear a weight belt, too, with just the right amount of weights on it. The weights help you get down without having to swim hard.

The BC, or *buoyancy compensator*, is very important. It's like a vest and can be filled with air. You can put a little air into the BC and make yourself weightless so you can float underwater without sinking or rising. If you want to come up, you can put more air into your BC.

The most important equipment is the tank of com-pressed air on your back. One part of the regulator screws on the tank, and the other part, at the end of the short

hose, goes into your mouth. You breathe in and out, nice and easy, as long as you have air in your tank. That's why you need a pressure gauge. It shows how much air you have in your tank. I've always been amazed that a tank is so heavy on land. It weighs more than thirty pounds—but once I'm in the water, I hardly feel it!

Your dive watch shows how long you've been under. And your depth gauge shows how deep you are.

It's a good idea to wear cotton or rubber gloves. You don't want to hold onto strange coral with your bare hands. You might get scratched, and fire coral can sting.

When you go on a night dive, you must carry your own light so you can see what's out there on the reef. Mom has thought of something else, too—light sticks that glow green in the dark. She fastens one to the back of my tank and puts another on her tank. That way, I'll be able to tell where she is at all times. And she'll know where I am.

Mom is wearing a compass. It's especially important at night to be able to find your way back to the boat.

Jim says having the right equipment is crucial. It makes you feel safer. It makes the whole diving experience easier. You don't have to swim hard or breathe hard or worry about anything not working. Your dive lasts longer when you take it nice and easy and don't get upset.

Jim makes an announcement. "You've all dived with me before so you know the rules. We'll make a backward entry. That's when you sit on the side of the boat and fall over backwards," Jim explains. "It sounds hard, but it's an easy way to get into the water. Stay close together and stay with me. The boat light will be on all the time. And another light hanging from the boat into the water will help guide you back. We'll enter the water and go down the line. We'll meet on the reef, thirty feet below the boat. Then we'll begin exploring the reef. At some point, I'll give a signal by twirling my light. That means you should turn off your lights for a minute or two."

Turn off our lights! It's bad enough having only a tiny little beam of light in that huge black sea. But to be in total darkness? No way. I won't do it. I'm leaving my light on all the time.

I sit on the side of the boat. Jim helps me on with my tank and turns on my air.

"Let's get wet," he calls.

This is it.

I look out at the smooth black water, gulp, and roll over backward into the night-dark sea.

I'm in the water, but where's Mom? For a moment, I feel panic rising in me. Everywhere there is pitch black, except for the narrow beam of my light in front of me.

Something touches me from behind. I whirl around. It's Mom. I tell myself to calm down. Mom takes my hand, and we start down the line.

Is that the noise of my air bubbles or my heart beating like a drum? My light shows up specks in the dark water as we make our way slowly down to the reef. The specks are *plankton*—tiny creatures drifting through the water.

On day dives, I usually get very excited the minute I hit the water. I just love the feeling of being weightless, like an astronaut—a feeling half like a bird and half like a fish as I swim slowly over the reef or stand on my head.

But tonight I feel only fear. I can hardly tell up from down. The stick of glowing light on Mom's tank comforts me a little.

I look up. The light hanging from the boat is a pale green hazy ball. I see the lights of the other divers below me. I aim mine in front of me. Dozens of shrimplike creatures dance in the beam of the light, like moths around a candle. They are *larvae*, babies of sea animals. When I move my light, they go away. When I keep the light still, they come back.

My fins touch the sandy bottom. It takes only one minute to go down thirty feet but it feels like ten minutes.

I count lights. There are eight of us, including Jim. Jim said we would be able to see the moonlight. He was right. It shimmers on the surface of the water like a pool of light.

I start to move away. Mom pulls me back. Jim has begun his signal. He is twirling his light around and around.

One by one, the divers turn off their lights. I guess I have to now. My heart pounds as I turn off my light.

Now there is nothing but darkness. Then little by little I begin to see the shapes of the divers. I move my arm. A stream of tiny stars trails from my fingertips.

Jim begins to swim around us. As he swims, pinpoints

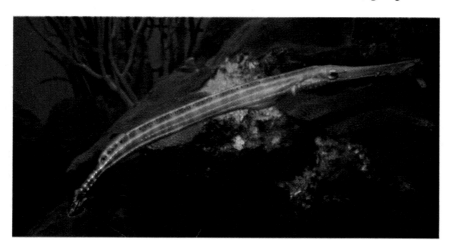

of light scatter around his body. The lights are made by a variety of tiny creatures. When they are disturbed, they glow like sparklers and fireflies. There are millions of these creatures in the warm waters of the coral reef. Their glow is called *bioluminescence* (bī′ ō lōō′ mə nes′əns), which means "living light."

It's so different at night! The fish I see by the hundreds during the daytime are nowhere to be seen. Some fish sleep on the reef, deeper than divers can safely go. Some bury themselves in the sand at night. Others fit into tiny cracks and crevices of the coral and hide till daybreak.

The most common night fishes seem to be the red ones—the squirrelfish, the bigeye, and the soldierfish. Their big eyes help them find their prey. During the day I see them hiding under ledges in the coral, watching me. At night, they swim around freely. The little cardinalfish, too, are out in the open.

I see so many new things. My light seeks out a slow-moving trumpetfish. Whenever I get too close to this fish in the daytime, it swims away so quickly I hardly see it leave. But this trumpetfish is sleepy. It's moving very slowly toward the coral reef. It uses its fins as feelers,

guiding itself away from the sharp spines of spiny sea urchins.

Here's a sleepy blue tang in its night colors. It has stripes that I never see on a day dive.

I feel a tap on my arm. I turn to see Jim holding a spiny porcupinefish. He rubs it and it puffs up. It looks like a balloon with spines sticking out all over. I've seen porcupinefish on day dives with their spines flat against their bodies. Jim hands it to me. It feels a little squishy. When a porcupinefish is disturbed, it takes in water and blows up to almost three times its normal size. Its eyes are open wide. Its spines are sharp.

Mom and I see a stoplight parrotfish sleeping, wedged tight against a sponge. Parrotfish are large and come in many colors. They have sharp teeth that chomp on coral and help turn it into sand. The mouth of the parrotfish looks like a beak of a parrot and is just as strong.

And then I see it! A parrotfish sleeping in its see-through cocoon, wedged deep under a ledge.

I wave my light. Mom hurries over. I show her the sleeping parrotfish. She hugs me and settles down to study

536

it. I feel I've given her the best present in the world. And it's not even her birthday. Mom has told me that the nighttime cocoon keeps in the parrotfish's smell—and keeps the moray eels from finding it. Jim thinks it might give the parrotfish a warning if an enemy breaks through.

I check my air. How could it get that low so fast? I shine my light on Mom's gauge. She's used up most of

her air, too. I look at my watch. It can't be! We've been under almost an hour. It seems like seconds.

Jim checks our gauges. Then he shines his light on his hand and gives the thumbs-up signal. Other divers are going up, too.

Just think. An hour ago, I hated the idea of a night dive. And now I don't even want to get out of the water.

Night diving. It's still spooky, still scary. But I must admit, it's kind of magical, too.

CHECK FOR UNDERSTANDING

1. Why did Jim challenge the girl to take part in a night dive?
2. Why is having the right equipment important when someone is diving?
3. Why was the girl, who was an experienced diver, afraid of diving at night?
4. What happened when the divers turned off their lights underwater?
5. Why are some fish that are hard to get a look at in daytime diving easier to watch at night?
6. For what two reasons was finding the cocoon of a parrotfish so important to the girl?

WRITE ABOUT *"Night Dive"*

Think about all the information in the selection that would be useful to someone who wanted to learn scuba diving. Use this information to write a report on how a beginner would go about learning to dive and becoming a certified diver.

THE WAYS OF
LIVING THINGS

by JACK PRELUTSKY

There is wonder past all wonder
in the ways of living things,
in a worm's intrepid wriggling,
in the song a blackbird sings,

In the grandeur of an eagle
and the fury of a shark,
in the calmness of a tortoise
on a meadow in the dark,

In the splendor of a sea gull
as it plummets from the sky,
in the incandescent shimmer
of a noisy dragonfly,

In a heron, still and silent
underneath a crescent moon,
in a butterfly emerging
from its silver-spun cocoon,

In a fish's joyful splashing,
in a snake that makes no sound,
in the smallest salamander
there is wonder to be found.

READING TABLES AND GRAPHS

Read this paragraph.

Different activities require different amounts of energy. Riding a bicycle burns 210 calories in one hour. Bowling takes 270 calories an hour, while table tennis requires 350. Walking also uses up 350 an hour, and downhill skiing uses 450. When you dance to fast music, you burn up 600 calories an hour. Even more calories are needed for swimming (750) and running (900).

Now try to answer these questions:

1. Which two activities use the same amount of energy?
2. Which burns up more calories—swimming or dancing?

Now look at the following **table**. It contains the same information as the paragraph you just read, only it is organized differently. It is easier to find the answers to the questions above on the table. Why?

How Much Energy Do You Burn?	
Activity	**Calories per Hour**
Bicycling	210
Bowling	270
Walking	350
Table Tennis	350
Downhill skiing	450
Dancing (fast)	600
Swimming	750
Running	900

There is still another way of presenting the same information. It is called a **bar graph**. On this graph, bars of different lengths show how many calories each activity requires. How does the bar graph help you answer the two questions?

How Much Energy Do You Burn?

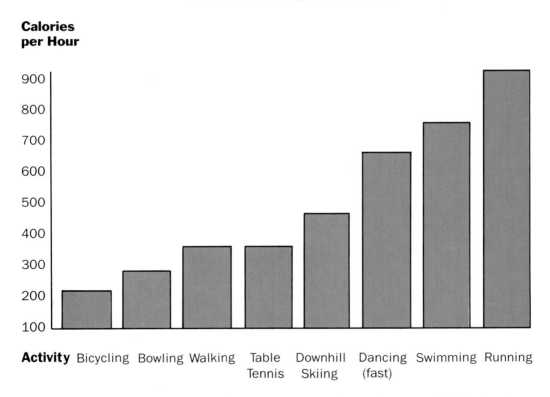

Calories per Hour

Activity: Bicycling, Bowling, Walking, Table Tennis, Downhill Skiing, Dancing (fast), Swimming, Running

Tables and graphs are good ways of showing certain kinds of information. Whenever there are a great many figures or you want to be able to compare and contrast things, a table or graph will usually be more helpful than a paragraph or a page of text.

Here is another kind of graph. It is called a **circle** or **pie graph** because of its shape. Each percentage is shown as a wedge of the pie. How does this make it easier to compare items? What would the same information look like on a table?

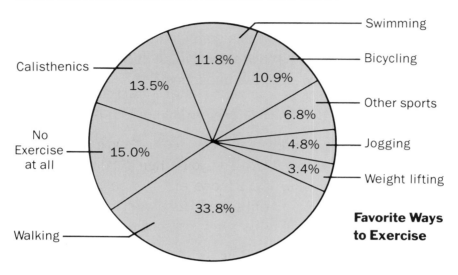

Favorite Ways to Exercise

Another way to present information visually is on a **line graph.** A line graph is a good way to show growth and change. For example, the graph below shows how a runner's performance in the marathon depends on the runner's training.

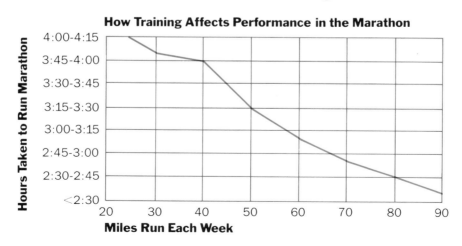

How Training Affects Performance in the Marathon

542

What else does the graph show? How would you give this same information in words? Which shows more dramatically the relationship between training miles and marathon performance?

Using What You Have Learned

1. Copy the table below and use the following information to complete it. Decide how to group the sports and their calorie costs. Will you arrange the table in alphabetical order or will you put the sports that use the most calories per minute first?

When you plan a fitness program, find out how many calories—or energy units—it will cost you. Then plan to give your body the proper fuel to meet those energy needs. If you like cross-country skiing, you will spend 12 calories a minute when you ski a flat surface. Climbing a hill costs 8.2 calories a minute, while climbing a mountain costs 10. A game of basketball uses 11 calories a minute, football uses 16, and table tennis uses 5. Sit-ups cost 3 calories a minute, standing in place is worth 1.5, and sleeping costs 1 calorie a minute.

Energy Costs By The Minute	
Activity	**Calories per Minute**
_____	_____
_____	_____
_____	_____
_____	_____
_____	_____
_____	_____
_____	_____
_____	_____

STUDY SKILLS

2. Copy and complete the bar graph using the information you arranged for 1. Choose five activities and arrange them from lowest to highest or from highest to lowest.

Calories per Minute

16
15
14
13
12
11
10
9
8
7
6
5
4
3
2
1

Sport ———— ———— ———— ———— ————

3. There are 20 students in the Fitness Club at Locus Ridge School. When they surveyed the club to find out which sports or exercises they liked best, these were the results. Eight members of the club liked bicycling best; two members liked walking. Swimming and basketball were tied with five members each. Draw a circle graph showing the results of this survey. (MATH HINT: The walkers represent 10% of the club, the swimmers and basketball players represent 25% each. Can you figure the percentage that like bicycling best of all?)

4. Marcella started a training program so that she could make the track team. The first week she ran three times a week, the second week she had a cold and ran only twice, the third week, she felt pretty good and ran four times, and finally, in the fourth week ran five times. Copy and complete Marcella's line graph using the following model.

Training Graph: MARCELLA JOHNSON

Times
per Week

5
4
3
2
1

   Week 1   Week 2   Week 3   Week 4

Expanding Your Skills

Work on a Fitness Profile of your class. Begin by taking a survey of favorite sports and exercise activities. Arrange the results in a table or a bar graph. Then pick a sport or activity that you like and set up a weekly training goal for yourself that you will be able to do for the next four weeks. Keep track of your activites with a line graph. At the end of four weeks, tell the class if filling in the graph helped you meet your goals.

by KEITH MONROE

When was the last time you took on a difficult task just because it was difficult? This is what the Scouts of Troop 2 do when they take "The Longest Shortcut."

What preparations do the hikers make for their trip? Why do you think people are willing to spend time and energy to meet a challenge when there is no prize or reward if they succeed?

It sounded almost impossible. Also crazy.

Walk clear across the Sierra Nevada? Walk seventy-two miles west to east, up and over Mount Whitney? Very few old-time mountain men ever tried that. The pioneers never did. Neither did the Spanish explorers. Today's Sierra hikers go mostly north-south along the John Muir Trail.

Glance at a map and you'll begin to see why. The Sierra range splits the length of California for hundreds of miles. The central Sierras are just a big blank spot on most maps. There are no roads, no settlements. This is the heart of California's hinterlands.

It is the area called the John Muir Wilderness, in honor of the bearded Scot who joyously explored it. He urged lowlanders, "Climb the mountains and get their good tidings!"

The Sierra range is almost as large as the French, Italian, and Swiss Alps combined. It is a tip-tilted slab of granite. The upper edge of a colossal platform, it slopes west into the floor of a great agricultural valley. It's like a huge box sunk half in the earth. The eastern edge of this

mass is more than two miles above sea level. It rises to the loftiest ridge in the forty-eight states.

It has always been a barricade to anyone who felt they had to cross it. Passes through the central Sierras are few, high, and narrow. The pioneers' California Trail wound through gaps farther north (where highways run today) near Lake Tahoe. In those passes many people died. They had to climb seven or eight thousand feet. No one attempted to cross the mid-range's 10,000-foot notches. So why would a modern-day Scout troop want to try?

Probably because John Dahlem offered to lead.

His enthusiasm is catching. He told the troop of wild splendor that few people ever see. He told of up-and-down toil across a series of high ridges and icy streams. He knew it was possible. He and his wife had done it.

He was challenging Troop 2, from Franklin School, Santa Monica, California. This was his

old troop. There he did his first backpacking and earned his Eagle. Ever since, he'd been a zestful outdoorsman, as well as a coach of state championship high school wrestlers.

Scouts asked what gear they'd need. He explained that the Sequoia National Park, by law, preserves the area as Wilderness with a capital W. It limits pack animals (they wear down trails). Hikers must carry tents, bedrolls, food, and everything else they need. It allows no open fires above timberline (they blacken rocks). Cooking must be on tiny backpacker stoves approved by Park rangers. No garbage may be left. A ranger with a walkie-talkie checks.

Therefore each Scout must carry forty pounds. "To get in shape we'll train four months," Dahlem said. "Work up to seven-mile runs plus a hundred push-ups. About fifty sit-ups in one minute. Plenty of climbing with full packs."

Tebb Kusserow, football coach at Santa Monica High,

took charge of progress checks. Anyone in the troop who wanted to qualify could try. Thirteen made it, including four thirteen-year-olds. Lean and rangy, all were ready in late July, along with five troop adults who'd trained, too.

They started in Giant Forest—the famed grove of *sequoia gigantea*, Earth's largest living things. They stared at trees 2,000 years old, thick enough to block a city street from curb to curb. Then they hit the lonely trail up-canyon through shadows of ponderosa and pine, in the warm spicy air. The air cooled as they took the slopes. In a few hours they were on a path that clung to a thousand-foot cliff. They weren't yet used to the thin air at 7,600 feet. So they stopped often to breathe deeply and admire the glory that spread below.

The plan was to camp at Mehrten Creek, five miles out. But Dahlem said, "Let's go on about a mile to Little Blue Dome." (He knew, but didn't say, that Mehrten was becoming a favorite spot for black bears seeking campers' food.) No one complained. All secretly wanted to prove their own ruggedness no matter what. "Tally ho," they said, and went on.

At Blue Dome a milepost indicated they'd hiked eight and a half miles that day. It seemed farther. Dr. John Sellman, a veteran backpacker, said, "These trail signs are generally accurate within a few miles." From then on "a Dahlem mile" was the code phrase for a long, long distance.

After supper came "bearbagging." All back country campers now hang food in the air. But bears can climb and have learned to chew or scratch through rope tied to a tree, making the grub bag fall. So Troop 2 used counterbalance. You tie a small stone to thirty feet of rope. Throw it over a slim branch at least sixteen feet up and far from the trunk, so a bear won't climb out. Then you put a food bag on each end of the line. Push up until the bags are about equally high. If you can touch them by jumping

There was blinding sunshine and dense fogs. Campsites among waterfalls and huge mountains. Quiet green lakes where trout leapt. Torrents where Dahlem crossed first to stretch a rope, while the others put on tennis shoes to keep from slipping. One razorback trail a yard wide with a six-hundred-foot drop on each side. One hot spring to lie in luxuriously. There were no bears, just wilderness. John Muir or crusty old geologist Josiah Whitney (first to measure Mount Whitney) might have passed by yesterday.

they're much too low. You must try again.

Next day was mostly cold rain. "Hiking in rain gear was fun," one Scout wrote in his diary, "thinking how dry I was and how wet everything else (including bears) was getting."

The next dawn flared windy-red on Kaweah Gap, 10,700 feet. As they crossed the gap, leaning into the wind, Dahlem proclaimed: "The first real climb." They were in a moonscape of stone where the few trees were tortured and dwarfed.

Then days melted together.

At last they came to the enormous granite bowl 3,000 feet below Mount Whitney. They climbed up the steep west wall. Thunder crashed. And in bright flashes of lightning the Scouts saw each other's pale faces. Static electricity made their hat-brims crackle. Dahlem said, "It straightens my beard. Let's wait here."

Fine hail stung them. Soon it was ankle deep. But as quickly as the storm had started, it passed. Troop 2 struggled on, stopping to rest every few steps.

At the top, 14,495 feet, they saw other peaks nearly as high. And they saw the flat desert far below to the east.

They slid down the slippery eastern trail's ninety-seven switchbacks, camping at 12,000 feet. By noon on the seventh day they were at Whitney Portal. They were as clean and calm as if they'd taken a short walk. Their families came to drive them home.

A tough hike? Well, yes. Tough enough to talk about for a lifetime.

CHECK FOR UNDERSTANDING

1. Who was John Muir?
2. Why did every hiker have to carry forty pounds of gear?
3. What preparations did the hikers make for their trip?
4. What was a "Dahlem mile"? Why did the hikers start using that term?
5. Why do you think people are willing to spend time and energy to meet a challenge when there is no prize or reward if they succeed?

WRITE ABOUT *"The Longest Shortcut"*

Write a travel advertisement for the hike across the Sierra Nevada. Describe the beautiful sights that can be seen. Also describe the preparation and requirements for taking this trip.

Alive with Music

by WILLIAM McMORRIS

Meeting a challenge does not always involve a test of physical endurance. Working to develop your talents is another way of meeting a challenge.

What personal qualities does Charles Kim have that enable him to compete with musicians twice his age? In what way is training and physical endurance as important for Charles Kim as it was for the Scouts in the "The Longest Shortcut"?

A Master Class for classical musicians is nothing like the "parents' night" recital so many music students have given. A Master Class is much tougher. If parents' night can bring on an attack of butterflies for a performer, a Master Class can create an onrush of great zooming, furry bats.

The bats were ready to zoom in the performance hall at Aspen Music School in Aspen, Colorado, one August evening. A large group of musicians, mostly college age, had trekked through a chilly mountain rain to watch a few very gifted young artists show their skills before Robert McDuffie. Mr. McDuffie, a concert violinist of international fame, would be "master" of the class.

As each young violinist played from memory a complex piece of classical music, Mr. McDuffie would sit on the stage with the performer. He would interrupt any time he thought the musician could benefit from criticism. Also looking on would be many of the performer's competitors for honors, scholarships and—some day soon—concert dates. The chances for learning—and public embarrassment—were outstanding.

One of the young artists scheduled that rainy evening was thirteen-year-old Charles Kim. Charlie seemed to be in trouble even before he reached the stage. His accompanist, Denise Dahlgren, looked at him in disbelief.

"But Charlie, I'm quite sure that I gave *you* the music," Denise said.

Charlie stared solemnly up at her from behind his dark-rimmed glasses. He shook his head as if puzzled.

"Charlie!" Denise's voice slid up the scale of alarm by at least three notes.

In ten minutes they were due on stage. The sheet music was important. A sympathetic bystander offered to drive Charlie to retrieve the music. That was too much. Charlie couldn't hold his bewildered frown any longer. He began to smile. "I've got it," he confessed and produced the score.

Denise took the music with a mock scowl at the grinning Charlie. A few minutes later they were on stage.

Mr. McDuffie complimented Charlie on his playing, made a minor correction in one passage, and moved on to the next performer. Charlie settled down beside some friends in the audience to watch the rest of the class.

Charlie's ability to stay calm under the eye of a master violinist and the knowing gaze of other fine young musicians comes from several qualities.

First, Charlie seems naturally cheerful and humorous. His good nature doesn't let him stay worried for long. In addition, and perhaps more important, he has confidence in his talent. Beyond that, he works hard at his music. He has been playing at a high level of skill for ten years.

"I started at the age of four," Charlie says. "My older brother, Richard, was taking piano. He was good, and my folks thought maybe we could play duets. I liked the violin right away."

Richard has since decided against a music career. He plans to be a doctor like their father, Jae Kyung Kim, a radiologist. But Richard's duets with Charlie started something for his brother.

"Somebody heard me and said maybe I ought to try out for the Julliard Pre-College Program," Charlie says. "I was only six and most of the students in that program were thirteen or fourteen. But I tried and I made it."

That's the casual way Charlie tells how he became the youngest

student ever accepted in the program offered by the world-famous Julliard School in New York City.

Charlie is aiming for the top of the classical music world. If his career continues to go well, he will become a concert soloist. Very few performers reach that goal. For as far in the future as anyone can imagine, Charlie will be working to develop his talent. This means,

among other things, hours of practice on the violin every day.

Already Charlie's left hand is clearly larger and more developed than his right, even though he is right-handed. That is because his left hand moves over the fingerboard of the violin while his right controls the bow. That left hand sometimes moves so fast it becomes a blur. But every time he presses a string, it must be in exactly the right spot and with exactly the right pressure for precisely the right instant of time. This is what produces, in part, the "clean" sound all good violinists strive for.

Charlie plays a wide variety of classical music. "I like all composers from all periods," he says.

Charlie likes sports, too. He plays baseball, basketball, and tennis when he can. "I like football, but I can't play because of my fingers."

Charlie is not yet as good with a tennis racquet as he is with a violin. But he has a good time on the court. He threatens to make a cannonball serve. Then laughs and shrugs when the ball crashes into the net. Sometimes he makes fun of himself when he misses a shot, but he moves well and keeps trying.

Physical stamina is important for a violinist. Anyone who has watched a concert musician in action knows the effort required is great. "When I practice and really concentrate, sometimes I sweat a little bit," Charlie says, "but in

performance, sweat pours down my face. Sweat gets in my eyes and stings. My glasses slip down my nose. My fingers are usually OK, but my arms or shoulders cramp sometimes."

Tired or not, a concert performer can't think of stopping. And some violin pieces may last forty-five minutes.

Charlie likes performing better than any other part of his music life right now. "Sometimes you get two or three times better in performance than when you are just practicing." His voice becomes more enthusiastic when he talks about performing and a gleam comes into his eyes.

"Of course, sometimes you think you are two or three times worse," he laughs. "On stage when you have all the audience listening, you get kind of excited. And you go out and some things just 'pop' on the stage."

Perhaps that is the reason Charlie pays the price in practice hours, study, and sweat. It could be why he pursues such a difficult career. When all his talent, love of music, imagination, and strength are focused on his art, something "pops" that wasn't there before. All at once he's playing better than he thought he could. That rare feeling may be all he needs to reach his goal.

CHECK FOR UNDERSTANDING

1. What personal qualities does Charles Kim have that enable him to compete with musicians twice his age?
2. Why did Charlie's left hand become larger than his right by the time he was thirteen?
3. In what way is training and physical endurance as important for Charles Kim as it was for the Scouts in "The Longest Shortcut"?
4. Why does Charles Kim enjoy performing more than any other part of his music life?

Fact and Opinion

Years ago there was a detective on a television show who always cautioned a witness, "The facts...just the facts."

When you read, you don't always get "just the facts." Often what you read is a mixture of facts, which can be proved, and opinions, which reveal how the author thinks or feels about the subject. As a careful reader, you must be able to recognize opinions and to decide whether or not you agree with the opinions.

Facts Supporting Opinions

Sometimes a statement of opinion will be supported by facts. At other times an opinion will be presented as a conclusion based on facts. Read these two paragraphs. Which sentence in each paragraph states an opinion?

> To walk across the Sierra Nevada—up and over Mount Whitney—is the greatest challenge any hiker can take on. Very few mountain men ever tried to cross the central Sierras. Pioneers and California-bound gold-seekers used a pass farther north, where a highway runs today.
>
> In the central Sierras there are no roads and no settlements. There are few passes, and those that exist are high and narrow. The hike requires training and stamina. But viewing a wild and beautiful landscape that few people see is worth all the hardships.

The first sentence in the first paragraph and the last sentence in the second paragraph are statements of opinion. All the other sentences state facts. These facts can be proved by historical records and by firsthand accounts and observation.

Implied Opinions

Sometimes an author does not actually state an opinion. Instead the author may present "just the facts." But the facts may be presented in such a way that the author's opinion is clear. Read this paragraph. Which type of skiing do you think the author prefers?

There are two types of skiing: Alpine, or downhill, and cross-country. Downhill skiing requires a mountain to ski down and some form of lift to get you to the top of the mountain. People usually must travel some distance from their homes to get to a ski area. They often must wait in line to get on the lift. Cross-country skiing, however, requires only snow-covered ground. This can be found in city parks, golf courses, and in open country fields.

This paragraph is made up of nothing but facts. Every statement made can be proved. Yet the facts that are presented strongly support the opinion that cross-country skiing is better than downhill skiing.

Suppose you wanted to write a paragraph about cats. You wanted your paragraph to support the opinion that cats make good pets. Which of these facts would you *not* mention in your paragraph?

1. Cats keep themselves clean.
2. Cats have claws that can ruin furniture.
3. Cats do not have to be walked.
4. Cats shed.
5. There are many different breeds of cats.
6. Cats have an instinct for returning home.
7. Cats love to play with humans or by themselves.

559

When people you care about are in danger, it is difficult to accept the idea that there is no way you can help them. When you are determined enough, you find a way. In this story, Tessa Noble must find a way to help her family sail safely back to Snapper Bay.

Why isn't the Hammerhead Light already on in this stormy night? Which is worse for Tessa, the tension of trying to start the light, or the tension of waiting after it is on?

Needs a Lighthouse

by COLIN THIELE

Tessa Noble lives in a small fishing village on Snapper Bay in Australia. Her family has been away for a week, sailing in their boat, the Cuttlefish, *to a place called Kangaroo Island. Now they are on their way back. It is a stormy night, and the Anvil Beacon, the lighthouse that would guide the* Cuttlefish *safely to Snapper Bay, is not working.*

Tessa's only hope is the Hammerhead Light. But the old lighthouse has not been used for years. With the help of her friend Uncle Axel, who used to be the lighthouse keeper, Tessa is determined to light a safe path for the Cuttlefish.

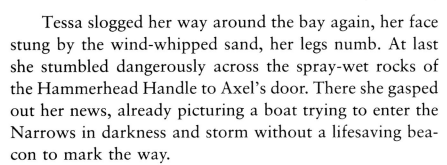

Tessa slogged her way around the bay again, her face stung by the wind-whipped sand, her legs numb. At last she stumbled dangerously across the spray-wet rocks of the Hammerhead Handle to Axel's door. There she gasped out her news, already picturing a boat trying to enter the Narrows in darkness and storm without a lifesaving beacon to mark the way.

"What are we going to do?" she asked fearfully. "They *must* see a light."

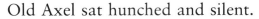

Old Axel sat hunched and silent.

"Could we tell them to go back?" she pleaded.

He shook his big tousled head. "Too late," he said, "especially with a big storm coming."

"A lamp on the headland, then? We've got a kerosene lantern."

"It would be doused in a second—snuffed out by the wind and the spray."

"We could shelter it."

"Wouldn't work. They wouldn't see it anyway."

"On the Point they might."

He shook his head again. "A few candlepower! Hopeless. They'd be onto the rocks before they got a glimpse of it."

"Two lamps, then. Lots of lamps. I could run back and get some from the town."

He sat there shaking his head. "Need far more than that, especially on a night like this. Need a great beam like a searchlight."

"Needs a lighthouse," she said tonelessly.

He nodded. "Yes, a lighthouse."

Suddenly she seemed to tremble a little as if she'd had an attack of fever. "A lighthouse," she repeated in a whisper. She turned to him, her face bright and her eyes shining. "Needs a lighthouse!" she cried, jumping to her feet and seizing him by the arm. "And here we are sitting underneath one. The best and biggest lighthouse on the coast."

He stood up slowly, his mouth opening in amazement. "Yes, Tessa."

"The Hammerhead," she cried.

"The Hammerhead! You can see its light halfway to Antarctica."

She was waiting for him to act, hardly daring to hope. "Can you get it going, do you think?"

"Worked for years."

"How long will it take?"

"With the two of us—not long."

They clambered up quickly into the next room where Axel grabbed a lantern, a box of matches, and some rags. Then up the spiral they went to the floor above, where he seized a big can of kerosene and a small one of methyl alcohol.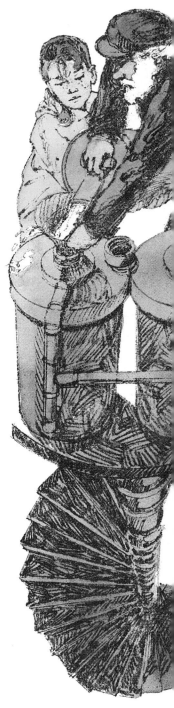

"First job, Tessa girl," he said, panting from the fast climb up the staircase. "Fuel supply."

There were two cylinders fixed side by side near the central column of the lighthouse. Axel unscrewed the cap from one of them. Together they poured in the kerosene, using an old funnel. The can was heavy and they spilled some in their haste.

"Never do, this spilling business," Axel said. "Too dangerous. In the old days we'd be hauled over the coals for sure."

When they had poured in about five gallons they screwed on the cap and put aside the empty drum.

"Second job, Tessa girl," said Axel rather breathlessly. "Start pumping."

There was a hand pump beside the second cylinder, and Axel seized it, giving a few quick pushes on the plunger. "Good, it still works."

He left her alone with the pump while he hurried up to prepare the light. "Pump as long as you can," he called

back, "and then stop. At the moment we need just enough pressure to get a start."

It was dreadful work. After a few minutes her arms felt like lead and the pump handle weighed a ton. Then her back started to ache and the pain spread like a hot stain right across her shoulders. Perspiration stood out on her forehead and the drops began to join and trickle down into her eyes. She was surprised at the way they stung. But still she worked on. If her family's safety depended on the light, and the light depended on pressure, then she would see that there was plenty of it.

"That'll do," Axel called at last. "We can finish pumping later. You can come up and help here now."

She could have cried with relief. "Coming," she called, as soon as she had gathered enough breath to speak.

He had opened one of the bull's-eyes, taken out the burner, and cleaned it thoroughly. As she joined him he was replacing it and fitting a new mantle.

"Just as well they left everything behind when they closed down the lighthouse," he said.

"Do you think it'll work?" she asked, twisting her fingers.

"It'll work." It almost sounded as if he was gritting his teeth as he said it.

He stepped back, picked up the can of methyl alcohol, and filled the preheating dish below the burner. Then he struck a match and watched for a while as the blue flame swayed and danced.

"Now," he said. "Third job while we're waiting."

She looked at him cannily. "Not more pumping?"

"Winding."

"Oh, no!"

"I'll give you a hand."

So they turned the big handle together, slowly winding up the weights from the bottom of the shaft.

"How often do we have to do this?" she asked after a while.

"Every two hours."

"It's torture," she said. "Gives you needles in your back and blisters on your hands."

"It's good for you. Builds your muscles."

Standing there side by side with their hands together on the handle in the half dark, Tessa was aware more clearly than ever of his strength and patience and skill. And his knowledge of so many things. He was a clever, kindly man, a great man.

"Reminds me of winding up the capstan," he said. "Did plenty of that in my time."

"Were you a sailor for long?"

"Twenty years. Sailor, donkey man, stoker, fireman, deckhand, cook."

"Scientist, teacher, lighthouse keeper."

"And a hippy in a hut." He chuckled at that picture of himself and whistled three bars of an old sea chanty as he wound up the weights.

"Nearly time," he said after three or four minutes "The burner should be hot enough."

He made a long taper from a piece of rolled up newspaper, lit one end of it, and held it above the mantle.

Tessa watched breathlessly. "It's not working," she said with sudden disappointment.

"Half a minute, half a minute," he said. "Wait till I open the valve."

He turned on a small tap in a metal pipe on the side of the frame. There was a sharp hiss and the next moment the mantle ignited in a brilliant white glow.

"Presto," he cried delightedly.

"It works," said Tessa, hugging him. "It works. It works."

He extinguished the taper and put it aside. "Not too fast," he said. "The last test is still to come."

"What's that?"

"The optics. To see if they turn."

"Of course."

"No use if they don't."

He swung the bull's-eye shut like a solid glass door and clipped it into place. Then he let the whole frame ride free. It started to turn at once in a slow deliberate circle that seemed as steady and as certain as the movement of the earth.

Axel grinned so broadly that his whole face glowed through his beard. "Fifteen seconds for a full turn," he said. "Three bull's-eyes in the system, a five-second gap between signals." His grin widened still more. "The Hammerhead Light is shining again."

She laughed with relief. "I hope it lights a track for the *Cuttlefish* all the way back into Snapper Bay."

"The five-second flash."

"The five-second flash of the Hammerhead Light."

By the time they had pumped up the air cylinder to full pressure and wound the weights to the top of the tower it was almost seven o'clock. Then they both stood watching. Axel refused to leave because the mantle had bucked and fluttered once or twice at the beginning. He was afraid that a bit of grit might suddenly block the jet and plunge everything into darkness.

And so they waited and talked. Seven o'clock went by, half past seven, eight o'clock. The light was burning beautifully—bright, incandescent, clear. Axel stretched and yawned. "Just like old times," he said. "Only thing missing is the head lightkeeper to keep us on our toes."

"Shall I get you something to eat or drink?" Tessa asked.

"Hardly worth bothering."

"No trouble."

"A couple of biscuits, then. That'll do till the boat comes in."

She skipped the staircase to the first floor and swung herself from the iron ladder to the ground level, where she found a lantern, lit it, and put it on a hook.

She gathered up the bag of biscuits, two apples, and her radio, and went clambering back up to Axel again.

As she was about to put her foot on the first step of the spiral staircase a shudder like the one she had noticed earlier passed through the tower and a piece of metal clanged above her head like a broken bell. She jumped back, looking upward quickly, afraid that something was about to fall on her head. But it was only the clockwork weights. They were halfway down again now, swinging and jangling like a jolted pendulum instead of hanging straight and still as good weights should. She could hear

the wind outside and feel the power of the sea. And she was afraid. If the sea could send tremors through hills of solid rock, what could it do to a little boat that was as weak as a walnut shell?

She shuddered. But then, when she looked up the high tunnel of the staircase toward the pinnacle above her, she was hopeful, too. For up there the lenses were slowly turning—silent, unfaltering, dependable—hurling out their great beam like a solid bolt of light. Over the yeasty whitecaps, over the spume and spindrift, high above the rocks and the tortured storm-wracked breakers, the Hammerhead Light was flinging out its light again like a challenge. As it had done for a hundred years.

Tessa stood where she was, one hand on the spiral handrail. Her face was turned upward as if listening to a far message—the voices of a million voyagers in the dark. Even now, perhaps, her father was adding the final shout: "It's the Hammerhead, Jody, the Hammerhead Light. The five-second flash of the Hammerhead Light."

A tremendous wave struck the cliffs and the handrail shivered in Tessa's palm. The whole tower creaked. She roused herself and climbed quickly back to Axel.

He was standing in front of the thick glass panels peering into the darkness. He hadn't heard her coming. Again, she looked at him; she felt proud and grateful that he was her friend. The broad back still seemed so young, the big shoulders so strong, the huge shock of hair so fiercely independent.

"Come on," she heard him say under his breath. "Come on, come on."

She moved up beside him, offering apples and biscuits.

"What's the time, Tessa?" he asked.

"Nearly half past eight."

"Should be time." He paused. "*Must* soon be time."

She was heartened and frightened, all at the same time. "As early as this?" she asked.

He paced from pane to pane, munching and peering.

"With the wind behind them they should be traveling like a speedboat, *Cockleshell* or no *Cockleshell*."

"*Cuttlefish*," she corrected.

"*Coddlefish*," he said wryly.

Nine o'clock came. They pumped up the air cylinder again and wound up the weights. Half past nine . . . ten o'clock. Still there was no sign.

They were both very tense now. Tessa was close to tears, but held them back sternly so as not to disgrace herself in front of him. They both listened to the ten o'clock news and weather report. Then she hastily switched off the radio. The gales were already causing havoc in the gulfs, the reporter said, and the storm front was moving rapidly eastward.

"What are they doing?" Axel blurted out impatiently. "What on earth are they doing?"

Another half hour went by. Tessa was very frightened now. She felt that she was trapped and helpless in the center of giant forces of terrible power and violence. So were her father and mother, and Jody and Bridget, and there was nothing anyone could do.

"Perhaps they've turned back after all," she said at last. Her voice was thin and unconvincing.

"Couldn't," he answered tersely. "Madness to head into a storm like that."

"Then perhaps they've run for shelter somewhere?"

"There isn't any shelter. It's Snapper Bay or nothing." They were silent again.

"We would . . . we could see their lights, couldn't we, Uncle Axel?" she asked timidly.

"Should see their masthead lights, even in this mash—unless they've had the stuffing knocked out of them."

She had no way of knowing what he was really thinking now—whether he was starting to give up, admitting to himself that the *Cuttlefish* was already at the bottom of the sea. She told herself that she wouldn't give up, not ever. She would go on hoping to midnight, to daybreak, to midday tomorrow if she had to.

"There!"

Axel almost sprang at the glass, pouncing forward, jabbing with his stubby finger.

"Where? Where?"

"Still well out . . . See the red lights?"

She missed them at first, but then she saw them winking and dipping like tiny pinpricks. "Yes, yes, I see them, I see them." She cried then, just a bit, and tried to pretend that she was laughing, to cover up the tremors in her voice. "Yes, I can see them now."

Axel had his nose right against the pane. "They're coming in," he said. "They're coming in!"

CHECK FOR UNDERSTANDING

1. What is the setting of this story?
2. Why was Tessa so concerned about getting the light started?
3. Why wasn't the Hammerhead Light already on in this stormy night?
4. Why did Uncle Axel know so much about getting the light started?
5. Which was worse for Tessa, the tension of trying to start the light, or the tension of waiting after it is on?

WRITE ABOUT "Needs a Lighthouse"

The story is told from the point of view of Tessa and Axel on land. Write a short story from the point of view of Tessa's family on the *Cuttlefish*. Use the details mentioned in the story about the boat, the land, and the sea. Include in your story the moment when Tessa's family sees the Hammerhead Light.

The Fugitives

by PERCY BYSSHE SHELLEY

The waters are flashing,
The white hail is dashing,
The lightnings are glancing,
The hoar-spray is dancing—
      Away!

The whirlwind is rolling,
The thunder is tolling,
The forest is swinging,
The minster bells ringing—
      Come away!

The earth is like ocean,
Wreck-strewn and in motion:
Bird, beast, man and worm
Have crept out of the storm—
      Come away!

Sometimes people take on challenges to test themselves. At other times, people are faced with challenges that must be met in order to survive. It is this kind of a challenge that Pitohok and his sister Upik face in the middle of a long Arctic winter.

What makes Pitohok so determined to get the caribou back home? How would you explain what the grizzly bear does at the end of the story?

Long Claws

by JAMES HOUSTON

The long Arctic winter had been a time of near-starvation for Pitohok, his sister Upik, their mother, baby sister, and grandfather. For three days they had had no food at all. Then with the help of a snow owl, Pitohok and Upik found some frozen trout. But the winter was not yet over, and when the fish were gone they would again be without food. Their only hope was a frozen caribou that Grandfather had buried in the fall, three days' walk from their igloo. Grandfather had left the caribou because he had not been strong enough to carry it. It was now up to Pitohok and Upik to find the caribou and bring it back.

With a crude sled made from frozen caribou skin and with the last of the frozen trout, Pitohok and Upik set out on their journey. They found the caribou without difficulty, loaded it on the sled, and began the long trek home.

THE AKLA

Pitohok took up the sled's long pulling straps, and together he and Upik headed back toward their home. They hauled the welcome weight of meat behind them, following their own footprints eastward, hurrying until it was almost dark. Then, as they had each night of their journey, they built a small igloo and slept exhausted.

Many times the following morning Upik looked back at the precious caribou lashed to the creaking sled. She tried to fight off her hunger by saying, "Just think of the wonderful smell that meat will make as it simmers in our mother's pot."

The morning sun had risen high above the plain when Pitohok stopped and pushed up his wooden goggles. He shaded his eyes, then pointed at a small dark speck far away. "Do you see it?"

"Yes, what is it?" Upik asked him as she watched it moving slowly toward them across the endless plain of snow.

"I don't know," said Pitohok as he pulled down his goggles to protect his eyes again. "It's not a caribou or a man. But it is certainly something that's alive."

"Let us hurry home," said Upik. "I don't like the look of that moving spot. It sways from side to side in a heavy way that frightens me."

By midafternoon the brown speck had grown much larger.

"It is moving faster than we can walk. What is it?" Upik asked her brother.

"I am not sure," he said, handing her one of the straps. "Let us run for a while together, then walk, and run again. Perhaps it will turn and go away."

In the late afternoon they had to stop and rest because their legs were too tired to go on.

"Can you tell now what it is," Upik asked, "that thing that is coming closer to us?"

"Yes," Pitohok said. "It is Akla, a barren-ground grizzly bear. It is moving in our footprints, following our scent."

"I am afraid," said Upik. "I have

never seen an akla, but I have heard terrible things about them. Hunters call them 'Long Claws.' "

"Let us walk fast again," said Pitohok.

When the sun started to sink into the west, Pitohok knew that they could not get away from the huge, hump-shouldered grizzly that came shambling after them, rolling its enormous hips, gaining on them with every step it took.

"We've got to do something," Pitohok gasped, and now his voice was full of fear. "That akla's going to catch us no matter how fast we walk. And if we run now, it may get excited and attack. Grizzlies are tireless in following their prey and can make short, fast bursts of speed. Grandfather has told me that strong aklas in their prime can sometimes catch a running caribou."

"What shall we do?" Upik asked him, and Pitohok could tell by her voice that she was almost crying.

Pitohok stopped and drew his grandfather's rifle out from under the sled lashings. He put their last stone-nosed cartridge inside its barrel. Looking at his sister, he said, "I hope we don't have to use it."

He stood the rifle upright in the snow. Then quickly he bent and unlashed the frozen caribou and rolled it off the sled. With his short, sharp knife he cut the bindings that held the sled together. As it fell apart, Pitohok grabbed one of the runners. Whirling it around his head, he threw it as far as he could along the trail toward the oncoming grizzly. The second runner he flung far to the right, hoping to draw the big bear away from their path.

576

The akla stopped, raised its massive head and stared at the two human creatures. Pitohok and Upik could hear its stomach rumbling with hunger as it ambled forward and sniffed the runners made from folded caribou skin. Placing one paw upon it, the grizzly tore it into pieces with its teeth and began devouring it.

Pitohok knelt down beside the frozen caribou and grasped it by its front and rear legs. "Quick!" he said to Upik. "Help me heave this meat onto my shoulders."

She did so, scarcely able to believe how heavy it was.

As soon as Pitohok rose to his feet, he started walking, hurrying once more along their own trail that would lead them home.

"You bring the rifle and the snow knife and the last two fish," he called back to his sister. "One sleeping robe will have to do us. Tie it around yourself. Leave the other one. Move!" Upik could hear a sound of horror creeping into his voice again. "Don't let that Long Claws near you!"

Upik's legs ached with tiredness, but she hurried after him, afraid to look back, afraid she would find the grizzly close behind her.

The evening sun turned red as it slid down and touched the long, flat white horizon. Pitohok looked back then and groaned beneath the heavy weight of caribou. "Long Claws is still coming after us. Give him a fish. Hurry and fling it back toward him."

Upik did as she was told. Pitohok looked again, then slowed his pace. "He's lying down," Pitohok gasped. "He's eaten the trout. He looks now as if he's going to sleep." It was growing dark and Pitohok was staggering with weariness. "Hold onto me," he groaned. "Help me. I've got to make my feet carry me over that next snow ridge so the akla won't see us stop to build our igloo."

When they were beyond the huge bear's sight, Pitohok collapsed, letting the caribou fall to the snow. Upik helped him up, but Pitohok was so exhausted that he

could scarcely rise. With the snow knife Upik cut a shallow gravelike hole and they slid the caribou in and carefully covered it with snow. They built their igloo on top of it.

Once inside, Pitohok wedged a snow block firmly into place, trying to jam the entrance. "Let us share our one last fish," he said. "I have never been so hungry before or so tired in all my life."

Even while they were eating, they listened carefully. But they did not hear the akla. Upik could not finish her share of the fish, so exhausted was she from their terrible journey. They rolled themselves into the caribou robe and slept, not knowing if the akla would let them live to see the next day dawn.

When Pitohok awoke, he said, "The weather's changed. Can you not smell and feel spring's dampness in the air?"

Cautiously he cut away the en-trance block and crawled outside. Upik followed him. The land was blanketed in lead-gray fog that hung heavily above the snow, hiding everything from view. The huge akla might have been very close to them or very far away.

Pitohok dug up the caribou and, cutting a larger entrance in their igloo, shoved the frozen animal outside.

"There is Long Claws. He is waiting for us," Upik whispered with terror in her voice.

Pitohok looked up and saw the dark outline of the akla standing watching them. It was less than a stone's throw away, its wide back glistening with silver hoarfrost, which made the coarse hair on its massive shoulders bristle like countless needles.

"Shall I try to shoot him now?" Pitohok whispered to his sister.

"No," she said. "No! I'm afraid

that last bullet will break and the noise will only anger him."

"Then hurry," he cried. "Help me get this caribou up onto my back. I don't know how far I can carry it today. My legs feel weak as water. But we've got to get it home."

Swaying its huge head back and forth, the grizzly let a low growl rumble in its throat. It was so close now that for the first time Upik could see the akla's long, sharp claws. They cut deep furrows in the snow when it came shambling toward them. Its beady black eyes watched every move they made.

"Leave our caribou sleeping skin in front of the igloo. That may fool him," Pitohok whispered. "If he goes inside, he will surely smell the place where the caribou lay last night. He may stay there digging long enough for us to lose him."

Together they hurried away, trying to hide themselves from Long Claws in the heavy ice fog.

They walked and walked until they came to a riverbed that seemed familiar to them. Violent winds had blown one bank free of snow, but in the swirling fog they could not tell where it would lead them. Pitohok struggled up onto stones that formed the bank of the frozen river. His sister had to help him by pushing at his back.

"Be careful not to leave a single track up here," Pitohok gasped. "Step from rock to rock," he warned her. "The wind is at our back. If the akla cannot see us or smell our footprints, we may lose him."

Together they traveled on the stony river bank until about midday, following a twisted course, leaving no path behind them.

"I hope we are far enough away from him," Pitohok gasped. "I can walk no farther."

He sank to his knees and let the heavy weight of the caribou sag down until it rested on the wind-cleared stones. He lay against it, his

579

chest heaving as he tried to catch his breath. Although the air was stinging cold, Upik had to kneel and wipe the frost-white sweat from her brother's face.

"He's gone." Upik sighed, glad to rest the heavy rifle in the snow. She looked around in the still-thick fog. "Which way do we go now?"

Pitohok peered over his shoulder and felt cold sweat trickling down his spine. He could see no sign of the sun. Everything was hidden by a wall of fog.

"I . . . I don't know," he admitted. "I was trying so hard to get away from the akla that now . . . we're lost!"

THE SNOWY OWL

Pitohok struggled painfully onto his knees and looked in all directions. He saw nothing but gray ice fog that drifted in phantom swirls along the frozen river.

"Oh, I wish someone would help us," Upik whispered aloud, and as if in answer to her words, the snowy owl came toward her, winging low out of the fog. Upik saw the owl turn its head as though it had seen the bear, then stare at her with its huge golden-yellow eyes. Suddenly, the owl changed its wingbeat, hovering as if by magic at the very edge of the smokelike mists. It seemed to signal Upik. Then, turning sharply to the right, it flew off, cutting a dark trail through the ice-cold wall of fog.

Upik stood up, and, using all her strength, helped her brother heave the caribou onto his back. She struggled to ease the heavy burden as she stood upright.

"We should follow her," said Upik. "I think she knows the way."

Her brother's answer was a moan when the full weight of the frozen caribou settled on his tired, cramped shoulders. "Yes, follow the owl," he whispered.

Upik tried to steady Pitohok while they walked. She looked back only once at the zigzag trail they left in the snow as her brother's strength grew less and less. Both of them had lost all sense of distance and of time. Upik followed the owl's course through the dense fog, wondering if they would ever reach their home.

They had not gone far before Upik heard the sound of heavy breathing. She turned, then screamed in terror. The huge grizzly, its heavy head rolling, its tongue lolling out of its mouth, came padding after them. It was only a pace behind Pitohok. Upik saw Long Claws raise its head and sniff at the rich burden of caribou, which had softened a little because of the heat of Pitohok's body. The grizzly stretched out its neck and licked the frosted nostrils of the caribou.

"What's the matter?" Pitohok asked her. Then turning, he, too, saw the bear. His voice caught in his throat. "You've got to . . . to try and shoot him," Pitohok gasped. "I can't do it. My arms are too tired. My whole body is trembling from carrying this weight. Let him get close to you," he said, "then shoot him . . . in the head."

Upik stopped, raised the heavy rifle and tried to sight along its wavering barrel. "I can't," she said. "I am afraid . . . afraid this last stone bullet will break." She was weeping. "Drop the caribou," Upik begged her brother. "Let Long Claws take it. We can walk away alive. It will stop and eat. Please drop the caribou. I am afraid that the akla is going to kill you for that meat."

Pitohok hunched his shoulders and struggled forward, as if he had not heard her plea. But now Upik could see that he held his short knife in his hand and that he would not give up their prize of meat without a fight.

Once more she heard an angry rumble in the grizzly's throat and saw it reach out with one terrible paw and rake the caribou along the whole length of its back. As its claws hooked against the caribou's antlers, Pitohok was thrown off balance and stumbled sideways, falling onto his knees. The big bear moved closer. Driven by fear and desperation, Pitohok rose and continued walking, his eyes narrowed,

his mouth drawn down with strain.

The huge akla, with lips drawn back to show its enormous teeth, came after him again. Upik once more raised her grandfather's rifle and looked along its sights. The bear must have heard the safety catch click off, for it stopped, turned its head and stared straight up the gun barrel at her. At that moment, looking into its eyes, Upik realized that the bear was neither good nor evil. It was a hunter like themselves, desperate to feed itself and remain alive in the lonely, snow-filled wilderness. She lowered the rifle. She could not bring herself to try to kill the bear.

At that moment, Pitohok whispered hoarsely, "I see the owl again! She's sitting on our family's empty food cache. Can it be?" he sobbed. "Are we . . . almost home?"

The bear moved in again behind him and, raising up on its hind feet, struck out angrily at the caribou's plump haunches. Pitohok reeled from the heavy blow and staggered to his knees. He tried to rise, then sank back onto the snow.

"I can't go on," he said. "I'm finished." He had lost his knife. There were tears in his eyes, but his teeth were clenched in anger. He tightened his grip upon the caribou.

"Let go," Upik begged her brother. "Let him have the meat."

"No," Pitohok said. "If I lose this caribou to that bear and return home with nothing, none of us will live, and I myself would die of shame."

He turned away from the hot breath of the snarling grizzly whose great swaying head was not more than an arm's length from his face.

"Run!" Pitohok whispered to his sister. "Run for the igloo and save yourself."

Upik bent and grabbed her brother underneath the arms, trying to help him up, but he was too weak. Then she turned around so that she stood directly between him and the akla's gaping jaws.

"No—don't do that," Pitohok gasped. He was hunched over like an old man. "Put the rifle under the caribou to help me support this weight," he moaned, "or I . . . shall never rise. You run!" he begged his sister. Pitohok wept aloud as he whispered, "I can't do any more. All my strength has gone. It's going black . . . I'm going to . . ."

"You are coming with me, now!" cried Upik. "I can see our igloo. It's not far from us. Can you not see it through the fog?"

The big grizzly raked its claws through the snow. Upik put her left shoulder underneath the caribou and her arm around her brother's waist and strained with all her might. Together they rose from the snow and staggered off toward their family's house. Pitohok stumbled once again and fell onto one knee. He hung there gasping for breath.

The akla snarled and opened its mouth wide to take the caribou's leg and Pitohok's mitted hand between its crushing jaws.

"*Unalook! Kukikotak!*" Upik screamed at the bear. "We shared our fish with you. Don't you dare to harm my brother. He must take this food to our family. They are starving . . . don't you understand?"

The huge bear let go of Pito-

hok's hand and the caribou's leg and stood there glaring back at her.

"Quick! Get back on your feet," Upik whispered. "We have only a little way to go."

The grizzly must have seen the snowhouse, too, for suddenly it shambled around in front of them, blocking Pitohok's way.

"I warned you not to hurt my brother," Upik screamed again.

As if ruled by magic, the huge bear stepped back and let them pass.

"Mother! Mother! Come and help us!" Upik wailed.

Long Claws turned its head and stared at her when Upik's mother burst out of their igloo entrance. She saw the great humped shoulders of the akla and, like her daughter, screamed at it, then turned and rushed inside again.

Upik tried to take half of the caribou's weight on her own shoulders while pulling Pitohok to his feet. Slowly he rose, but his knees would scarcely support him.

"Don't drop it now," Upik said in a stern voice. "We're almost there."

Together they staggered painfully toward the igloo.

"Everything is whirling around," cried Pitohok. "It's going black again . . . I'm falling. . . ."

Because she no longer had the strength to hold him, Upik and her brother collapsed together on the snow. She shook him, but Pitohok seemed to have lost the power to hear or move or speak. Upik tried to drag him toward the igloo, but his arms remained locked tight around their precious burden of meat.

Long Claws turned once more and shambled after them, snarling like a huge and angry dog. It grasped the caribou's neck in its powerful jaws and started backing away, dragging the carcass and Pitohok, pulling both of them into the swirling fog.

The snow knife, the rifle, and Pitohok's short knife were gone. Upik had no weapons but her hands and teeth. She turned and saw her grandfather crawling out of the igloo on his hands and knees. In his left mitt he held his huge curved bow and in his mouth a pair of arrows. Right behind him came their mother, her parka hood puffed out with icy wind, screaming aloud, raging to protect her children, ready to do battle with

the enormous bear. Her hands outstretched like claws, their mother raced forward to attack.

Upik heard her grandfather call out, "Stop, woman. Hold! If you help me, we can pierce him right from here."

The grandfather knelt unsteadily and notched an arrow to the braided string. His hands shook with strain when he tried to draw the powerful bow. But he could not. In desperation Upik's mother knelt and helped to draw the heavy weapon almost to a full curve. The point of the arrow wavered wildly when the grandfather tried to aim.

"Don't!" Upik cried, spreading her arms and running between her grandfather's unsteady arrow and the bear. "You might hit Pitohok."

Looking back, she saw her brother still being dragged across the snow behind the bear. In sudden anger she whirled around and ran straight between her brother and the akla, screaming, *You let go of him! Let go!*

Surprised, the huge grizzly released the caribou for a moment and raised its head.

587

"Here, this is for you," she yelled and reaching into her parka hood, she snatched out the last piece of frozen trout that she had saved and flung it beyond the bear.

The akla looked at her, grunted, then turned and moved away from Pitohok, who still clasped the caribou as fiercely as an Arctic crab. The grizzly snatched up the piece of fish. Then, with its hips and frosted shoulders rolling, it disappeared into the silver wall of icy fog.

Pitohok's mother and his grandfather knelt beside him, trying to unlock his arms from the caribou.

Pitohok opened his eyes and stared at them. "I thought that akla would surely snatch the caribou away from me," he whispered.

"I, too, believed he would take

it from you," his grandfather agreed. "But no human knows exactly what the animals will do."

"Upik was afraid of the akla. We were both afraid of him. Yet she ran and put her body between me and the grizzly's snarling jaws. Grandfather, did you believe my sister would do that?"

"No. I did not know what she would do. Nobody knows the strength or courage that humans possess until real danger comes to test them."

CHECK FOR UNDERSTANDING

1. How did the akla first appear to Pitohok and Upik? What made it frightening even before they knew what it was?
2. How did Pitohok try to keep the akla away from them the first time?
3. What made Pitohok so determined to get the caribou back home?
4. What were two reasons why Upik didn't want to shoot the akla?
5. What did Upik do to save Pitohok from the akla?
6. How would you explain what the akla did at the end of the story?

WRITE ABOUT *"Long Claws"*

There are two possible explanations for why the bear went away at the end of the story. It could be that the bear felt outnumbered and was satisfied with the frozen trout Upik threw. It could also be that the bear somehow understood Upik's anger and responded to the courage she showed. Which do you believe? Write two paragraphs giving your opinion and supporting it with details from the story.

LITERATURE

Science Fiction

What will the world be like fifty years from now? Do you ever wonder what cars will look like, or if there will even *be* cars? Do you ever wonder whether your children will grow up on another planet? Do you ever wonder whether you will meet a being from another world? Every time you use your imagination to think about the future this way, you are creating a special kind of story known as *science fiction.*

Science fiction stories usually transport you into the future. The author makes an effort to imagine what life will be like at some future time. The predictions the author makes for the future are usually based on the scientific work actually going on in the author's own time. By using his or her imagination about the real science of the day, the author creates science fiction that is believable and enjoyable to read.

In many ways, science fiction stories are like fantasies. A fantasy involves impossible characters, an impossible setting, or events that could not possibly happen. A story in which a cat visits a magic kingdom and learns to play a trumpet is a fantasy because magic kingdoms do not exist and cats do not really play trumpets.

In science fiction the characters, the setting, and the events may all be possible but no one knows this for certain yet. The main characters in science fiction are usually just like real people who live on Earth today. Some of the characters, however, are usually fantastic—beings from another planet or other worlds, with unusual or extraordinary powers. The setting may be a planet that really exists, but since no one has ever visited that planet yet, the fact that people are there is fantastic. The events that take place in a science fiction story are usually a combina-

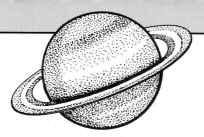
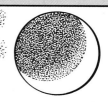

tion of realistic events and extraordinary events. The characters may do something familiar and ordinary, like going to school, and then do something extraordinary, like traveling to the next galaxy for a weekend vacation.

The success of a science fiction story depends on how well the author makes you feel part of the story. For this reason, most science fiction stories combine familiar things from the present with imagined things from the future. In the story you are about to read, "We Are at Shine," the central characters are a family. The members of the family may remind you of your own family in some ways. For example, in one part of the story, they spend some time together looking at family slides. They act toward each other just the way most families do. They should seem familiar to you.

The things that will seem familiar to you about the family help you get involved in the parts of the story that are unfamiliar. Even though the events in the story are not ones that have ever happened to you, they will seem believable.

Another sign of a good science fiction story is how believable the future seems. Jules Verne, a French writer who died in 1905, is considered to be the first science fiction writer. His books and stories are well-known today for the way they predicted a future he had no way of knowing about. He predicted flight across great distances. He predicted underwater boats. He predicted space travel so accurately that some details in his stories seem like modern newspaper reports.

As you read the next selection, think about how the future is presented. Ask yourself how real the details seem, and whether the future the author predicts might come true.

The Green Book

by Jill Paton Walsh

Almost everyone has mixed feelings about the challenge of moving from an old home to a new one. But try to imagine how you would feel if, like the people in "We Are at Shine," you were moving from an old *planet* to a new one.

Why could the people take only very few things with them? What are some differences between Earth and Shine that the people notice when they first arrive?

We Are at Shine

Father said, "We can take very little with us." The list was in his hand. "Spade, saw, file, ax, for each family. Seeds, etc. will be provided. For each voyager a change of clothing, a pair of boots, *one* or *two* personal items *only*; e.g., a favorite cooking pan, a musical instrument (small and light), a picture (unframed). Nothing under this heading will be taken if it is bulky or heavy, fragile or perishable. One book per voyager."

It was easy to pack. We were allowed so little, and we didn't have to bother about leaving anything tidy behind us. Only the books caused a little delay. Father said, "I must take this." He showed us an ugly big volume called *A Dictionary of Intermediate Technology*.

"But you must choose for yourselves," he said. "It wouldn't be fair of me to choose for you. Think carefully."

We didn't think. We were excited, disturbed, and we hadn't really understood that everything else would be left behind. Father looked wistfully at the shelves. He picked up *The Oxford Complete Shakespeare*. "Have you all chosen your books?" he asked. "Yes," we told him. He put the Shakespeare back.

We had time to waste at the end. We ate everything we could find.

"I don't want to eat iron," Pattie said, but nobody knew what she meant.

Then Father got out the slide

projector, and showed us pictures of holidays we had once had. We didn't think much of them.

"Have they all gone brownish with age, Dad?" said Joe, our brother, the eldest of us.

"No," said Father. "The pictures are all right. It's the light that has changed. It's been getting colder and bluer now for years . . . but when I was young it was this lovely golden color, just like this—look."

But what he showed us—a beach, with a blue sea, and the mother we couldn't remember lying on a towel, reading a book— looked a funny hue, as though someone had brushed it over with a layer of treacle.

Pattie was glad that Father wasn't going to be able to take the slide projector. It made him sad.

And the next day we all went away, Father and Joe, and Sarah, and Pattie, and lots of other families, and left the Earth far behind.

When this happened, we were all quite young, and Pattie was so young that later she couldn't remember being on the Earth at all, except those few last hours, and even the journey was mostly forgotten. She could remember the beginning of the journey, because it was so exciting. When we could undo our seat belts, and look out of the windows, the world looked like a Chinese paper lantern, with painted lands upon it, and all the people on the ship looked at it, and some of the grown-ups cried. Father didn't cry; he didn't look, either.

Joe went and talked to Father by and by, but Sarah and Pattie stood at a porthole all day long, and saw the world shrink and shrink and diminish down till it looked like a round cloudy glass marble that you could have rolled on the palm of your hand. Pattie was looking forward to going past the moon, but that was no fun at all, for the ship passed by the dark side, and we saw nothing of it. And then we were flying in a wide black starry sky, where none of the stars had names.

At first there were voices from the world below, but not for long. After two days the ship was flying in radio silence, alone, and navigating with a calculator program on the computer, and a map of magnetic fields.

The journey was very boring. It was so long. The spaceship was big enough to frighten us when we thought of it flying through the void. Joe kept telling Pattie not to worry. "Heavy things *don't* fall down in space," he told her. "There's nowhere for them to fall; no gravity."

"When I knock things over, they fall down, just like at home," Pattie said, doubtfully.

"That's just the ship's gravity machine, making it happen inside the ship," said Joe. "To make us feel normal."

But the ship was *small* enough to frighten us, too, when we thought of spending years inside it. "We will still be here when I'm fourteen!" said Joe, as though he found that as hard to believe as Pattie found the lack of gravity.

We did get used to being on the ship, in the end. A funny thing happened the way people felt about it. At first, everyone had hated it, grumbled all the time about tiny cubicles, about no exercise, about nothing to do. They had quarreled a lot. Grown-up

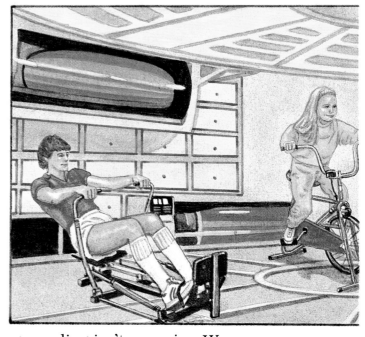

quarreling isn't very nice. We were luckier than most families. We didn't seem to quarrel, though we got very cross and scratchy about things, just like other people. But time went by, and people settled down to playing games, and sleeping, and talking a little, and got used to it, and so when at last everyone had had four birthdays on the ship, the journey had been going on for what seemed like forever and ever, and the Guide told us all there were only months to go now, people were worried instead of glad.

"We shall be lucky if we can walk more than three steps, we're so flabby," said Father, and people began to do pushups in their cabins, and line up for a turn on the cycle machine for exercising legs.

Joe began to ask a lot of questions. He didn't like the answers he got and he talked to Pattie and Sarah about it after lights-out in sleeping times. "They just don't know what this place is going to be like," he told them. "They *think* it should support life. They know there is plant growth on it, and they suppose that means we could grow wheat. But there may be wild animals, or any kind of monster people on it already, they don't know."

A time came when we reached the light of a new sun. Bright golden light filled the spaceship from the starboard portholes. The roosters woke up and crowed as if for all the missing mornings on the whole long trip. The sun warmed the ship, and made it hard to sleep at sleeping time. And then the new planet loomed up on the starboard side. It looked unlike the Earth, said the grownups, who could remember what the Earth had looked like. It was redder and shinier; it had no cloud drifts around it. When it got near, it looked like maps in bright colors. It didn't look green. People spent all day looking anxiously through the portholes at it, trying to guess the meaning of what they could see. Just before touchdown, we could all see a land with mountains, craggy and rocky, and large lakes lying on the land surface everywhere, but as the ship came into land, nightfall was racing us

across the ground—a big black shadow engulfing everything, moving faster than we were ourselves, its crescent edge going at a dizzy speed, and leaving us behind, so that we landed in total darkness. It was an auto-control landing anyway. It happened smoothly. The ship landed at a steep angle, but immediately straightened up by leveling its podlike legs. Then it switched off its own gravity and hummed quietly into run-down cycles.

When the gravity machine switched off, everyone felt light-headed, and, indeed, light. The planet's own gravity was less than the ship had got us used to. Pattie found she could jump up and touch her cabin roof, and land without thudding enough to make anyone cross. Everyone felt full of energy, and eagerness to get out. But the Guide said the ship must be kept locked till daylight. So little was known, it would be dangerous to go out.

Arthur, the head of one of the families, said he would go and have a look, at his own risk, and then the Guide spoke to us very sternly.

"It's natural to feel excited," he said. "But this is not a holiday. We are a handpicked group; we are the minimum number that can possibly survive and multiply. Among us we have the skills we require. But the loss of a single member of our party will endanger the survival of us all. There is no such thing, Arthur, as 'your own risk.' Not any more. And may we all remember that."

We sat around, fidgeting, restless, talking together in lowered voices, waiting for dawn. None of the games interested us now. Pattie couldn't sleep, though Father made her lie down on her bunk. The feeling of suspense, the unfamiliar rhythm of the machines running themselves toward shutdown, the altered pitch of the voices around her kept her awake so late, so long, that when dawn broke at last she was fast asleep and did not see it.

But Sarah told her it had come like a dark curtain being swept aside in a single rapid movement; for a few minutes there was a deep indigo light, and after that, brilliance.

The Guide walked around the ship, looking out of each porthole in turn. All that he could see was rocks, white and gray, rather glittery crags, all very near the ship, blocking any distant view. They gave Arthur a breathing mask and put him through the inner door to the ship's main hatch, closing it behind him before he opened the outer door. He came back very quickly. "Come out," he said. "The air is good."

So we trooped down the ramp and found ourselves in the shadow of the ship, a narrow gully between one rock face and another. It seemed to be a sort of hanging valley in a hill. A tiny runnel of flowing clear liquid threaded between rocks in the bottom of the dip, over a bed of silver-white sand and pebbles. Malcolm, the party's chemist, took a sample of the stream in a little specimen bottle, to test it.

Pattie was so sleepy after the

night before that she could hardly walk, and Father picked her up and carried her, nodding with drowsiness, rather than leave her alone in the ship. She went in his arms, up the slope toward a gentle saddle between one side of the valley and the other, where all the others were walking. It was easy to walk, even up the slope; Pattie felt light and easy to carry. So up we all went to the rim of the hollow, and looked over.

Before us lay a wide and gentle plain sloping to the shores of a round wide lake some miles across. Beyond the lake, a very high mountain with perfectly symmetrical slopes rose into the sky, topped with snow. A mirror image of the lovely mountain hung inverted in the lake, quite still, for the surface was like glass, perfectly unruffled by even the slightest impulse of the air. The surface of the plain was gray and silver, shining like marcasite in places, in others with a pewter sheen. To the left and right of the plain, on gentle hills, were wide sweeps of woodland, with quite recognizable and normal trees, except that the leaves upon them were not green but shades of red, and shining, like the blaze of an amazing autumn. It was very beautiful and perfectly silent, and perfectly still.

The children ran forward onto the open expanse of land before them, shouting. And at once we were limping, crying, and hopping back. We were still wearing the soft ship slippers we had been given to keep down the noise in the corridors of the spacecraft, and the pretty gray grass and flowers had cut through the thin leather at once, and cut our feet. The Guide ordered the crate of boots to be brought from the store and unpacked. Someone fetched ointment and bandages. Meanwhile, we stooped and picked the sharp plants, which broke easily in our fingers when gathered; they seemed to be made of glass, sharp and shining like jewels. But as soon as we all had boots on, we could walk over them safely, for the growth was crushed beneath the soles, as fragile and as crunchy to walk on as the frost-stiffened grass of winter on Earth.

We all walked over the crisp and sparkling frost plain, down toward the shores of the lake. It took an hour to reach it. The lake shore was wide silver beach, made of soft bright sand, like grains of worn down glass. And all the time we walked toward the lake, it did not move, or ruffle, even enough to shake the curtains of reflected mountain and reflected sky that hung in it. And though the air smelled good and sweet to breathe, it was windless, and as still as the air in a deep cave underground. Only the little rivulet that followed us across to the lake from the crag valley where the ship had lodged moved, it chuckled gently from stone to stone, and sparkled as brightly as the glass leaves and grass. When we got to the beach, Pattie went to look where it joined the lake, to see if it would make some splash or ripples for just a little way, but it seemed to slide beneath the surface at once and made only the faintest ripple ring, quickly dying in the brilliant mirror of the lake.

"I think we may be lucky," said the Guide. "I think this place is good."

601

People laughed, and some of the grown-ups kissed each other. The children ran to the edge of the lake and made it splash. Jason's mother ran along the beach, calling to the wading children not to drink from the lake until Malcolm had made sure it was water. Everyone was thirsty from walking, and the lake looked clear and good, but we all obediently drank from the flagons of recycled water from the ship.

"Right," said the Guide. "We shall begin the settlement program. And first we need to name the place we are about to build. The instructions suggest that the youngest person present should give the name. That can't include the real babies, obviously; Pattie or Jason—which is the youngest?"

Jason's mother and Pattie's father spoke together.

"It is Pattie, by a few days," said Father. "Well, Pattie, where are we?"

"We are at Shine, on the first day," said Pattie, solemnly.

"Good girl," said the Guide. "This place, then, is Shine. And now we must all work, and fast, for we do not know how long the days are here, or what dangers there may be." And he began to hand out jobs to each one in turn.

What will life be like at Shine? Why did these people have to leave Earth? To find out, read the rest of the novel **The Green Book,** *by Jill Paton Walsh.*

CHECK FOR UNDERSTANDING

1. Why could the people take only a very few things with them?
2. If you were going to a new planet and could take only *one* book with you, which book would you select?
3. How long did it take the spaceship to get to the new planet? What was the trip like?
4. Why did the Guide refuse to let Arthur go out to investigate the new planet at his own risk?
5. What were some differences between Earth and Shine that the people noticed when they first arrived?
6. Why do you think Pattie named the planet "Shine"?

WRITE ABOUT *"We Are at Shine"*

One of the striking features of Shine is that there is no wind. Think about the history of life on Earth and about the way our planet looks. How would a complete lack of wind affect the Earth? What inventions and vehicles would have been useless? What parts of the Earth would look different? Write two paragraphs explaining how Earth would be different without wind.

THINK ABOUT IT

Think about the challenge that was faced in each selection.

- In "Blue Beach," Carlota had to survive the deadly grip of the burro clam.
- In "Night Dive," the girl had to overcome fear of the unknown in order to discover the beauty of diving at night.
- In "The Longest Shortcut," the hikers had to overcome fatigue, discomfort, and their own doubts.
- In "Alive with Music," Charles Kim meets the challenge of preparing for a demanding and difficult career.
- In "Needs a Lighthouse," Tessa had to find a way to help her family get safely back to harbor.
- In "Long Claws," Pitohok and Upik had to survive the threat of death from starvation and from the fierce grizzly bear.
- In "We Are at Shine," the colonists faced the challenge of building a new life on a new planet.

What personal qualities were required to meet each challenge? Was there one quality that all the people and characters in the selections shared? Is it possible to identify a single quality that is most necessary to help someone meet a challenge? Explain your answer.

WRITE ABOUT IT

Think about a challenge you have faced in your life. It might have been the challenge of doing something that was difficult or frightening. It might have been the challenge of responding to an emergency or potential danger. Write two paragraphs describing the challenge and explaining how your normal ability to deal with situations was increased or altered by the demands of the challenge.

READ ABOUT IT

O the Red Rose Tree by Patricia Beatty. William Morrow & Co., 1972. In Washington in the 1890s, Mrs. Hankinson needs scarce materials to make a dream quilt. Four girls resolve to find the materials.

My Side of the Mountain by Jean Craighead George. E. P. Dutton, 1959. A New York City boy goes to live on some abandoned land in the Catskills. Although he brings few possessions with him, he learns that the mountains can provide him with food, shelter, and even friends.

The Wind Is Not a River by Arnold A. Griese. Thomas Y. Crowell Co., 1978. During World War II when Japanese soldiers capture Attu Island, two children escape discovery. They help their neighbors and learn to love even their enemy.

Zia by Scott O'Dell. Houghton Mifflin Co., 1976. Zia, a young Indian girl, and her brother Mondo set forth on a dangerous journey from Santa Barbara, California, to a deserted island.

The Night of the Twisters by Ivy Ruckman. Thomas Y. Crowell Co., 1984. "Tornado alert! Tornado alert!" Dan, his best friend, and his infant brother are the only ones at home when a twister strikes.

GLOSSARY

A

a·ban·don (ə ban′ dən) *n.* complete giving over to excitement or other emotion.

a·ban·doned (ə ban′ dənd) *adj.* deserted; given up.

ab·sence (ab′ səns) *n.* the state of being away or not present.

ab·sent·mind·ed·ly (ab′ sənt mīn did lē) *adv.* in a manner showing that one is lost in thought.

ac·quaint·ed (ə kwān′ tid) *adj.* known to each other.—**to get acquainted,** to come to know each other.

ac·quire (ə kwīr′) *v.,* **ac·quired, ac·quir·ing.** to get; gain as one's own.

af·fec·tion (ə fek′ shən) *n.* a tender, warm feeling.

af·ter·deck (af′ tər dek′) *n.* the deck at the rear of a ship.

a·ghast (ə gast′) *adj.* filled with shock or fear.

ag·ri·cul·tur·al (ag′ rə kul′ chər əl) *adj.* having to do with farming.

al·ma·nac (ôl′ mə nak′) *n.* a book arranged by days, weeks, and months covering the tides, the weather, and the rising and setting of the sun.

a·loof (ə lo͞of′) *adj.* distant; reserved; cold or unfriendly.

am·ble (am′ bəl) *v.,* **am·bled, am·bling.** to walk slowly.

am·bush (am′ boosh) *n.pl.,* **am·bush·es.** a surprise attack from a hidden position.

a·midst (ə midst′) *prep.* in the middle of; surrounded by; amid.

an·nex (ə neks′) *v.* to add or attach to something larger.

an·tic·i·pate (an tis′ ə pāt) *v.,* **an·tic·i·pat·ed, an·tic·i·pat·ing. 1.** to expect. **2.** to predict and deal with in advance.

an·ti·sep·tic (an′ ti sep′ tik) *n.* a product that kills germs.

ap·par·ent·ly (ə par′ ənt lē) *adv.* clearly; in a way that is obvious.

a·rise (ə rīz′) *v.,* **a·rose, a·ris·en, a·ris·ing. 1.** to rise or move upward. **2.** to stand or get up. **3.** to appear or originate.

ar·riv·al (ə rī′ vəl) *n.* **1.** somebody or something that arrives or has arrived. **2.** the act of arriving.

as·sign·ment (ə sīn′ mənt) *n.* something that is given out such as a task or job.

a·stern (ə sturn′) *adv., adj.* at or toward the rear of a boat or ship.

at·tempt (ə tempt′) *n.* an effort; a try.

at·trac·tive (ə trak′ tiv) *adj.* pleasing; charming; attention winning.

au·thor·i·ty (ə thôr′ ə tē) *n.pl.,* **au·thor·i·ties.** an expert.

B

balk (bôk) *v.* to stop and refuse to go on.

bar·na·cle (bär′ nə kəl) *n.* little shellfish that attaches to things underwater.

bar·racks (bar′ əks) *n.pl.* buildings used to house soldiers.

bar·ren (bar′ ən) *adj.* to have little or no plant life.

bar·ri·cade (bar′ ə kād) *n.* a barrier that does not allow passage.

bay·o·net (bā′ ə net′) *n.* a large knife that can be attached to the front end of a rifle barrel.

bea·con (bē′ kən) *n.* a lighthouse or other object that guides ships.

be·grudge (bi gruj′) *v.* **be·grudged,**

be·grudg·ing. to want to deny someone the possession or pleasure of
something.

ben·e·fit (ben′ ə fit) *v.* to receive help.

be·tray (bi trā′) *v.* **1.** to make known or
give away (a secret). **2.** to be false to;
to fail to honor a promise to.

bi·ol·o·gist (bī ol′ ə jist) *n.* someone who
is an expert in biology.

black·smith (blak′ smith′) *n.* a person
who works with iron, heating it and
hammering it into shape.

bland (bland) *adj.* lacking flavor; dull.

blare (bler) *v.* to make loud harsh sounds.

blurt (blurt) *v.* to say suddenly or without
thinking.

bob·ber (bob′ ər) *n.* a cork or plastic float
attached to a fishing line.

brawl·er (brôl′ ər) *n.* a noisy, rough
fighter.

bribe (brīb) *v.,* **bribed, brib·ing.** to offer
money or gifts to convince someone
to do something.

bris·tle (bris′ əl) *v.,* **bris·tled, bris·tling.** to
be full of or covered with.

bron·co·bust·er (brong′ kō bəs′ ter) *n.*
one who tames wild horses.

brood (brood) *v.* to think in a worried
manner for a long time.

buck·eye (buk′ ī′) *n.* the shiny brown
nutlike seed of a small tree that is related to the horse chestnut.

bull's eye (boolz ī) *n.* a lens with an outward curve.

bu·oy (boo′ ē; boi) *n.* a floating object that
is anchored to warn ships of dangers.

buoy·an·cy (boi′ ən sē) *n.* the power of
something to rise in the water or
float.

bur·lap (bur′ lap) *n.* a rough cloth.

butte (byoot) *n.* a steep, flat-topped
mountain.

C

cache (kash) *n.* a hiding place or storage
place, especially for treasure or
provisions.

ca·hoots (kə hoots′) *n. Slang.* partnership,
especially to plot secretly.

cal·cu·la·tion (kal′ kyə lā′ shən) *n.* the
product or result of calculating.

cal·lous (kal′ əs) *adj.* hardened and thick-
ened as a callus on the skin.

can·ni·ly (kan′ ə lē) *adv.* knowingly;
shrewdly.

can·ta·loupe (kan′ tə lōp′) *n.* a melon
with thick, rough skin and sweet
orange flesh.

can·teen (kan tēn′) *n.* a metal container
used for carrying water.

can·vas (kan′ vəs) *n.* heavy cloth made of
cotton, flax, or hemp.

cap·stan (kap′ stən) *n.* a device with an
upright spindle that is turned by
motor or by hand to wind up a cable
or rope, as in raising an anchor.

cap·tiv·i·ty (kap tiv′ ə tē) *n.* the state of
being under another's control.

car·cass (kär′ kass) *n.* an animal's dead
body.

cas·cade (kas kād′) *n.* **1.** a small waterfall
or a series of small waterfalls. **2.** anything like a waterfall.

PRONUNCIATION KEY
at; āpe; cär; end; mē; it; īce; hot; ōld;
fôrk; wood; fool; oil; out; up; turn;
sing; thin; this, hw in white; zh in
treasure; ə stands for a in ago, e in taken,
i in pencil, o in lemon, u in circus.

ca·tas·tro·phe (kə tas′ trə fē′) *n.* a sudden, great misfortune or disaster.

ca·ter (kā′ tər) *v.* to provide food, supplies, and other services for parties or meals.

cel·e·bra·tion (sel′ ə brā′ shən) *n.* **1.** the act of celebrating. **2.** the festivities or ceremonies carried on to celebrate something.

cer·ti·fi·ca·tion (sur′ tə fi kā′ shən) *n.* **1.** the state of being certified. **2.** a certified statement.

chan·ty (chant′ ē) *n.* a song sailors sing in rhythm with their work.

char·i·ty (char′ ə tē) *n.pl.*, **char·i·ties.** a group set up for helping the poor or needy.

check (chek) *v.* to hold in control; to prevent from acting.

chem·ist (kem ist) *n.* an expert in chemistry.

chron·ic (kron′ik) *adj.* returning again and again, or lasting a long time.

cir·cu·lar (sur′ kyə lər) *adj.* having the form of a circle; round.

civ·i·li·za·tion (siv′ ə li zā′ shən) *n.* a society that has an orderly and highly developed system for meeting human needs.

clamp (klamp) *n.* a device used to hold something in place.

coast·al (kōst′ əl) *adj.* located on a coast or at the edge of an ocean.

col·lapse (kə laps′) *v.*, **col·lapsed, col·laps·ing.** to fall down helpless; to lose strength.

co·logne (kə lōn′) *n.* a scented liquid used as perfume.

co·los·sal (kə los′ əl) *adj.* extremely large.

com·et (kom′ it) *n.* a bright heavenly body made of frozen gases, ice, and dust particles with a visible, long tail pointing away from the sun.

com·mence (kə mens′) *v.*, **com·menced, com·men·cing.** to start or begin.

com·mo·tion (kə mō′ shən) *n.* noisy activity; confusion.

com·plex (kom pleks′) *adj.* hard to do or understand.

com·plex·ion (kəm plek′ shən) *n.* the color of the face or skin.

com·po·si·tion (kom′ pə zish′ ən) *n.* the parts that make up a whole.

com·press (kəm pres′) *v.* to squeeze together tightly.

com·pul·sion (kəm pul′ shən) *n.* an urge or sudden desire to do something.

con·cept (kon′ sept) *n.* a general idea; an idea or an image developed from knowledge or experience.

con·front (kən frunt′) *v.* to face boldly.

con·sec·u·tive (kən sek′ yə tiv) *adj.* following one after the other.

con·ster·na·tion (kon′ stər nā′ shən) *n.* feelings of amazement or alarm that lead to fear or confusion.

con·struct (kən strukt′) *v.* to build; to put together.

con·tem·po·rar·y (kən tem′ pə rer′ ē) *adj.* of the present time.

con·trast (kon′ trast) *n.* a difference made clear by comparing two things.

con·tri·bu·tion (kon′ trə byoo′ shən) *n.* something that is given.

con·triv·ance (kən trī′ vəns) *n.* something created, invented, or designed, such as a mechanical object made for a particular purpose.

co·op·er·ate (kō op′ ə rāt′) *v.*, **co·op·er·at·ed, co·op·er·at·ing.** to work or act together for a common purpose.

coun·ter·bal·ance (koun′ tər bal′ əns) *n.* weights used to balance other weights.

cou·pon (ko͞o′ pon; kyo͞o′ pon) *n.* an advertisement or part of an advertisement that gives the person using it some right, usually a lower price on a service or product.

cow·er (kou′ ər) *v.* to crouch, trembling in fear.

crag (krag) *n.* a rugged, steep cliff or rock.

crag·gy (krag ē) *adj.* rough, uneven, steep, with many crags.

cramp (kramp) *n.* painful, sharp tightening occurring suddenly in a muscle.

cray·fish (krā′ fish) *n.* a small, freshwater shellfish that resembles a lobster.

cre·o·sote (krē′ ə sōt′) *n.* an oily liquid used to preserve wood.

cres·cent (kres′ ənt) *adj.* having the shape of the moon during its first or last quarter.

crev·ice (krev′ is) *n.* a narrow crack through or into something.

cringe (krinj) *v.*, **cringed, cring·ing.** to pull back because of fear or pain.

crit·i·cism (krit′ ə siz′ əm) *n.* a remark or statement that expresses an opinion (often bad) about something.

croon (kro͞on) *v.* to sing softly.

cross·bred (krôs′ bred′) *n.* an animal that is a mix of two different breeds.

cru·cial (kro͞o′ shəl) *adj.* critical, very important.

cu·bi·cle (kyo͞o′ bi kəl) *n.* a small partitioned area, room, or compartment.

cul·vert (kul′ vərt) *n.* a drain for water that passes under a road or driveway.

cu·mu·lus (kyo͞o′ myə ləs) *n.* a dense cloud with a flat base and rounded mounds piled upward.

cyl·in·der (sil′ ən dər) *n.* a chamber in which a piston of a pump moves up and down.

D

deaf·en·ing (def′ ən ing) *adj.* extremely loud; stunning to the ears.

de·bris (de brē′, dā′ brē) *n.* scattered remains of something broken or destroyed; rubbish; trash.

de·fi·ance (di fī′ əns) *n.* a challenge of power; lack of respect for authority or an opponent.

deign (dān) *v.* to consider fit or worthy of oneself.

de·lib·er·ate (di lib′ ər it) *adj.* **1.** unhurried in movement or action. **2.** slow and careful; not quick.

de·lib·er·ate·ly (di lib′ ər it lē) *adv.* carefully planned out; intentionally.

del·i·ca·cy (del′ i kə sē) *n.pl.*, **del·i·ca·cies.** an especially good or rare food.

dem·on·stra·tion (dem′ ən strā′ shən) *n.* an act of showing by means of example.

de·pos·its (di poz′ itz) *n.* natural layers as of an ore, coal, or gas.

de·prive (di prīv′) *v.* **de·prived, de·priv·ing.** to take away from; to keep from having or using.

PRONUNCIATION KEY
at; āpe; cär; end; mē; it; īce; hot; ōld; fôrk; wood; fo͞ol; oil; out; up; turn; sing; thin; **th**is, **hw** in white; **zh** in treasure; ə stands for **a** in ago, **e** in taken, **i** in pencil, **o** in lemon, **u** in circus.

de·ri·sive (di rī′ siv) *adj.* scornful; communicating a feeling that someone is foolish.

de·spair (di sper′) *n.* a complete loss of hope.

des·per·a·tion (des′ pə rā′ shən) *n.* the loss of hope often resulting in recklessness.

de·tect (di tekt′) *v.* to discover, find out, or notice.

di·ag·o·nal (dī ag′ ən əl) *adj.* having a slanting line.

dig·ni·ty (dig′ nə tē) *n.* self respect, nobility of manner and character.

di·lute (di lo͞ot′; dī lo͞ot′) *v.* **di·lut·ed, di·lut·ing.** to thin or make weaker by adding liquid.

di·min·ish (di min′ ish) *v.* to become less; to grow smaller.

dis·a·gree·a·ble (dis′ ə grē′ ə bəl) *adj.* unpleasant; bad-tempered.

dis·ci·pline (dis′ ə plin) *v.,* **dis·ci·plined, dis·ci·plin·ing.** to train to be obedient; to keep under control.

dis·may (dis mā′) *v.* to fill with fear or alarm; to trouble.

dis·miss (dis mis′) *v.* to put out of mind; refuse to think seriously about.

dis·patch (dis pach′) *v.* to send off quickly.

dis·rupt (dis rupt′) *v.* to throw into confusion; to upset.

dis·tress (dis tres′) *n.* a state of suffering for the body or mind.

dis·trib·u·tor (dis trib′ yə tər) *n.* a device that causes the spark plugs in an engine to fire in the correct order.

dole·ful·ly (dōl′fəl ē) *adv.* sadly.

dom·i·nant (dom′ ə nənt) *adj.* having control.

dor·mer (dôr′ mər) *n.* a window that is set straight up and down in a sloping roof, covered by a small peaked roof.

dote (dōt) *v.,* **dot·ed, dot·ing.** to show affection beyond what is usual.

dra·per·y (drā′ pər ē) *n.pl.,* **dra·per·ies.** a heavy cloth hung or arranged in loose folds over or at the sides of a window.

drow·si·ness (drou′ zē nis) *n.* the inclination to sleep; to be half asleep.

du·ly (do͞o′ lē; dyo͞o′ le) *adv.* to the extent that is proper.

du·pli·cate (do͞o′ pli kāt′; dyo͞o′ pli kāt′) *v.,* **du·pli·cat·ed, du·pli·cat·ing.** to make an exact copy of.

E

eb·on·y (eb′ ə nē) *n.* a hard, black wood. *adj.* like ebony, especially in color.

ed·dy (ed′ ē) *n.* a current of water moving against the main current, especially with a circular motion.

ed·it (ed′ it) *v.* **1.** to improve or correct. **2.** to review, cut, and prepare for presentation.

e·di·tion (i dish′ ən) *n.* **1.** all the copies of a publication printed at the same time. **2.** one of the different issues of a newspaper printed for a single day: *the morning edition.*

ef·fi·cient (i fish′ ənt) *adj.* effective, competent, with little waste of effort.

el·e·gance (el′ ə gəns) *n.* grace; excellence in appearance, performance, or manner.

em·blem (em′ bləm) *n.* a symbol used to identify something.

em·brace (em brās′) *v.* **em·braced, em·brac·ing.** to hug.

em·pha·sis (em′ fə sis) *n.pl.*, **em·pha·ses** (em′ fə sēz) special importance.

en·coun·ter (en koun′ tər) *n.* an unexpected meeting.

en·dear (en dēr′) *v.* to make dear or loved.

en·dure (en door′; en dyo͞or) *v.* to continue without yielding; to suffer without yielding.

en·force (en fôrs′) *v.*, **en·forced**, **en·forc·ing.** to make sure that a rule or the like is observed.

en·gulf (en gulf′) *v.* to swallow up.

en·ter·prise (en′ tər prīz′) *n.* a project or undertaking.

en·thu·si·as·ti·cal·ly (en tho͞o′ zē as′ tik lē) *adv.* eagerly; with strong interest.

e·rupt (i rupt′) *v.* to throw something suddenly and violently.

e·rup·tion (i rupt′ shən) *n.* the sudden and violent throwing forth of steam, liquid, or lava.

e·vac·u·a·tion (i vak′ yo͞o ā′ shən) *n.* the situation or action of being forced to leave.

ewe (yo͞o) *n.* a female sheep.

ex·as·per·ate (eg zas′ pə rāt′) *v.*, **ex·as·per·at·ed**; **ex·as·per·at·ing.** to provoke to anger, to irritate.

ex·ca·vate (eks′ kə vāt) *v.*, **ex·ca·vat·ed**, **ex·ca·vat·ing.** to uncover by digging.

ex·ca·va·tion (eks′ kə vā′ shən) *n.* the act or process of uncovering by digging.

ex·er·tion (eg zur′ shən) *n.* hard, labored effort.

ex·panse (eks pans′) *n.* a wide area.

ex·pe·di·tion (eks′ pə dish′ ən) *n.* 1. a journey made for a particular purpose. 2. the people and equipment involved in such a journey.

F

fa·tigue (fə tēg′) *n.* tiredness; weariness.

fa·vor (fā′ vər) *v.* to look like someone; resemble.

fence (fens) *v.*, **fenced, fenc·ing.** to fight with a sword.—**fenc·ing** *n.*

fes·tiv·i·ty (fes tiv′ ə tē) *n.pl.*, **fes·tiv·i·ties.** 1. joyful celebrating. 2. celebration activities.

feud·ing (fyo͞od′ ing) *adj.* quarreling.

fic·ti·tious (fik tish′ əs) *adj.* not real; made-up.

fidg·et (fij′ it) *v.* to make restless movements.

fi·nance (fi nans′; fī′ nans) *v.*, **fi·nanced**, **fi·nanc·ing.** to provide money for.

flag·on (flag′ ən) *n.* a large container with a handle and cover used to hold liquids.

fleece (flēs) *n.* the wool cut from a sheep at any one time.

flour·ish (flur′ ish) *n.pl.*, **flour·ish·es.** a showy action or display.

fo·li·age (fō′ lē ij) *n.* the leaves on trees and plants.

for·bid·den (fər bid′ ən) *adj.* not permitted or allowed.

fore·fa·ther (fôr′ fä′ thər) *n.* an ancestor.

for·mu·la (fôr′ myə lə) *n.pl.*, **for·mu·las** or **for·mu·lae** (fôr′ myə lē) a liquid food prepared for babies or young animals.

frame (frām) *n.* body structure; build.

PRONUNCIATION KEY
at; āpe; cär; end; mē; it; īce; hot; ōld; fôrk; wood; fo͞ol; oil; out; up; turn; sing; thin; this, hw in white; zh in treasure; ə stands for a in ago, e in taken, i in pencil, o in lemon, u in circus.

fran·tic·al·ly (fran′ tik əl lē) *adv.* excitedly; in a very disturbed and alarmed manner.

fren·zy (fren′ zē) *n.*, a state of great excitement or of greatly disturbed emotions.

fum·ble (fum′ bəl) *v.* to make a clumsy or awkward attempt at something.

fun·nel (fun′ əl) *n.* a utensil with a wide, conelike mouth at one end and a tube at the other, used to pour something into a container with a small opening.

fur·row (fur′ ō) *n.* a narrow, long channel or groove, like a rut.

G

gad·get (gaj′ it) *n. Informal.* a small mechanical device.

gales (gālz) *n.* strong, high velocity winds.

gal·le·on (gal′ē ən) *n.* a large, sailing ship used from the fifteenth to the seventeenth centuries.

gauge (gāj) *n.* an instrument used for measuring or indicating measurement.

gen·u·ine (jen′ yōō in) *adj.* real, true; actually what it seems to be.

gi·gan·tic (jī gan′ tik) *adj.* huge; enormous.

gild (gild) *v.*, **gild·ed** or **gilt, gild·ing.** to cover with a thin layer of gold.

girth (gurth) *n.* a strap passed under the belly of a horse to hold a saddle in place.

glam·or·ous (glam′ ər əs) *adj.* attractive; full of excitement and charm.

glim·mer (glim′ ər) *n.* **1.** a faint, shimmering light. **2.** a faint hint; a slight suggestion of something: *a glimmer of excitement.*

gnaw (nô) *v.* to bite repeatedly; to chew on.

gorge (gôrj) *n.* a narrow, deep passage or opening between the steep, rocky sides of a mountain.

gos·sa·mer (gos′ ə mər) *n.* a fine, filmy material.

gran·ite (gran′ it) *n.* a hard rock with specks or veins of dark minerals in it.

grat·i·fy·ing (grat′ ə fī ing) *adj.* pleasing or satisfying.

grat·ing (grā′ ting) *n.* scraping sound.

gren·a·dier (gren′ ə dēr′) *n.* a soldier, especially a member of the first regiment of the British Army.

groove (grōōv) *n.* a long, narrow channel in a surface.

gul·let (gul′ it) *n.* the throat.

H

hail (hāl) *v.* to gain the attention of someone through motions or calls.

ham·let (ham′ lit) *n.* a small village.

ham·mock (ham′ ək) *n.* a swinging bed of a length of material hung between two poles or other supports.

hatch·et (hach′ it) *n.* a small ax.

haunch (hônch) *n.pl.*, **haunch·es.** the upper leg of a four-footed animal.

hav·oc (hav′ ək) *n.* great ruin or destruction.

hawk (hôk) *v.* to offer goods for sale by calling out.—**hawk·er,** *n.*

heart·en·ed (härt′ ənd) *v.* encouraged, cheered, given heart to.

heave (hēv) *v.* to raise or lift with great effort or force.

heft·ed (hef′ tid) *v.* lifted up, heaved.

helm (helm) *n.* the wheel or tiller used to steer a ship.

hes·i·ta·tion (hez′ ə tā′ shən) *n.* a delay due to fear, uncertainty, or doubt.

high·hand·ed (hī′ han′ did) *adj.* done without concern for the effect on other people.

hin·ter·lands (hin′ tər landz′) *n.* regions that are far away from towns or cities; back country.

hoard·er (hôrd′ ər) *n.* one who saves and hides something away.

hob·ble (hob′ əl) *v.*, **hob·bled, hob·bling.** to walk awkwardly.

hoist (hoist) *v.* to lift or pull up.

hor·rid (hôr′ id, hor′ id) *adj.* causing horror or dread; terrible.

hos·tile (host′ əl) *adj.* showing or feeling strong dislike or hatred.

host (hōst) *v.* to be a host for or serve as one.

hov·er (huv′ ər) *v.* **1.** to linger or remain nearby. **2.** to remain suspended in air around a certain spot.

huff·i·ly (huf′ ə lē) *adv.* in an impatient, quickly angered manner.

hy·brid (hī′ brid) *adj.* being a mix of two different plants or two different animals: *a hybrid corn.*

hys·ter·i·cal (his ter′ i kəl) *adj.* frenzied; uncontrollably excited.

hys·ter·ics (his ter′ iks) *n.pl.* a sudden burst of emotion, especially of laughing or crying.

I

il·lus·trate (il′ əs trāt′; i lus′ trat′) *v.*, **il·lus·trat·ed, il·lus·trat·ing.** to provide with pictures or drawings.

im·pet·u·ous (im pech′ yōō əs) *adj.* having the tendency to act suddenly, without planning.

im·plor·ing·ly (im plôr′ ing lē) *adv.* pleadingly; in a begging manner.

in·au·gu·ral (in ô′ gyər əl) *adj.* relating to the ceremony to install a person in an office or a position.

in·can·des·cent (in′ kən des′ ənt) *adj.* shining brightly; sparkling.

in·cred·u·lous·ly (in′ krə dōō′ ləs lē) *adv.* in a manner that shows disbelief.

in·dig·nant (in dig′ nənt) *adj.* angry at something that seems unfair or cruel. —**in·dig·nant·ly,** *adv.*

in·di·go (in′ di gō′) *adj.* a very dark blue.

in·ev·i·ta·bly (i nev′ ə tə blē) *adv.* unavoidably; certain to happen.

in·hab·it·ant (in hab′ ət ənt) *n.* resident; an animal or person that lives in one place permanently.

in·spire (in spīr′) *v.*, **in·spired, in·spir·ing.** to have a positive influence or effect on.

in·su·late (in′ sə lāt′) *v.*, **in·su·lat·ed, in·su·lat·ing.** to cover with a material that does not conduct electricity, heat, or sound.

in·ten·tion (in ten′ shən) *n.* plan; something that is meant.

in·ter·pret·er (in tur′ prə tər) *n.* someone who translates from one language to another orally.

in·ter·sect (in′ tər sekt′) *v.* to meet and cross: *Main Street intersects High Street.*

PRONUNCIATION KEY
at; āpe; cär; end; mē; it; īce; hot; ōld; fôrk; wood; fōol; oil; out; up; turn; sing; thin; this, hw in white; zh in treasure; ə stands for a in ago, e in taken, i in pencil, o in lemon, u in circus.

in·ter·sec·tion (in′ tər sek′ shən) *n.* a place where two roads cross.

in·ter·val (in′ tər vəl) *n.* a period of time between two events.

in·ti·mate (in′ tə māt′) *v.*, **in·ti·mat·ed, in·ti·mat·ing.** to hint or imply.

in·ti·mate (in′ tə mit) *adj.* personal or private.

in·vert (in vurt′) *v.* to turn upside down.

i·sin·glass (ī′ zin glas′) *n.* thin sheets of mica, a mineral that light passes through but you cannot see clearly through.

J

jeer (jēr) *v.* to speak in a scornful way.

jerky (jur′ kē) *n.* a kind of meat, especially beef, that is dried and cured.

jut (jut) *v.*, **jut·ted, jut·ting.** to stick out.

K

keen (kēn) *adj.* sensitive; sharp: *The bloodhound can use its keen sense of smell to find the trail they took.*

kin·dling (kind′ ling) *n.* small pieces of wood or twigs used to start a fire.

L

la·bored (lā bərd) *adj.* not easy, forced, done with great effort.

lad·en (lād′ ən) *adj.* weighed down, burdened.

la·goon (lə gōōn) *n.* a shallow body of water partially cut off from the sea by a narrow piece of land.

land·scape (land′ skāp′) *n.* an area of land or scenery that can be viewed from one point. *The landscape was filled with flowering trees.*

lar·i·at (lar′ ē ət) *n.* a long rope with a loop at one end; lasso.

lei·sure·ly (lē′ zhər lē; lezh′ ər lē) *adj.* unhurried; relaxed.

lev·ee (lev′ ē) *n.* earth built up along the banks of a river to prevent flooding.

lev·er·age (lev′ ər ij; lē′ vər ij) *n.* increased power.

lin·i·ment (lin′ ə mənt) *n.* a liquid rubbed on the skin to relieve pain or stiffness.

list·less (list′ lis) *adj.* showing little interest; lacking energy.

lit·er·al·ly (lit′ ər ə lē) *adv.* actually; in actual fact.

lo·cust (lō′ kəst) *n.* **1.** a grasshopper that travels in swarms. **2.** an insect like a fly with large clear wings; cicada. The male makes a loud, shrill sound.

loll (lol) *v.* to droop, hang loosely.

lull (lul) *v.* to calm with soothing sounds.

lunge (lunj) *v.*, **lunged, lung·ing.** to move forward suddenly.

lurk (lurk) *v.* to lie hidden: *The cat lurks in the bushes, watching for birds.*

lush (lush) *adj.* covered by a rich growth of plants: *the lush forest.*

lux·u·ri·ous·ly (luk shoor′ ē əs lē; lug zhoor′ ē əs lē) *adv.* in a manner adding to one's comfort or pleasure.

M

ma·neu·ver (mə nōō′ vər) *v.* to control and direct the movement of: *I maneuvered the car into the small parking space.*

man·tle (mant′ əl) *n.* a lacy hood of heat resistant material that gives off incandescent light when placed over a flame.

man·u·fac·ture (man′ yə fak′ chər) *v.*, **man·u·fac·tured, man·u·fac·tur·ing.** to make or produce, usually by machine.

mar·ca·site (mär′ kə sīt) *n.* a mineral similar to iron pyrite.

mas·sage (mə säzh′) *v.*, **mas·saged, mas·sag·ing.** to rub parts of the body to increase movement of the blood or relieve muscle strain or ache.

mas·to·don (mas′ tə don′) *n.* a mammal, now extinct, that resembled an elephant.

maw (mô) *n.* the throat, mouth, jaw or stomach of an animal.

me·an·der (mē an′ dər) *v.* to wander, stroll.

mel·o·dra·ma (mel′ ə drä′ mə; mel′ ə dram′ ə) *n.* a sentimental story that usually has a happy ending.

mem·o·ra·ble (mem′ ər ə bəl) *adj.* not to be forgotten; worth remembering.

men·ac·ing (men′ is ing) *adj.* seeming dangerous; threatening.

merge (murj) *v.*, **merged, merg·ing.** to become one: *The two lanes of traffic merged into one lane.*

me·sa (mā′ sə) *n.* a mountain or hill with a flat top, steeply descending to a plain.

mil·lion·aire (mil′ yə ner′) *n.* a person who has a million dollars or more.

min·i·a·ture (min′ ē ə chər; min′ ə chər) *adj.* reduced in size; very small.

mock(mok) *adj.* not real, pretend.

molt (mōlt) *v.* to shed feathers and replace with new growth.

mo·men·tar·y (mō′ mən ter′ ē) *adj.* lasting only a short time.

moor·ing (moor ing) *n.* a place where a ship can be held in place with ropes.

moor·land (moor′ land) *also,* **moor** (moor). *n.* an area of open, hilly, wild land, containing marshes and often low bushes.

mo·rose (mə rōs′) *adj.* bad-tempered; gloomy.

mor·sel (môr′ səl) *n.* a small bite of food or a small quantity.

mum·my (mum′ ē) *n.pl.*, **mum·mies.** a dead body treated and dried so as not to decay.

muse (myo͞oz) *v.* **mused, mus·ing.** to think or reflect.

mus·ter (mus′ tər) *n.* the act of calling troops together.

N

niche (nich) *n.* **1.** a hollow or recess in a wall. **2.** something that resembles a hollow or recess in a wall.

no·mad (nō′ mad) *n.* a person who wanders from place to place without a permanent home.

nos·tril (nos′ trəl) *n.* either one of the two outer openings of the nose.

O

ob·vi·ous·ly (ob′ vē əs lē) *adv.* clearly; in an open manner.

o·men (ō′ mən) *n.* an event taken as a sign of good or bad luck to come.

P R O N U N C I A T I O N   K E Y
at; āpe; cär; end; mē; it; īce; hot; ōld; fôrk; wood; fo͞ol; oil; out; up; turn; sing; thin; this, hw in white; zh in treasure; ə stands for a in ago, e in taken, i in pencil, o in lemon, u in circus.

om·i·nous·ly (om′ ə nəs lē) *adv.* in a threatening way.

out·fox (out foks′) *v.t.* to trick by using the mind; outsmart.

out·set (out′ set′) *n.* the beginning; the start.

o·ver·take (ō′ vər tāk′) *v.*, **o·ver·took, o·ver·taken, o·ver·tak·ing.** to come upon suddenly.

P

pad·dock (pad′ ək) *n.* a small enclosed field where animals can graze and exercise.

pan·try (pan′ trē) *n.pl.*, **pan·tries.** a closet or room where food is stored.

par·al·lel (par′ ə lel′) *adj.* going in the same direction and staying the same distance apart.

par·tic·i·pate (pär tis′ ə pāt′) *v.* to take part in an activity.

par·ti·tion (pär tish′ ən) *n.* a structure that divides a room into parts.

pass·a·ble (pas′ ə bəl) *adj.* capable of being traveled on or through.

pas·sion (pash′ ən) *n.* something about which a person has strong feelings or enthusiasm: *Dancing was her passion.*

pat·ent leath·er (pat′ ənt leth′ ər) *n.* a smooth, soft glossy leather.

pave·ment (pāv′ mənt) *n.* **1.** material used to make a street, sidewalk, or road. **2.** an area covered with this material.

peat bog (pēt bog) *n.* wet, spongy ground made up chiefly of rotted plant matter; swamp.

pe·cul·iar (pi kyool′ yər) *adj.* strange; odd.

ped·i·gree (ped′ ə grē′) *n.* a line of ancestors.

per·cep·tion (pər sep′ shən) *n.* what one becomes aware of through the senses, especially sight.

per·ish (per′ ish) *v.* to die, especially in a terrible or violent way.

per·spec·tive (pər spek′ tiv) *n.* the method of representing objects on a flat surface in a way that makes them appear to have depth, distance, or thickness.

per·spi·ra·tion (pur′ spə rā′ shən) *n.* the moisture given off through the pores of the skin; sweat.

pet·ri·fy (pet′ rə fī′) *v.*, **pet·ri·fied, pet·ri·fy·ing.** to turn to stone.

pew·ter (pyoo′ tər) *n.* an alloy made of tin, copper, and antimony. —*adj.*, having the color or appearance of pewter.

phan·tom (fan′ təm) *n.* a ghost. —*adj.* like a ghost.

pheas·ant (fez′ ənt) *n.* a long-tailed bird. The male will often have brilliantly colored feathers.

phi·los·o·phy (fə los′ ə fē) *n.pl.*, **phi·los·o·phies.** the study of the basic nature of life and the universe.

phys·i·cal ther·a·pist (fiz′ i kəl ther′ ə pist) *n.* a person trained in the treatment of injuries or illnesses by methods such as exercise, heat, or massage.

pin·cer (pin′ sər) *n.* a grasping claw, such as that of a shellfish.

pin·na·cle (pin′ ə kəl) *n.* a tall, pointed peak such as a mountaintop.

plague (plāg) *v.*, **plagued, plagu·ing.** to annoy or bother; to trouble.

pla·teau (pla tō′) *n.pl.*, **pla·teaus, pla·teaux** (pla tōz′) an area of flat land higher than the land around it.

plum·age (ploo͞' mij) *n.* the feathers of a bird.

plume (ploo͞m) *n.* **1.** a large, fluffy feather. **2.** anything resembling a plume.

pom·mel (pum' əl; pom' əl) *n.* the knob at the front of a saddle.

pom·pous (pom' pəs) *adj.* overly proud of one's own importance.

pon·der (pon' dər) *v.* to think over or consider.

pore (pôr) *v.*, **pored, por·ing.** to read earnestly or study with great attention.

port·hole (pôrt' hōl') *n.* a circular, small window in a ship or boat.

pos·i·tive·ly (poz' ə tiv lē) *adv.* **1.** in a way that shows approval or acceptance; with certainty. **2.** definitely; clearly.

pos·sess (pə zes') *v.* to own; have as one's own.

pre·cede (pri sēd') *v.* to come before in time, or order of importance.

prey (prā) *n.* **1.** any animal hunted for food. **2.** a person or animal who is a victim.

pri·ma·ry (prī' mer' ē) *n.pl.*, **pri·ma·ries.** one of nine or ten strong feathers at and near the tip of a bird's wing.

prin·ci·ple (prin' sə pəl) *n.* a scientific rule or method: *the principle of gravity.*

pro·ce·dure (prə sē' jər) *n.* a particular series of actions or events.

pro·nounced (prə nounst') *adj.* obvious; very easily noticed; definite.

pro·pose (prə pōz') *v.*, **pro·posed, pro·pos·ing. 1.** to suggest. **2.** to plan.

prune (proo͞n) *v.*, **pruned, prun·ing.** to cut off; to trim.

pueb·lo (pweb' lō) *n.* an Indian village with houses made of stone and adobe.

punt (punt) *n.* a flat-bottomed boat with square ends.

pu·ri·fy (pyoor' ə fī') *v.*, **pu·ri·fied, pu·ri·fy·ing.** to make pure or clean.

py·thon (pī' thon) *n.* a large snake that is not poisonous but that coils around its prey to crush it or smother it.

Q

quake (kwāk) *v.*, **quaked, quak·ing.** to shake or tremble, as with terror.

R

rasp·ing (rasp' ing) *adj.* rough-sounding; grating.

ra·tion (rash' ən; rā' shən) *n.* amount of food allowed.

ra·vine (rə vēn) *n.* a deep, narrow valley.

re·ac·tion (rē ak' shən) *n.* an action in response to something.

re·as·sure (rē' ə shoor') *v.*, **re·as·sured, re·as·sur·ing.** to bring back confidence or courage to.

re·cede (ri sēd') *v.*, **re·ced·ed, re·ced·ing.** to move back or away.

re·ceipt (ri sēt') *n.* a written statement that something has been received.

re·cep·tion (ri sep' shən) *n.* the act of receiving or being received.

PRONUNCIATION KEY
at; āpe; cär; end; mē; it; īce; hot; ōld; fôrk; wood; foo͞l; oil; out; up; turn; sing; thin; this, hw in white; zh in treasure; ə stands for a in ago, e in taken, i in pencil, o in lemon, u in circus.

re·cite (ri sīt′) *v.* to repeat something from memory.

re·cline (ri klīn′) *v.*, **re·clined, re·clin·ing.** to lie back.

rec·ol·lec·tion (rek′ ə lek′ shən) *n.* a thing remembered; a memory.

re·cord·er (ri kôr′ dər) *n.* a musical wind instrument with eight finger holes.

reel (rēl) *v.* **1.** to stagger from a blow. **2.** to move unsteadily.

re·flect (ri flekt′) *v.* to mirror or give back an image.

re·fresh (ri fresh′) *v.* to restore strength, revive, or make fresh.

ref·uge (ref′ yo͞oj) *n.* something that provides safety, protection, or shelter.

reg·u·lat·or (reg′ yə lā′ tər) *n.* something that adjusts time, rate, or amount.

re·hearse (ri hurs′) *v.*, **re·hearsed, re·hears·ing.** to prepare by practicing.

re·in·force (rē′ in fôrs′) *v.* **re·in·forced, re·in·for·cing.** to make stronger.

re·jec·tion (rē′ jek′ shən) *n.* the act of refusing to accept or approve.

re·joice (ri jois′) *v.* **re·joiced, re·joic·ing.** to express great joy about something.

rel·ic (rel′ ik) *n.* something from the past that has lasted to the present.

re·luc·tant·ly (ri luk′ tənt lē) *adv.* unwillingly; not done or said readily.

rem·e·dy (rem′ ə dē) *n.pl.*, **rem·e·dies.** something that helps to relieve or cure a disease or other problem.

re·mote (ri mōt′) *adj.* **re·mot·er, re·mot·est.** far; not near.

re·pose (ri pōz′) *v.*, **re·posed, re·pos·ing.** to rest; to lie down.

rep·u·ta·tion (rep′ yə tā′ shən) *n.* a general opinion of a person.

res·er·va·tion (rez′ ər vā′ shən) *n.* **1.** public land set aside for a particular use: *an Indian reservation.* **2.** doubt; an uncertain or uneasy feeling about something.

res·ig·na·tion (rez′ ig nā′ shən) *n.* to submit to or accept something without complaint or protest.

re·sist (re zist′) *v.* to keep from giving in to.

re·trieve (re trēv′) *v.*, **re·trieved, re·triev·ing.** to get back; to fetch.

re·un·ion (rē yo͞on′ yen) *n.* an instance of friends or relatives gathering.

re·vive (ri vīv′) *v.*, **re·vived, re·viv·ing.** to bring back to consciousness.

rheu·ma·tism (ro͞o′ mə tiz′ əm) *n.* a disease that causes swelling and stiffness, especially in the joints.

rile (rīl) *v.*, **riles, ril·ing.** to provoke, annoy, or irritate.

riv·u·let (riv′ yə lət) *n.* a tiny stream.

roan (rōn) *adj.* reddish brown mixed with gray or white.

rouse (rouz) *v.*, **roused, rous·ing.** to stir up; to awaken.

row·dy (rou′ dē) *adj.* rude, unruly, disorderly.

rub·ble (rub′ əl) *n.* rough, broken pieces of rock, stone, or other solid material.

rud·der (rud′ ər) *n.* a steering device at the rear of a boat, that is flat, broad and made of metal or wood.

rud·dy (rud′ ē) *adj.* **rud·di·er, rud·di·est.** having a healthy reddish color.

run·nel (run′ əl) *n.* a small brook or stream.

rut (rut) *n.* a groove or track in the ground made by a wheel.

S

sage (sāj) *n.* **1.** a small plant. **2.** sagebrush; a shrub that grows on the western plains.

salt·box (sôlt' boks) *n.* a small house with two stories in front and one in back, with a long sloping roof.

salve (sav) *n.* a greasy substance, often containing medicine, spread on the skin to aid healing and to stop pain.

saun·ter (sôn' tər) *v.* to walk in a slow, unhurried way.

scan (skan) *v.* to search thoroughly or look over a wide area.

schol·ar (skol' ər) *n.* a person with knowledge and interest in learning.

schol·ar·ship (skol' ər ship') *n.* monetary aid given to help a student continue studies.

scorn·ful (skôrn fəl) *adj.* showing anger and dislike.

scoun·drel (skoun' drəl) *n.* a villain, rogue, or dishonest, wicked person.

scroll (skrōl) *n.* a roll of paper, parchment, or silk with writing on it.

scur·vy (skur' vē) *n.* a disease of the gums caused by lack of vitamin C.

se·date·ly (si dāt' lē) *adv.* calmly; slowly.

seem·ing·ly (sē' ming lē) *adv.* appearing to be or to be like.

sen·ti·nel (sent' ən əl) *n.* a person who keeps watch and warns others of danger.

se·vere·ly (sə vēr' lē) *adv.* sternly, strictly, in a very serious manner.

sham·ble (sham' bəl) *v.* **sham·bled, sham·bling.** to shuffle; to walk awkwardly or unsteadily.

shan·ty (shan' tē) *n.* a cabin or hut.

shear·er (shēr' ər) *n.* one who cuts the wool from sheep.

sheen (shēn) *n.* gloss; brightness.

shield (shēld) *v.* to defend from harm.

shin·gle (shing' gəl) *n.* a thin piece of wood or other material used on roofs and outside walls.

shoal (shōl) *n.* a sandbar or sandbank of a river.

shrewd (shrood) *adj.* keen or very clever, astute in practical matters.

shuck (shuk) *n.* the outer covering of an ear of corn.

shut·ter (shut' ər) *n.* a panel that covers a window.

sil·hou·ette (sil' oo et') *n.* a dark outline seen against a lighter background.

skulk (skulk) *v.* to move in a sneaky way.

slink (slingk) *v.* **slunk, slink·ing.** to move quietly, carefully, and secretly.

slur (slur) *v.* **slurred, slur·ring.** to speak unclearly by running sounds together.

smock (smok) *n.* loose garment.

sneer (snēr) *v.* to look hatefully.

snor·kel (snôr kəl) *n.* a tube that allows a person to breathe when swimming with the face underwater.

sock·et (sok' it) *n.* a hollow place or opening that something fits into.

som·ber (som' bər) *adj.* dark; gloomy.

sor·rel (sôr' əl) *adj.* a reddish brown color.

spar (spär) *n.* a pole that holds open a ship's sail.

PRONUNCIATION KEY

at; āpe; cär; end; mē; it; īce; hot; ōld; fôrk; wood; fool; oil; out; up; turn; sing; thin; this, hw in white; zh in treasure; ə stands for a in ago, e in taken, i in pencil, o in lemon, u in circus.

spec·i·men (spes′ ə mən) *n.* a sample of something taken for the purpose of testing.

spec·tral (spek′ trəl) *adj.* like a ghost.

spec·u·lat·or (spek′ yə lā′ tər) *n.* a person who buys and sells property in the hope of making a large profit.

spell·bound (spel′ bound′) *adj.* held as if by a spell; entranced.

spew (spyo͞o) *v.* to spit up or out.

spi·ral (spī′ rəl) *n.* a curve that keeps winding like the curves of a spring.

splen·dor (splen′ dər) *n.* a brilliant or magnificent display.

splint (splint) *n.* a device, made of strips of wood or metal, to hold a broken bone. —**splint·ed,** *adj.*

spraw·ling (sprôl′ ing) *adj.* in a straggly, spread out manner.

squinch (skwinch) *v.* to draw together tightly or squint the eyes.

stag·nant (stag′ nənt) *adj.* foul or stale from standing still: *stagnant air.*

stam·i·na (stam′ ə nə) *n.* the ability to endure physical hardship or fatigue.

stan·chion (stan′ shən) *n.* a pair of bars loosely fitted around the neck of an animal to keep it from moving.

stan·za (stan′ zə) *n.* a group of lines in a poem or song.

stark (stärk) *adj.* harsh.

sta·tus (stāt′ təs; stat′ əs) *n.* position.

stealth·y (stel′ thē) *adj.,* **stealth·i·er, stealth·i·est.** moving in a secret or sneaky way.

steel (stēl) *v.* to cause to be strong like steel.

stern (sturn) *n.* the rear part of a boat or ship.

sti·fle (stī′ fəl) *v.,* **sti·fled, sti·fling.** to hold back: *stifle a giggle.*

stress (stres) *n.* emotional or mental strain or pressure.

struc·ture (struk′ chər) *n.* anything built.

stun (stun) *v.,* **stunned, stun·ning.** to shock or to overwhelm.

sub·dued (səb do͞od′; səb dyo͞od′) *adj.* lacking force or enthusiasm.

sub·mit (səb mit′) *v.,* **sub·mit·ted, sub·mit·ting.** to give in; to choose not to protest.

suc·ces·sion (sək sesh′ ən) *n.* a series of things following one after the other.

su·per·vi·sion (so͞o′ per vizh′ ən) *n.* the act of guiding or controlling; direction.

sup·ple·ment (sup′ lə ment′) *v.* to improve or add to something.

sur·ly (sur′ lē) *adj.* **sur·li·er, sur·li·est.** bad-tempered; unfriendly.

sur·vey·or (sər vā′ ər) *n.* a person who examines and measures land.

sur·viv·al (sər vī′ vəl) *n.* the state or act of remaining alive.

sus·pend (sə spend′) *v.* to hang.

sus·pi·cion (sə spish′ ən) *n.* doubt; a lack of trust; an act of suspecting something wrong.

sym·met·ri·cal (si met′ ri kəl) *adj.* having parts that are alike on each side of a central point.

sym·pa·thet·ic (sim′ pə thet′ ik) *adj.* expressing compassion; in agreement with. —**sym·pa·thet·i·cal·ly,** *adv.*

T

tan·trum (tan′ trəm) *n.* an outburst of temper and anger.

taut (tôt) *adj.* drawn tightly.

tech·nique (tek nēk′) *n.* the manner or method used to bring about a desired result.

ten·sion (ten′ shən) *n.* strain on the emotions or mind; nervousness.

ter·rain (tə rān′; te rān′) *n.* the features of the surface of the land: *wooded terrain; hilly terrain.*

terse·ly (turs′ lē) *adv.* in a manner that is short and to the point; abruptly.

teth·er (teth′ ər) *n.* a rope used to lead an animal or keep it confined.

the·o·ry (thē′ ər ē) *n.pl.,* **the·o·ries.** an idea that provides an explanation.

ther·mos bot·tle (thur′ məs bot′ əl) *n.* a container in which liquids can be kept hot or cold for many hours.

thigh (thī) *n.* the upper part of the leg.

this·tle·down (this′ əl doun′) *n.* the light and silky down on the flower of the thistle plant.

thong (thông; thong) *n.* a narrow strip of leather.

thor·ough·bred (thur′ ə bred′) *n.* an animal of pure breed.

thrash (thrash) *v.* to toss violently; to make wild movements.

thwart (thwôrt) *n.* a crosswise seat in a boat.

tis·sue (tish′ o͞o) *n.* a soft, thin piece of paper used as a handkerchief.

toil (toil) *n.* exhausting, hard effort or work.

tongs (tongz) *n.pl.* a device with two connected arms used for grasping objects.

tor·rent (tôr′ ənt; tor′ ənt) *n.* an overwhelming, often violent flow.

tor·ren·tial (tô ren′ chəl) *adj.* in a strong, rapid flow.

trai·tor (trā′ tər) *n.* **1.** one who aids the enemy. **2.** a person who changes from being loyal to one thing to being loyal or useful to another.

tran·quil (trang′ kwəl) *adj.* calm; peaceful.

trans·par·ent (trans per′ ənt) *adj.* **1.** allowing light to pass through. **2.** clear; easily understood.

trea·cle (trē′ kəl) *n.* another word for molasses.

trek (trek) *v.,* **trekked, trek·king.** to travel in a slow difficult manner.

trem·u·lous (trem′ yə ləs) *adj.* affected by trembling; shaky.

trench (trench) *n.pl.,* **trench·es.** a long, narrow ditch.

trig·gered (trig′ urd) *adj.* set; ready to be set off.

tun·dra (tun′ drə) *n.* a huge, treeless plain with an arctic climate and frozen soil beneath a surface that never thaws.

tur·quoise (tur′ kwoiz; tur′ koiz) *n.* a bluish-green mineral valued as a gem.

U

un·bend (un bend′) *v.,* **un·bent, un·bend·ing.** to relax.

un·daunt·ed (un dôn′ tid) *adj.* not frightened; bold and fearless.

un·err·ing (un ur′ ing; un er′ ing) *adj.* without mistakes or faults.

PRONUNCIATION KEY
at; āpe; cär; end; mē; it; īce; hot; ōld; fôrk; wood; fo͞ol; oil; out; up; turn; sing; thin; this, hw in white; zh in treasure; ə stands for a in ago, e in taken, i in pencil, o in lemon, u in circus.

un·seem·ly (un sēm′ lē) *adj.* **un·seem·li·er, un·seem·li·est.** not proper; not considered correct for the time or place.

V _____

va·cant (vā′ kənt) *adj.* unoccupied or empty.

val·or (val′ ər) *n.* great courage or bravery.

va·ri·e·ty (və rī′ ə tē) *n.* a group of different things.

veer (vēr) *v.* to change direction or course quickly.

vein (vān) *n.* a mineral deposit surrounded by rock.

ven·ture (ven′ chər) *v.* to expose to danger, to take a risk.

vet·er·an (vet′ ər ən) *adj.* having past experience.

vid·e·o·tape (vid′ e o′ tāp) *n.* magnetic tape used to record sound and picture.

vig·or·ous·ly (vig′ ər əs lē) *adv.* forcefully; powerfully.

vil·lain (vil′ ən) *n.* an evil person.

vin·dic·tive (vin dik′ tiv) *adj.* wanting to punish someone; spiteful.

vi·o·la·tion (vī′ ə lā′ shən) *n.* failure to obey or respect.

vi·o·lent (vī′ ə lənt) *adj.* characterized by force or intensity.

vis·u·al·ize (vizh′ o͞o ə līz′) *v.*, **vis·u·al·ized, vis·u·al·iz·ing.** to form an image within one's mind; to imagine.

W _____

war·rant (wôr′ ənt; wor′ ənt) *v.* to provide reason or foundation for; show to be just or reasonable.

war·y (wer′ ē) *adj.* **war·i·er, war·i·est.** always on the alert for danger; watchful; cautious.

wa·ver (wā′ vər) *v.* to tremble; to be unsteady. *n.* a trembling or shakiness.

way·lay (wā′ lā′; wā′ lā′) *v.*, **way·laid, way·lay·ing.** to wait for and stop someone.

whin·ny (hwin′ ē) *v.* **whin·nied, whin·ny·ing.** a horse's low, gentle neigh.

wil·i·ness (wī′ lē nis) *n.* cleverness; slyness.

wist·ful·ly (wist′ fəl lē) *adv.* sadly wanting something.

with·er·ing (wi<u>th</u>′ ər ing) *adj.* fierce; belittling.

with·ers (wi<u>th</u>′ ərz) *n.* the highest part of a horse's back, between the shoulder blades.

wrench (rench) *v.* to hurt by twisting suddenly.

wrest (rest) *v.* to take away with force.

wry·ly (rī′ lē) *adv.* with humor; dryly.

Y _____

year·ling (yēr′ ling) *adj.* one year old.

yoke (yōk) *n.pl.*, **yoke.** a pair of work animals held at the neck by a single wooden frame.

Z _____

zest·ful (zest′ fəl) *adj.* full of excitement or enthusiasm.

(Acknowledgments continued)

"Dreams" is from THE DREAM KEEPER AND OTHER POEMS by Langston Hughes. Copyright 1932 by Alfred A. Knopf, Inc. and renewed 1960 by Langston Hughes. Reprinted by permission of Alfred A. Knopf, Inc.

"From the Diary of Leigh Botts" from pp. 39-49, 78-105 in DEAR MR. HENSHAW by Beverly Cleary. Copyright © 1983 by Beverly Cleary. By permission of William Morrow & Company and Julia MacRae Books.

"Galloping to Lexington" is adapted from MR. REVERE AND I by Robert Lawson. Copyright 1953 by Robert Lawson. By permission of Little, Brown and Company.

"A Get-Well Gift" is an adaptation of pages 76-92 in THANK YOU, JACKIE ROBINSON by Barbara Cohen. Copyright © 1974 by Barbara Cohen. By permission of Lothrop, Lee & Shepard Books (A Division of William Morrow & Company).

"Gone" from ONE AT A TIME: HIS COLLECTED POEMS FOR THE YOUNG by David McCord. Copyright © 1974 by David McCord. By permission of Little, Brown and Company.

"Horse Sense" is adapted from MEGAN'S MARE by Lynn Hall. Copyright © 1983 Lynn Hall. Reprinted with the permission of Charles Scribner's Sons.

"Ida Early" is from IDA EARLY COMES OVER THE MOUNTAIN by Robert Burch. Copyright © 1980 by Robert Burch. Reprinted by permission of Viking Penguin, Inc.

"Inside the Giant Peach" is from JAMES AND THE GIANT PEACH by Roald Dahl. Copyright © 1961 by Roald Dahl. Reprinted by permission of Alfred A. Knopf, Inc. and George Allen & Unwin and Puffin Books for the British Commonwealth.

"Jim Bridger's Alarm Clock" from JIM BRIDGER'S ALARM CLOCK AND OTHER TALL TALES by Sid Fleischman. Copyright © Sid Fleischman. Reprinted by permission of Bill Berger Associates for the author.

"The Last Crow in Piney Woods" is abridged and adapted from pp. 1-15 in THE CRY OF THE CROW by Jean Craighead George. Copyright © 1980 by Jean Craighead George. Reprinted by permission of Harper & Row, Publishers, Inc. and Curtis Brown, Ltd.

"The Last of the Dragons" is from THE COMPLETE BOOK OF DRAGONS by Edith Nesbit. Copyright © 1972 Hamish Hamilton Ltd. Reprinted with permission of Macmillan Publishing Company.

"Little Bit, the Chickaree Squirrel" from ANIMALS COME TO MY HOUSE by Esther Kellner. Text © 1976 by Esther Kellner. Abridged by permission of G. P. Putnam's Sons.

"Long Claws" is adapted from LONG CLAWS: AN ARCTIC ADVENTURE by James Houston. Copyright © 1981 James Houston. (A Margaret K. McElderry Book). Reprinted with the permission of Atheneum Publishers, Inc. and McClelland & Stewart.

"The Longest Shortcut" by Keith Monroe is from "The Longest Shortcut" which appeared originally in *Boys' Life*. Reprinted by permission of the author.

"Lost and Found" from SEE MY LOVELY POISON IVY by Lilian Moore. Copyright © 1975 Lilian Moore. Reprinted with the permission of Atheneum Publishers.

"The Lost Umbrella" from THE LOST UMBRELLA OF KIM CHU by Eleanor Estes. Copyright © 1978 Eleanor Estes. (A Margaret K. McElderry Book) Reprinted with the permission of Atheneum Publishers.

"The Medicine Bag" by Virginia Driving Hawk Sneve is reprinted by permission of the author.

"Miss Louisa and the Outlaws" by Frances B. Watts is from FIFTY PLAYS FOR JUNIOR ACTORS edited by Sylvia E. Kamerman. Copyright © 1963, 1966, 1981 by Plays, Inc. Reprinted by permission. This play is for reading purposes only; for permission to produce, write to Plays, Inc., 120 Boylston St., Boston, MA 02116.

"The Mountains of the Sangre de Cristo" is abridged and adapted from pp. 10-24 in...AND NOW MIGUEL by Joseph Krumgold (Thomas Y. Crowell Company). Copyright 1953 by Joseph Krumgold. Reprinted by permission of Harper & Row, Publishers, Inc. and Mrs. Helen Krumgold.

"My Vietnamese Grandmother" is the text abridged from pp. 52-61 from THE LAND I LOST: Adventures of a Boy in Vietnam by Huynh Quang Nhuong. Copyright © 1982 by Huynh Quang Nhuong. Reprinted by permission of Harper & Row, Publishers, Inc.

"Needs a Lighthouse" is the text abridged and adapted from pp. 72-82 in THE HAMMERHEAD LIGHT by Colin Thiele. Copyright © 1976 by Colin Thiele. Reprinted by permission of Harper & Row, Publishers, Inc. and Penguin Books, London.

"Night Dive" is from NIGHT DIVE by Ann McGovern. Copyright © 1984 by Ann McGovern. Edited with permission of Macmillan Publishing Company.

"The Night Traveler" is from ZEELY by Virginia Hamilton. Text Copyright © 1967 by Virginia Hamilton. Reprinted with permission of Macmillan Publishing Company and McIntosh & Otis, Inc.

"Optical Illusions" from pp. 9-10, 56, 57, 58, 58-59, 60-64, 66-68 in THE OPTICAL ILLUSION BOOK by Seymour Simon. Copyright © 1976 by Seymour Simon. Adapted by permission of William Morrow & Company.

"Over the Rockies with Lewis and Clark" is adapted from BOLD JOURNEY by Charles Bohner. Copyright © 1985 by Charles Bohner. Reprinted by permission of Houghton Mifflin Company.

"Planning the Nation's Capital" is from BENJAMIN BANNEKER: THE MAN WHO SAVED WASHINGTON by Claude Lewis. Copyright © 1970. Reprinted by permission of McGraw-Hill Book Company.

"The Rescue" is adapted from THE LONG JOURNEY

624